Digital
Systems Design

D. G. Wong

School of Electrical Engineering
University of Sydney

Edward Arnold

© D. G. Wong 1985

First published in Great Britain 1985 by
Edward Arnold (Publishers) Ltd
41 Bedford Square
London WC1B 3DQ

Edward Arnold, 300 North Charles Street
Baltimore, Maryland, USA

Edward Arnold (Australia) Pty Ltd
80 Waverley Road
Caulfield East, Victoria 3145
Australia

British Library Cataloguing in Publication Data

Wong, D. G.
  Digital systems design.
  1. Digital electronics   2. Logic design
  I. Title
  621.3815′3   TK7868.D5

ISBN 0 7131 3539 5

Printed in Great Britain by
Thomson Litho Ltd, East Kilbride, Scotland

PREFACE

The responses to a 1983 survey questionnaire from Nobel Prize winners in Science support the view that 'Computers, artificial intelligence and robots will be the technologies that will most strongly affect people's lives in the next century'. The characteristics which these technologies have in common are shared by 'Digital Systems' which involve the acquisition, transmission, storage, processing and utilisation of digital information.

The very rapid advances made in the technology of very large scale integrated circuits have caused a greater emphasis to be placed on digital systems (especially computers) within the curricula of secondary schools, universities and institutes of tertiary education.

The design of digital systems has been a university field of endeavour (teaching and research) for several decades. There are many books which cover various aspects of design methodology. However, because of the advances in the technology, there have been significant changes to the approaches and techniques which designers are using to achieve their objectives. There is, therefore, a need for books which provide an up-to-date overview of the field as well as a presentation of the necessary fundamental theory with design examples suitable for a university course. It is hoped that this book will help to satisfy this need.

Chapter 1 (Introduction to Digital Systems) provides a comprehensive overview of digital systems design. A unique feature of the book is the 'top-down' order of presentation of the material in this overview. The chapter starts with a review of applications of digital systems and discusses concepts relating to systems structure. The characteristics of some important systems components are then presented. Design methodology is summarised and the chapter ends with a description of the logical behaviour of fundamental logic gates.

Chapter 2 (Combinational Circuits) presents the basic theory and tools (Boolean algebra, Karnaugh maps etc.) for the analysis, minimisation and design of combinational circuits. These tools lead to methods for handling the universal logic elements (NOR- and NAND-gates) and larger combinational building blocks such as parity generator/detectors, adders, decoders and magnitude comparators.

Chapter 3 (Sequential Circuits) describes the characteristics of different types of flip-flops. Methods are then developed for the analysis and design of circuits (containing flip-flops) such as shift-registers and counters. Finally a systematic method of the design of the state transition logic of clocked sequential circuits is described.

Chapter 4 (Circuits for Arithmetic Operations) describes the two's complement, fixed-point representation of binary numbers and introduces the IEEE Standard (Standard 754) for floating-point binary numbers. The chapter describes serial and parallel implementations of circuits for the addition, subtraction, multiplication and division of numbers represented in two's complement, fixed-point binary notation. These circuits include iterative arrays for multiplication and division. Finally a full development of the carry lookahead adder is presented together with an analysis of the SN74181 and SN74182 integrated circuits.

Chapter 5 (Timing and Control Circuits) discusses the basic concepts and special needs of timing and control circuits. A number of examples of both synchronous and asynchronous timing are given. Finally the detailed design of a simple pushbutton and switch controlled timing unit is described.

Chapter 6 (Programmable-Logic-Arrays) describes the organisation of field-programmable-logic-arrays (FPLAs) and field-programmable-logic-sequencers. The detailed design is given of an arithmetic processor capable of the four arithmetic operations of addition, subtraction, multiplication and division. The implementation of the control signals for this arithmetic processor using field-programmable-logic-arrays is then described.

A set of questions is given in each of the Chapters 2 to 6. The last question of Chapter 6 concerns the PLA implementation of control signals for an arithmetic processor capable of sixteen operations. The standard of this question is representative of the levels of understanding and achievement which students should reach after studying this book.

This book is based on detailed notes prepared for undergraduate and post-graduate courses on Digital Systems given by the School of Electrical Engineering of the University of Sydney. The notes cover a wide range of material from 'combinational circuits' to 'microprocessor-based systems'. All this material could not be included in a single text and large sections on the following topics have been omitted: high-speed multipliers, floating-point arithmetic circuits, simulation of digital logic, memories, stored-program computers, microprocessors, and microprocessor-based systems.

Most of the material for Chapters 2 to 6 has been developed from 1977 onwards. Improvements have been made from time to time, and these chapters should now be in a very suitable form for first and second courses in Digital Systems at the undergraduate level. The overview of digital systems presented in Chapter 1 was written in 1983 and hence contains an introduction to some relatively new concepts and techniques such as 'systolic arrays' and 'data-flow computers'.

The author was strongly influenced in the development of material for this book by Frankel's paper on the description of the LGP-30 computer (Frankel, S.P., 'The Logical Design of a Simple General Purpose Computer', *Trans. IRE*, PGEC, **EC-6**, No. 1, March 1957). In this paper, a detailed description of the LGP-30 computer was given in the form of Boolean equations in less than half a page of typescript. What is important in this approach is the understanding of the function performed by the logic corresponding to a single term in one equation or associated terms in a number of equations. This approach has been taken in this book. Sets of equations are given, for example, to define an 8-bit magnitude comparator, a 16-bit carry lookahead adder and an arithmetic processor capable of the four arithmetic operations of addition, subtraction, multiplication and division.

I would like to acknowledge the assistance given me throughout my career by Professor J. M. Bennett, Basser Department of Computer Science, University of Sydney, Professor H. K. Messerle, School of Electrical Engineering, University of Sydney and Professor M. W. Allen, School of Electrical Engineering and Computer Science, University of New South Wales. Their friendship and professional advice on numerous occasions has been greatly appreciated.

I would like to thank my colleagues and students for their interest, encouragement and assistance. I would like to thank Ms P. Attwater for her accurate typing of the manuscript and her invaluable assistance in producing this book. Ms N. Strevens typed some of the notes on which this book is based. Messrs C. H. Barratt, J. G. Rathmell, K. R. Rosolen and D. T. Thomson assisted with proof-reading. Ms M. S. Reed assisted with some of the line diagrams. Their help is gratefully acknowledged.

D. G. Wong
Sydney, Australia
1984

CONTENTS

1 INTRODUCTION TO DIGITAL SYSTEMS

An overview of digital systems covering applications, organisation, component characteristics, techniques and design methodology

1.1 INTRODUCTION

The main functions performed by digital systems are the acquisition, transmission, processing, storage and utilisation of digital information. The applications of such systems are diverse, and the many improvements in community services which they have provided have been accepted by society-at-large as a natural development of the electronic age of the twentieth century.

Domestic applications of digital systems are well known. They include digital watches and clocks, calculators, controllers for sewing machines, microwave ovens, washing machines and other electrical appliances, alarms and security systems, educational toys, video games, digital recordings, optical disks, videotex terminals and personal computers.

Commercial applications are also very familiar. At supermarkets digital techniques are used in product labelling, automatic product scanning for checkout and point-of-sales terminals for inventory control. Offices are being automated with the increasing use of word processors, electronic filing systems, data banks, electronic mailing systems and distributed computing systems interconnected by local area networks. In banking, access to central account files is possible from a large number of widely distributed bank terminals, and 'auto banking' is becoming a popular banking service. Computing systems are indispensible tools for modern accounting practices, and the computer generated invoice, statement of account, reminder notice and cheque are integral parts of today's 'computerised society'.

Digital systems have many applications in transport systems. World-wide, on-line reservation systems play a key role in the efficient operation of international carriers. 'Fault-tolerant' control computers are used for the control of high-performance trains, aircraft and space vehicles, and are essential components of some aircraft under development which have aerodynamically unstable air-frames. Air traffic control and navigation aids also rely on computers and digital techniques. To achieve optimum fuel economy, automobile manufacturers are utilising microprocessors with integrated sensors for monitoring and controlling the automobile engine and for providing improved dashboard displays.

The industrial applications of digital systems cover a very wide field. Automated factories make extensive use of industrial robots and numerically controlled machine tools. Industrial processes are controlled by 'direct digital control' computers which replace analogue controllers, and process 'optimisation' is often performed by computers at various levels in a hierarchical structure. In complex, interconnected systems, such as power utilities, the problem of system instability is of paramount concern, and on-line computers for 'security assessment' and control are often employed.

Many military systems for both defence and war are highly dependent on advanced technology. Many reported hostile engagements in recent years have clearly demonstrated the military advantages which can be gained by using sophisticated digital systems for weapons control. Systems for 'command, control and communications' are essential for gaining supremacy in any protracted engagement involving large numbers of opposing strategic weapons. Future systems will require micro-electronic devices with capabilities of several orders of magnitude greater than those in use today. Hence it is very likely that the technology of micro-electronic devices will continue to advance. Industrial and commercial applications of these devices will follow in due course.

Communications systems are making increasing use of digital techniques. Many switched communications networks are designed to handle digitally-encoded speech, and high data rates are available from transmission media such as fibre-optic cable. Advances in communications technology will certainly improve services such as world-wide voice, data, telex, facsimile, television, tele-conferencing, videotex and distributed computing.

The processing of numerical data has been the traditional area of application of digital computers. The need to solve large sets of non-linear algebraic and differential equations, e.g. for the improved simulation of complex dynamical systems for nuclear engineering and weather forecasting, has stimulated the development of 'super-computers'. Higher performance has been achieved not only by using improved circuits and packaging techniques but also by innovative features which exploit a high degree of hardware 'parallelism'.

The computer processing of pictorial data has been used in many applications including space exploration, weather prediction, mineral surveying, military surveillance and medical tomography. The requirements of image processing have led to novel solutions, some of which have utilised recent advances in very-large-scale-integration.

Multi-processor systems containing high-performance microprocessors are providing very cost-effective solutions to many computational problems. Microprocessor-based systems in general are finding applications which affect many facets of our everyday life. Some of these have profound social implications.

1.2   THE ORGANISATION OF DIGITAL SYSTEMS

1.2.1   Components and functions

Digital systems contain components which perform the functions of:
   (i) acquisition of new or previously recorded data,
  (ii) transmission of digital information from one component to another,
 (iii) processing of numerical and non-numerical data for data reduction and for management of system resources,
  (iv) storage of data, and
   (v) utilisation of old or computed data.

The organisation shown in Fig. 1.2.1 is representative of the following broad classes of digital systems:
   (i) a large computer system with components structured around a *high-speed communication channel*,
  (ii) a distributed system based on a *local area network*,
 (iii) a *bus-structured* computer system,
  (iv) a *switched communication network*, and
   (v) a dedicated node computer.

The '*front-end computers*' of the large computer system provide an interface between the various input–output peripherals including user terminals and the powerful '*worker computers*' which take the form of large *main-frame* computers whose resources are managed by a *multi-processor operating system*. A front-end computer also handles the *communications protocols* pertaining to the switched communications network which allow the processing power of the large computer system to be distributed to a large number of remote user terminals.

A dedicated, high-speed communications link between the large computer system and a *node computer* is controlled by '*communications interface units*' (shown as CIUs in Fig. 1.2.1). This provides an effective method of handling a concentration of user terminals.

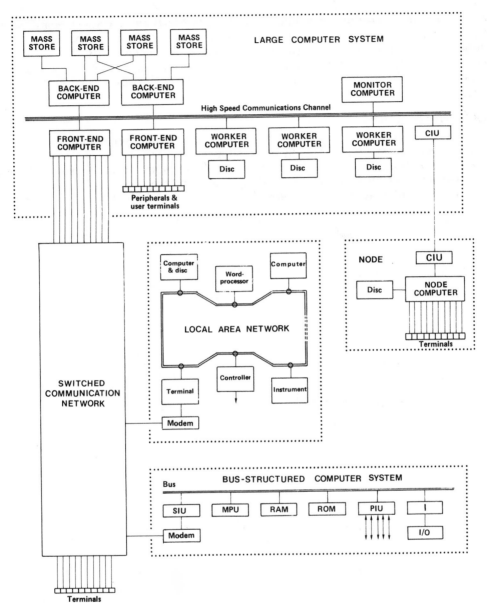

Fig. 1.2.1 Organisation of some digital systems

The '*back-end computers*' of Fig. 1.2.1 manage the expensive mass storage units which are shared by all worker computers. The integrity of the data-bases held in the mass storage units is guaranteed by a duplication of back-end computers and some mass storage units.

The '*local area network*' shown in part of Fig. 1.2.1 provides an effective means of communication between components of a computer system distributed throughout a factory, a large office, a building, a research establishment etc. The components connected to the local area network include word processors, personal computers, discs, data-acquisition systems, instruments, controllers, microprocessor development systems, etc.

The '*bus-structured computer system*' represented in Fig. 1.2.1 typifies a small *micro-*

processor-based system in which all components are interconnected via standard '*data*', '*address*' and '*control*' lines of a system *bus*. The components which can be so connected include a microprocessor unit (MPU), random-access memory (RAM), read-only memory (ROM), serial interface unit (SIU), parallel interface unit (PIU) and a wide variety of peripheral input–output units (I/O) such as keyboards, visual display units, floppy discs, etc.

1.2.2 Hierarchical structure

A hierarchical structure is an effective approach to the efficient organisation of complex systems. In digital systems, hierarchy is exploited in a number of distinct areas such as in *multi-level control* of complex industrial processes, in *memory organisation* using devices of widely different costs, access times and capacities, and the design of VLSI (very-large-scale-integration) systems where complexity management is important.

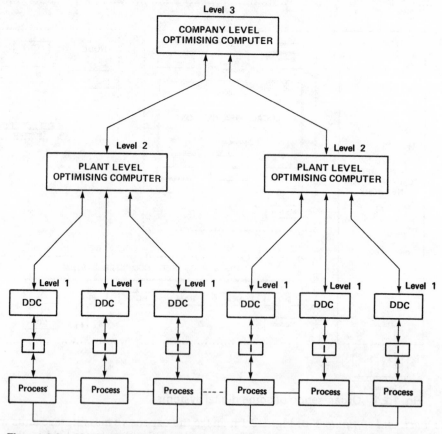

Fig. 1.2.2 Block diagram of hierarchical computer control system (DDC = direct digital control computer, I = interface)

Some features of a hierarchical structure will be described in terms of Fig. 1.2.2 which is a block diagram of a *hierarchical computer control system*. In this diagram, the word 'Process' represents the different industrial processes in a complex of interconnected processes run by a large company. The symbol DDC refers to a *direct-digital-control* computer which performs the *real-time control* of a process. The symbol I refers to the *interface* between a DDC computer and a process. This interface would normally consist of sensors (e.g. for temperature, pressure or flow), analogue-to-digital (A/D) converters, parallel interface units, digital-to-analogue (D/A) converters and process actuators. Each DDC computer is capable of performing the function of a number of analogue controllers on a time-shared basis. This results in improved, centralised control. However, hardware and software reliability is very important as the failure of a DDC computer would result in the closure of a complete process.

Fig. 1.2.2 refers to the hierarchical computer control system of a large company which operates many plants consisting of interconnected processes. The computers of the control system are arranged in several levels. The DDC computers (in Level 1) handle the real-time (second-by-second) monitoring and control of every process. The Level 2 computers have a *supervisory function* as well as performing *optimisation* at the plant level. Level 3 computers perform optimisation at the company level.

Several features of the hierarchical computer control system of Fig. 1.2.2 deserve some comment. Firstly, communication between computers is essentially between computers in adjacent levels of the hierarchy. The lowest level (DDC) computers handle large amounts of real-time data but only the modest amount of data relevant to the overall performance of each process is transmitted between the DDC computers and computers in the next higher level. Secondly a larger proportion of the company-wide operations is handled by a computer which is higher in the hierarchy. Finally a larger '*component size*' is used for sub-system optimisation by a computer which is higher in the hierarchy.

1.2.3 Structure for a real-time application

Real-time systems have *response times* which are '*time-critical*'. By implication they are *on-line* systems which receive stimuli from an environment and respond effectively to these stimuli within a time period which is less than a specified response time. Response times vary from application to application. In an airline reservation system, a satisfactory response time measured from the time an enquiry is keyed in by an operator to the time the required information is displayed on a visual display unit would be about a second. Many industrial processes have '*time constants*' varying from fractions of a second to many minutes. Suitable response times of a computer system which controls these processes vary from milliseconds to many seconds.

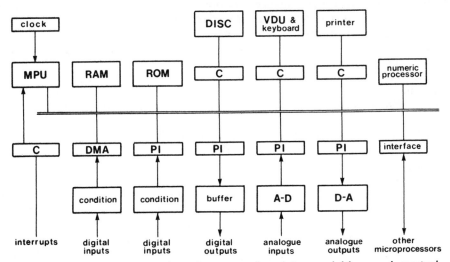

Fig. 1.2.3 Microprocessor-based system for data-acquisition and control (A–D = analogue-digital converter, D–A = digital-analogue converter, DMA = direct-memory-access channel, C = controller, PI = peripheral interface)

An example of a real-time system is the microprocessor-based system for data-acquisition and control shown in Fig. 1.2.3. The inputs to the system may be in either digital or analogue form. Digital input signals may require '*conditioning*' to transform voltages to levels acceptable to the microprocessor-based system. Analogue (voltage) inputs are converted to digital form by analogue-to-digital converters. The digital and analogue information acquired by the system is stored in the random-access memory and perhaps on disc. Output of this information may be via a visual display unit (VDU) or a printer.

The *control* function of the system of Fig. 1.2.3 is achieved by computing *feedback command signals* which take the form of digital outputs and analogue outputs from the microprocessor-based system. Digital outputs are *buffered* to provide the necessary electrical driving capability for relays, circuit breakers, etc. The analogue outputs produced by the digital-to-analogue converters are used by voltage-controlled actuators which control the process.

The '*direct-memory-access*' (DMA) channel provides a high-speed data-collection facility with data flowing from the monitored process directly to the random-access memory under the direction of the DMA controller and not the microprocessor (MPU).

The '*interrupt*' hardware provides a continuous monitoring of asynchronous events which may occur at unpredictable times but require action by the microprocessor within pre-defined time limits. *A priority interrupt* mechanism ensures that an interrupt signal corresponding to a more time-critical event is serviced with a response time which is less than that for a less time-critical (i.e. more patient) event.

The '*numeric processor*' (a 'co-processor' of the MPU) can perform arithmetic operations on *floating-point numbers* very rapidly, and hence significantly enhances the computational capability of the system.

1.2.4   Parallel structures

Multi-processing systems (i.e. systems involving concurrent processing by more than one processor) are structured to provide high performance. Examples of the functional partitioning of a system (e.g. front-end processor, back-end processor, worker computer, numeric processor, DMA channel) have been given in earlier sections. Many configurations of multi-processor systems have been used very successfully in the past, and with the availability of cheap, high-performance microprocessors and automated VLSI design procedures, interest in this area will certainly continue.

Processors in a multi-processing system may be *loosely coupled* or *tightly coupled*. Attributes of a loosely coupled system include geographically distributed processors and relatively low-speed communication links between processors. The objectives of interconnecting processors in such a system include the sharing of resources, the sharing of work load, the remote access to data-bases, data files and programs, improved processing availability and improved co-ordination of geographically distributed users contributing to a common computer project.

The attributes of a tightly coupled system include physically close processors and high-speed communication between processors. The objectives of designing such a system include high performance through *parallelism, fault-tolerance* and flexibility through a *reconfigurable* structure.

There are many problems, such as the real-time simulation of 3-dimensional systems defined by partial differential equations, which require computer capabilities far in excess of those of the fastest commercial computers. The architecture of the *super-computers* required to solve these problems is being actively studied. Many proposals are based on arrays of tightly coupled processors. The *interconnection networks* required to couple the processors take many forms such as *cross-point networks, ring networks, banyan networks, cube-connected networks, shuffle-exchange networks, tree-structured networks* and *systolic arrays*.

A simplified diagram representing the architecture of a super-computer based on tightly coupled processors is given in Fig. 1.2.4. In this diagram P represents a processor and M a memory unit. The concurrent operation of all processors is coordinated by the 'controller' (a special-purpose high-speed processor), and all elements of the system are interconnected via a high-speed interconnection network. The complexity of this interconnection network and its associated cost are very high. Hence compromises between *hardware complexity* and *generality of interconnections* are often made to provide cost-effective solutions.

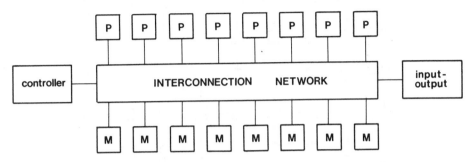

Fig. 1.2.4 Multiprocessor architecture for superfast computer (P = processor, M = memory unit)

The interconnection network which provides the highest generality of interconnection is the *cross-point switch*. This method of interconnection is shown in Fig. 1.2.5(a) for the case of eight processors (designated P) and eight memory units (designated M). Each switch of the network (designated by unlabelled squares) must be designed so that *any processor* may be connected to *any memory unit* and that *any combination* of the eight links between a processor and a memory unit is possible *simultaneously*.

The switches of the *banyan network* of Fig. 1.2.5(b) are shown with a *spread* of two and a *fan-out* of two. With this arrangement, any of the eight processors may be connected to any of the eight memory units. However every combination of links is not possible simultaneously. The banyan network has therefore a lower generality of interconnection than the cross-point switch. It has the advantage of less complexity and hence less cost. For n processors and n memory units the complexity of a cross-point switch varies as n^2 while that for a banyan network like Fig. 1.2.5(b) varies as $n \log n$.

An interconnection network which has very low generality of interconnection (i.e. high specialisation) is the *systolic array*. This method of interconnection becomes very cost-effective for specialised tasks. The concept of a systolic array is described by example in the next section.

Multi-microprocessor systems may be configured in many ways. Two of these are shown in Fig. 1.2.6 and Fig. 1.2.7. In the *shared memory* system of Fig. 1.2.6, all microprocessors communicate with one another by transmitting computed intermediate results to a shared memory. This memory is connected to the bus of one of the microprocessors called the *master* and it is accessed using an *address space* which has *global* significance, i.e. the *numeric addresses* used have the same meaning to every microprocessor in the system. For much of the time all microprocessors operate concurrently, and it is only when a microprocessor other than the master wishes to access the shared memory that *contention* of the bus associated with the master needs to be resolved by the master *bus arbitration hardware*.

In the multi-microprocessor system of Fig. 1.2.7, inter-processor communication is achieved via small random-access memories with *dual ports*. One port of each 2-port RAM

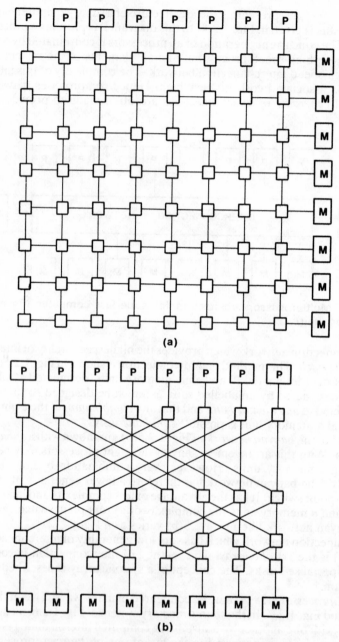

Fig. 1.2.5 Interconnection networks—(a)cross-point switch, (b) banyan network

is connected to the system bus and the second port is used exclusively by the associated microprocessor. An addressing scheme is used to allow any microprocessor to write-to or read-from any 2-port RAM. Again, for much of the time all microprocessors operate concurrently, and it is only when two or more microprocessors wish to use the bus simultaneously to access other 2-port RAMs that bus contention needs to be resolved by the arbitration hardware.

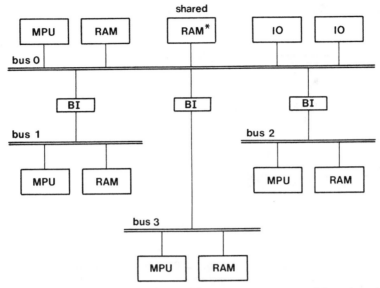

Fig. 1.2.6 Organisation of a multi-processor system with a shared memory (MPU = processor, RAM = local memory, RAM* = shared memory, BI = bus interface, IO = input-output peripheral)

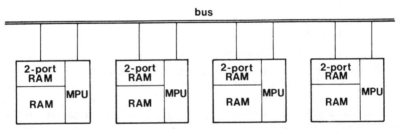

Fig. 1.2.7 Multi-microprocessor system in which any microprocessor can write into a (small) part of memory of any microprocessor connected to the bus

1.2.5 A systolic array

A *systolic array* is an array of special-purpose processors with a communication structure tailored to a specific class of problem. The structure is such that each processor communicates with only those processors which are its *nearest neighbour*, and for most of the time data required by each processor is provided by the processor's nearest neighbours. The input data and computed result of each processor are *latched*. This allows a *simultaneous* transmission of data and computed results between processors. The operation of every processor in the array is *synchronised* by a system clock, and during each clock period, each processor receives input data and computes an output result. All processors in the array '*pulsate*' with activity synchronously, and hence the use of the term *systolic*.

A processor used in systolic arrays designed for operations on *vectors* and *matrices* is represented by Fig. 1.2.8. This processor has been called an '*inner product step processor*' as it has been structured to perform the inner product step utilised by algorithms for operations on vectors and matrices. The processor has three inputs, A_{IN}, B_{IN} and C_{IN} with

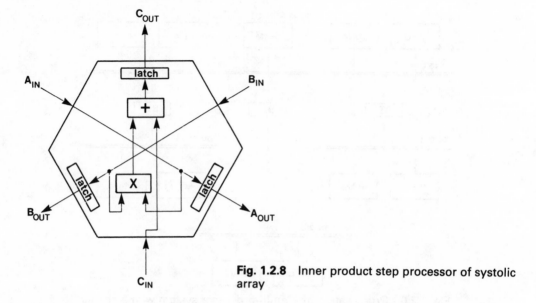

Fig. 1.2.8   Inner product step processor of systolic array

each input representing a number. The three outputs A_{OUT}, B_{OUT} and C_{OUT} are latched, and are related to the inputs by:

$$A_{OUT} = A_{IN}$$
$$B_{OUT} = B_{IN}$$
$$C_{OUT} = A_{IN} \times B_{IN} + C_{IN}$$

A systolic array which produces the product $C = (c_{ij})$ of two 3×3 matrices $A = (a_{ij})$ and $B = (b_{ij})$ is shown in Fig. 1.2.9. The array consists of nineteen *inner product step processors* defined by Fig. 1.2.8. The elements of matrix A are applied to processors 1, 2, 4, 9 and 14; the elements of matrix B are applied to processors 1, 3, 6, 11 and 16; and the elements of matrix C are produced by processors 4, 2, 1, 3 and 6. In order to understand how data and computed results flow through the array, each hexagon representing a processor in Fig. 1.2.9 is shown with a table of three columns and eleven rows. The three columns represent the three outputs A_{OUT}, C_{OUT} and B_{OUT} of the processor. The eleven rows represent eleven clock periods numbered 1 to 11 from top to bottom of the table. Blank entries represent zeros. Before clock period 1, all latches are cleared (i.e. set to zero).

The well-known product expansion for (c_{ij}) is reproduced below to facilitate the understanding of Fig. 1.2.9:

$$c_{11} = a_{11}b_{11} + a_{12}b_{21} + a_{13}b_{31}$$
$$c_{12} = a_{11}b_{12} + a_{12}b_{22} + a_{13}b_{32}$$
$$c_{13} = a_{11}b_{13} + a_{12}b_{23} + a_{13}b_{33}$$

$$c_{21} = a_{21}b_{11} + a_{22}b_{21} + a_{23}b_{31}$$
$$c_{22} = a_{21}b_{12} + a_{22}b_{22} + a_{23}b_{32}$$
$$c_{23} = a_{21}b_{13} + a_{22}b_{23} + a_{23}b_{33}$$

$$c_{31} = a_{31}b_{11} + a_{32}b_{21} + a_{33}b_{31}$$
$$c_{32} = a_{31}b_{12} + a_{32}b_{22} + a_{33}b_{32}$$
$$c_{33} = a_{31}b_{13} + a_{32}b_{23} + a_{33}b_{33}$$

In clock period 1, a_{11} is applied to processor 4 and b_{11} to processor 6. In clock period 2, these elements flow on to processors 7 and 8 respectively, and in clock period 3, they are concurrent inputs to processor 10. The entry c_{11} in column 2, row 3 of hexagon 10 indicates that the product term $a_{11}b_{11}$ is a term of the output c_{11}.

The entry a_{11} in row 4 of hexagon 13 indicates that a_{11} is an input of processor 13 in time period 4. The entry a_{11} in row 5 of hexagon 16 indicates that a_{11} is an input of processor 16 in time period 5. The reader should now be in a position to deduce how the elements of the input matrices flow through the array.

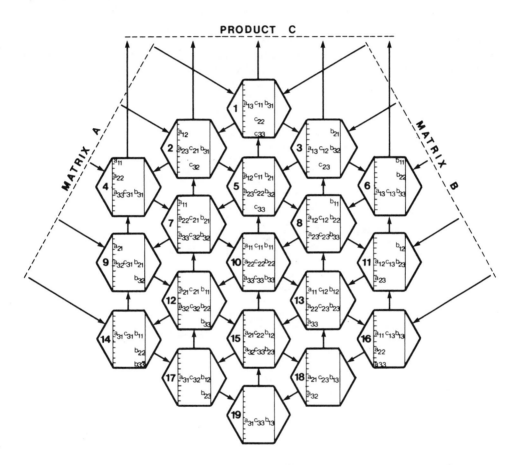

Fig. 1.2.9 Systolic array for multiplication of two 3×3 matrices

In order to see how the outputs are produced, consider the c_{11} entries in hexagons 10, 5 and 1. These indicate that $a_{11}b_{11}$ is produced in time period 3 giving an intermediate value of c_{11}. The term $a_{12}b_{21}$ is produced by processor 5 in time period 4 and added to the intermediate value of c_{11} computed earlier (in time period 3 by processor 10) giving an updated intermediate value of c_{11}. Finally, the term $a_{13}b_{31}$ is computed by processor 1 in time period 5 and added to the updated intermediate value of c_{11} computed earlier (in time period 4 by processor 5) giving a final value of c_{11}.

The entries in hexagons 4, 2, 1, 3 and 6 indicate when the elements of the matrix product are produced. The following is indicated: c_{11} is produced in time period 5 (by processor 1); C_{21} and C_{12} are produced in time period 6 (by processors 2 and 3); c_{31} and c_{13} in time period

7 (by processors 4 and 6); c_{22} in time period 8 (by processor 1); c_{32} and c_{23} in time period 9 (by processors 2 and 3) and c_{33} in time period 11 (by processor 1).

1.2.6   Arithmetic pipe-lines

An *arithmetic pipe-line* is a digital structure which provides a *high through-put* of arithmetic operations performed on *data streams*. It is an extremely effective structure for handling problems such as those found in many *signal-processing applications* which require the same arithmetic operations to be performed on long *vectors* or large *arrays* of data.

The principle of the arithmetic pipe-line is illustrated in Fig. 1.2.10. This diagram shows the organisation of a pipe-line with n stages. It is assumed that the arithmetic operation performed by the pipe-line may be sub-divided into n consecutive stages where the inputs

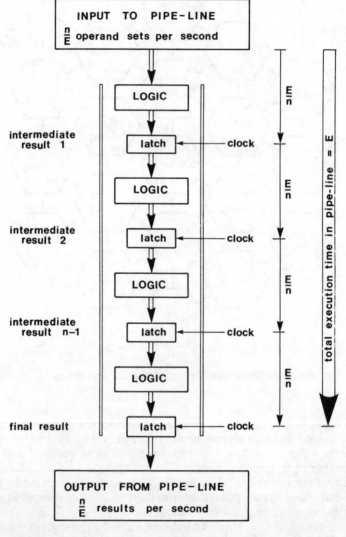

Fig. 1.2.10 Diagram illustrating the organisation of a digital-logic pipe-line with n stages (diagram drawn for $n = 4$)

to each stage are provided entirely from outputs of the previous stage, and execution times of all stages are the same. Latches are provided between the logic of consecutive stages so that all stages may be in operation concurrently. It is to be noted that at any point in time each stage of the pipe-line would be handling a part of the arithmetic operation for *different* sets of input operands.

Fig. 1.2.10 shows that if E seconds is the total execution time for a set of input operands to be processed in a pipe-line of n stages, then the rate at which operand sets are required at the pipe-line input is n/E operand sets per second and the rate at which results are produced at the pipe-line output is also n/E results per second. If approximately E seconds is required for the same arithmetic operation to be performed in an alternative arithmetic unit which is not pipe-lined, then the potential increase in speed which may be realised by pipe-lining (with n stages) is a factor of n. In practice, however, a speed increase of less

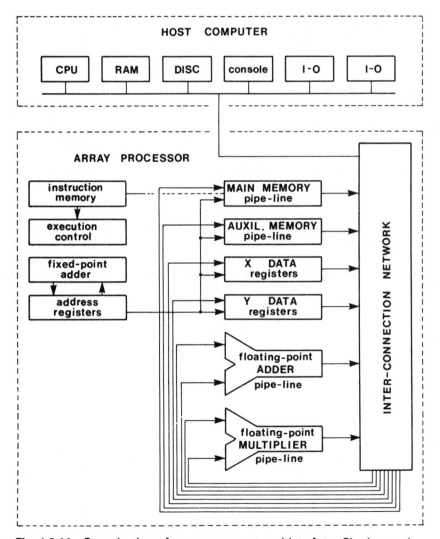

Fig. 1.2.11 Organisation of an array processor (data from Charlesworth, A. E., 'An Approach to Scientific Array Processing: The Architectural Design of the AP-1203/FPS-164 Family', *Computer*, Sept. 1981, pp 18–27)

than this amount results because of the time overheads involved in '*filling the pipe*' and in clocking the inter-stage latches.

Many computer structures utilise the inherent high speed of the arithmetic pipe-line. One such structure is that of the '*peripheral array processor*' of which an example is given in Fig. 1.2.11. The *peripheral array processor* is a special-purpose peripheral processor which can significantly enhance the capabilities of a host computer for processing large data arrays. Such a combination is extremely cost-effective for a class of *signal-processing* applications.

Peripheral array processors such as that represented by Fig. 1.2.11 possess one or more *pipe-lined floating-point adders* and one or more *pipe-lined floating-point multipliers*. There are several memory units and *register files* specifically for constant and variable data. These memory units and register files provide the data streams for the pipe-lined adder(s) and multiplier(s). They are also used to store processed intermediate results. All data memory units, register files and pipe-lines are interconnected by a flexible, high-speed interconnection network. *Instructions* which control the execution of arithmetic operations and transfers to/from memory are stored in a separate program memory. A high level of '*parallelism*' is therefore a major attribute of the peripheral array processor.

1.2.7   Data-flow computer

General-purpose, *stored-program* computers of the *von Neumann type* have two important characteristics. Firstly they have an *addressable memory* to store both *instructions* and *data*. Secondly instructions are executed *sequentially* under the control of a *program counter*. These characteristics impose fundamental limitations to the processing capabilities of computers of this type. Examples of *parallel structures* to improve performance have been given in previous sections. Another structure which is receiving a considerable amount of attention in laboratories for computer research and development is the structure of the *data-flow computer*.

A data-flow computer deals only with *values* and not with addresses. There is nothing like a program counter, and it is the data itself which 'drives the computation'. The program memory of a data-flow computer contains a representation of *data flow graphs*. Once the data for an operation becomes available that operation is despatched for execution by one of a multiplicity of processing elements. *Parallel processing* and *asynchronous operation* are, therefore, important attributes of the data-flow computer. These are the attributes which are being exploited to achieve high performance.

To illustrate the concept of data flow, consider the following sequence of assignment statements:

$$\begin{aligned}
1. \quad & C \leftarrow A + B \\
2. \quad & D \leftarrow A/B \\
3. \quad & E \leftarrow C * C \\
4. \quad & F \leftarrow C - D \\
5. \quad & G \leftarrow E + A
\end{aligned}$$

When values for A and B become available both statements 1 and 2 may be executed *simultaneously*. The *completion* of statement 1 *initiates* statement 3, and the completion of both statements 1 and 2 initiates statement 4. Completion of statement 3 initiates statement 5. The above illustrates the concept of *data-dependent* operations.

The organisation of a prototype data-flow computer developed at the University of Manchester is shown in Fig. 1.2.12. The five major units, viz. processing unit, switch, token queue, matching store and node store are connected in a pipe-lined ring around which *data tokens* flow. A data token consists of both data and control information. A structure referred to as a '*dynamic tagged data flow model*' is implemented by including a

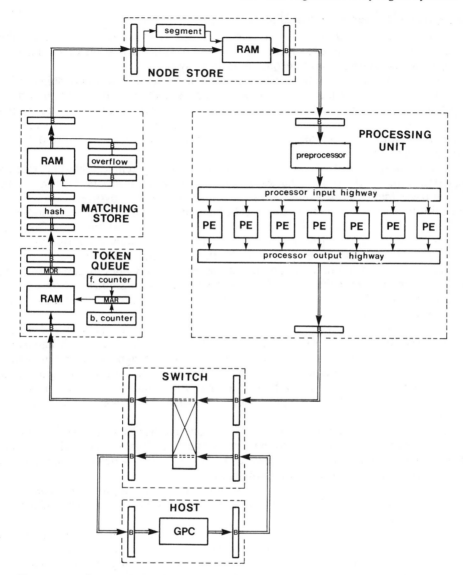

Fig. 1.2.12 Organisation of the prototype data-flow computer developed at the University of Manchester

label in each data token to identify the *context* of the data token. The data token also includes a specification of the *destination node* used in data flow graphs.

The *switch* allows the host computer to supply data tokens to the ring and to route data tokens to output devices. The *processing unit* executes node operations concurrently. Data tokens produced by the processing unit are stored temporarily in a *token queue*. The label and destination node fields of data tokens are matched by a *pseudo-associative memory* in the *matching store*. Matched data tokens are then sent to the *node store* where information defining the node operation is appended.

The *parallelism* of the structure very briefly outlined above is in the processing unit and in the pipe-lined ring which allows the operation of all units to be overlapped.

1.2.8   Parallel structures for reliability

Military and space *applications* provide classic examples of systems which require ultra-high reliability. Many other examples may be found in areas such as medicine, industrial control, data-base systems and telecommunications systems.

There are many *causes* of system failure. Some stem from faulty workmanship resulting in defects such as poor solder joints, poor hermetic seals, cracked insulation and contaminated parts, etc. Others result from the deterioration of the strength of a device from long exposure to fluctuations in operating and environmental conditions such as excess voltage, heat, vibration and radiation, etc. Some failures result from undetected 'bugs' in computer programs.

The term '*fault-tolerance*' of a digital system refers to the system's ability to perform its designed function in spite of some hardware failures and program errors. This implies that both '*hardware fault-tolerance*' and '*software fault-tolerance*' are involved.

The fault-tolerance (and hence reliability) of a digital system may be increased by the use of *redundancy techniques*. This involves the use of additional hardware (hardware redundancy) and additional (but not identical) programs (software redundancy).

Error-detecting-and-correcting codes such as the Hamming codes have been used for some time in digital computer components such as memories. Codes for the correction of single bit errors and for the detection of multi-bit errors are in common use. Some modern disc systems utilise a Fire code which can detect and correct isolated bursts of up to twelve consecutive error bits.

An example of a hardware redundancy technique is '*triple modular redundancy*' (TMR). This technique utilises three identical modules operating in parallel. The outputs of each module pass to a '*majority voting system*' whose output agrees with the majority of module outputs. This technique is an example of '*static redundancy techniques*' which utilise redundant hardware in such a way that the effect of a faulty module is instantaneously masked by other permanently connected and concurrently operating modules.

'*Dynamic redundancy*' involves the use of only one module at a time while spares are kept on-line ready to be switched into the system when a fault is detected. This technique therefore requires mechanisms for fault detection and dynamic switching of modules (i.e. faulty module switched out and spare switched in).

Further developments such as '*hybrid redundancy*', '*self-purging redundancy*' and '*reconfiguration schemes*' are based on extensions and combinations of static and dynamic redundancy techniques.

In a commercial system designed for high reliability, but which can tolerate a small amount of 'down-time', the concept of '*availability*' is useful. This is defined as 'the capability of an item, under the combined aspects of its reliability and maintenance, to perform its required function at a stated instant in time'. In order to provide a quantitative assessment of how redundancy techniques can improve the availability of a system, there must be a quantitative definition of the availability of each component of a system. One such definition is:

$$\text{Availability} = \frac{\text{MTBF}}{\text{MTBF} + \text{MTTR}}$$

where MTBF = mean-time-between-failure
       MTTR = mean-time-to-repair

The availability of a component or a system is therefore represented by a fraction less than unity which approaches unity when the availability is very high.

Fig. 1.2.13 illustrates how the availability of a computer system can be increased by duplicating components of the system. The symbols a_1, a_2, a_3 and a_4 represent the availabilities of the line controller, the computer, the file controller and the discs respec-

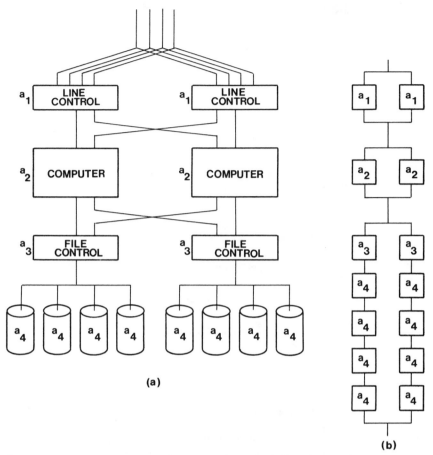

Fig. 1.2.13 Diagram illustrating the increase in 'availability' in a computer system with duplicated components—(a) computer system, (b) electrical circuit for computation of system availability

tively. The system availability is computed using a method analogous to that used for the analysis of electrical circuits containing series/parallel elements. Such a circuit is shown in Fig. 1.2.13(b). The system availability a is given by:

$$a = \{1-(1-a_1)^2\}\{1-(1-a_2)^2\}\{1-(1-a_3a_4^4)^2\}$$

Keeping in mind that all the as are fractions less than unity, the reader may readily show that the above expression for a is greater than $a_1a_2a_3a_4^4$ which is the availability of an alternative system without duplicated components.

1.3 CHARACTERISTICS OF SOME COMPONENTS OF DIGITAL SYSTEMS

1.3.1 Relative performance

Section 1.3 deals mainly with components which *process* and *store* digital information. Since the conception of the stored-program computer of the von Neumann type in the late 1940s, there has been an *evolution* of components which perform these functions. Many

bits   b

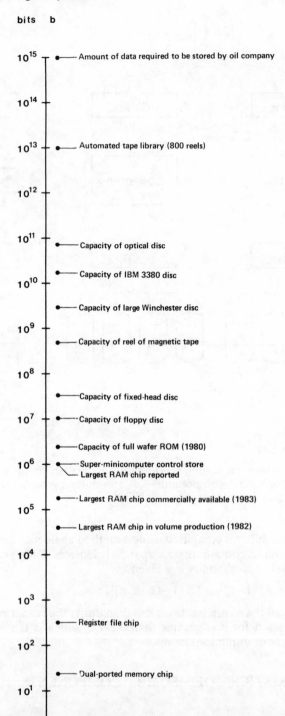

Fig. 1.3.1 Illustration of the order of magnitude of quantities defined by the unit 'bits' (b)

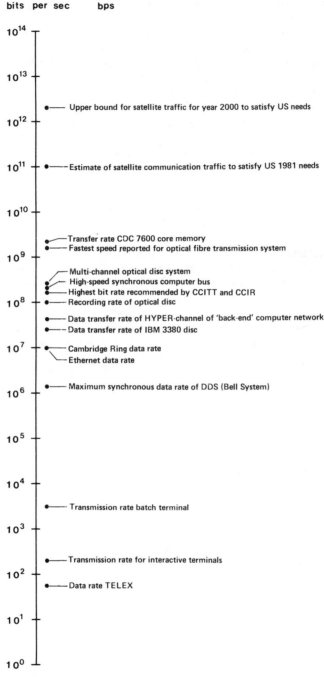

Fig. 1.3.2 Illustration of the order of magnitude of quantities defined by the unit 'bits per second' (bps)

devices have had *life cycles* with stages involving (i) active research and development, (ii) successful exploitation in commercial systems and finally (iii) obsolescence brought on by newer technologies. The technologies used in the main (high-speed) memories of digital computers present a good example. The *electrostatic, cathode-ray-tube store* used in early (parallel) computers was replaced by the *ferrite-core memory*—the dominant technology used for a long time in most second-generation and some third-generation computers. The ferrite-core memory still has some applications, especially those where *non-volatility* is important. However this type of memory has now been virtually replaced by the *semiconductor (MOS) random-access memory*. The *active element* of digital circuits has also been involved in evolutionary changes from the *vacuum tube* to the *discrete transistor* and then on to *integrated circuits* of increasing levels of integration.

The performance capabilities of the very large number of different types of processors and memories which have been used since the late 1940s differ by many orders of magnitude. There has been continual improvement, and technological advances in recent times, especially in the fields of *very-large-scale-integrated circuits* and *magnetic recording techniques* (such as 'vertical recording'), point to future improvements at an increased rate.

Because performance capabilities vary so widely and are improving so rapidly, it is important to have an understanding of the '*relative performance*' of digital components. An initial comparison on an '*order-of-magnitude*' basis is useful. To achieve this it is suggested that performance measures should be plotted on a logarithmic scale (e.g. equal increments for powers of ten). Two such plots are given in Fig. 1.3.1 and Fig. 1.3.2. The first provides an illustration of the order-of-magnitude of quantities defined by the unit 'bit', and the second provides an illustration of the order-of-magnitude of quantities defined by the unit 'bits/second'. The positions of points on these plots will certainly change as further technological advances are made in the years ahead. A suggestion for some points of interest (not all of which are plotted in Fig. 1.3.1 and Fig. 1.3.2) is given in the following lists:

Quantities defined by the unit 'bit'
- Data stored in flip-flop
- Capacity of largest memory chip
    - 'register file'
    - bipolar RAM
    - dual-ported
    - 'content-addressable' ('associative')
    - static RAM
    - dynamic RAM in volume production
    - dynamic RAM reported
    - non-volatile RAM
    - ROM reported
    - ultra-violet light erasable ROM
    - electrically erasable ROM
    - electrically alterable ROM
    - CCD
    - bubble memory
- Size of
    - microprocessor register file
    - super-minicomputer control store
    - large main-frame cache
- Capacities of
    - floppy diskette

  — fixed-head disc
  — moving-head disc
  — 'Winchester' disc
  — optical disc
  — one reel of magnetic tape
  — automated tape library
  — mass storage system
- Size of data-bases for
  — published works
  — suppliers of electronic components
  — inventory of parts used by a country's military forces
  — medical diagnosis
  — CAD system for semiconductor manufacture
  — airline reservation system
  — telephone directories
- Amount of data required to be stored for
  — direct digital control
  — security assessment of power utility
  — telecommunications switching computer
  — on-line banking system
  — insurance company
  — multi-national company
  — oil company

Quantities defined by the unit 'bits per second'
- 'Bandwidth' of main memory
- Data transfer rates of
  — floppy diskette
  — fixed-head disc
  — moving-head disc
  — largest commercially available discs
  — magnetic tape
  — optical disc
- Data rates available on switched telephone networks
- Data rates of digital carriers in telecommunication system
  — coaxial cable
  — optical fibre
- Highest reported data rate for optical fibre transmission system
- Data rates of microprocessor buses
- Data rate of local area network, e.g.
  — Ethernet
- Data rate of communication ring, e.g.
  — Cambridge ring
- Data rate of high-speed communication channel for 'back-end' communication network of large computer system
- Satellite communication traffic.

Performance measures of digital computers take the form of *'bench-mark'* tests. These tests involve both the *compilation* of programs written in high-level languages (such as PASCAL, ADA and FORTRAN) and the *execution* of compiled code to perform specific tasks. Examples of these tasks are the inversion of matrices, the sorting of data, the retrieval of data, the solution of complex simultaneous differential equations, the processing of non-numerical data and the real-time handling of input–output devices. The *execution times* to perform these tasks are used as a measure of the *relative performance* of digital computers.

Numeric performance measures of digital computers may also be obtained using a '*mix*', i.e. a *weighted sum* of the performance measures for individual operations and features. Examples of these individual operations and functions are the *cycle time* of main memory, the *execution time* for a floating-point addition, the *data rate* for transfers to and from secondary memory, the number of working registers, the 'richness' of the *instruction set*, the mechanism for handling *re-entrant subroutines*, the availability of *virtual addressing*, the ability to handle *interrupts* with assigned priority and so on. The assignment of the *weighting factors* used in these mixes can be based on the frequency of use of the individual operations for typical tasks. The assignment of numeric values to reflect the usefulness of features (such as subroutine re-entrancy) must be based on experience with many computer systems which do or do not possess these features.

A performance measure based on a mix of statements in a high level language such as FORTRAN, PASCAL or ADA is the 'Whetstone instructions per second', or WIPS.

Two simple performance measures of digital computers which are gaining increasing usage are (i) MIPS—*million instructions per second* and (ii) MFLOPS—*million floating-point operations per second*.

1.3.2   General-purpose computers

1.3.2.1   *Stored-program computer concepts*

A 'program' in a 'stored-program computer' consists of coded information representing computer-executable '*instructions*' and computer-recognisable '*data*'. Instructions and data are stored *in the same physical form* in a '*random-access memory*'. Such a memory contains '*locations*' in which computer '*words*' (sets of binary digits) representing instructions and data are stored. Each location is assigned a unique numeric 'address', and 'reading' from or 'writing' into a particular location is performed by firstly specifying the location's address. The time required to access (i.e., read from or write into) a location of random-access memory is *independent of the location's address*.

Most computers are organised as '*fixed word-length*' computers. This implies that circuits are provided for (i) the addressing of words in random-access memory, (ii) the transfer of words from one part of a computer to another, and (iii) the execution of arithmetic or logical operations on words. Word-lengths may vary from 8, 16 and 32 bits in microprocessors, 16 and 32 bits in minicomputers and up to 64 bits in main-frames.

The hardware of an elementary stored-program computer consists of (i) a random-access memory for program storage, (ii) an 'arithmetic logic unit' for performing the arithmetic or logical operations required by the set of executable instructions, (iii) 'control unit' for controlling instruction execution, and (iv) input–output devices.

The organisation of a simple (hypothetical) computer is shown in Fig. 1.3.3. This figure shows that there are two registers associated with the random access memory. These are the '*memory address register*' and the '*memory data register*'. To perform a '*read cycle*', the address of the location to be accessed must be loaded into the memory address register and a memory cycle initiated. During this read cycle, the contents of the addressed location are loaded into the memory data register, and at the end of this (overall non-destructive) cycle, the addressed location in memory is *left unchanged*. To perform a '*write cycle*', the data to be written into a location in memory must be loaded into the memory data register, the address of this location must be loaded into the memory address register and a memory cycle must be initiated. During this cycle, the contents of the memory data register are written into the location specified by the memory address register *overwriting* its previous contents.

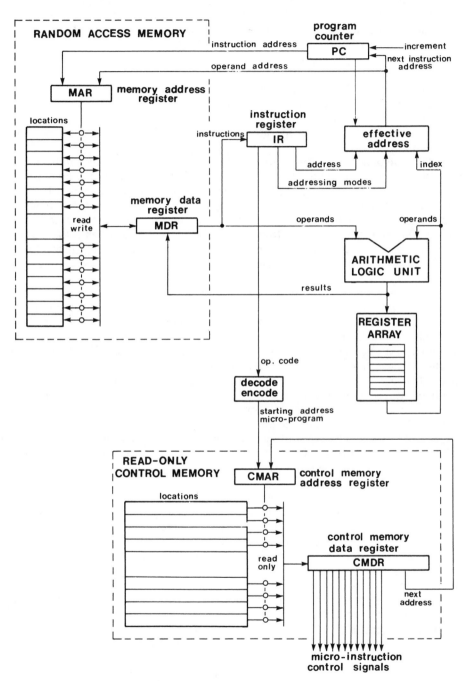

Fig. 1.3.3 Organisation of a computer with a micro-programmed control unit

The coded instructions have *formats* which differ from computer to computer. Each instruction must contain a *field* (i.e. a group of bits) which specifies the *type* of instruction which is to be performed. This field, often referred to as the *'operation code'* or *'op. code'*, has the additional function of defining the significance of other fields of the instruction. The format of an instruction may therefore contain the following fields:

(i)   operation code (mandatory),
(ii) addressing mode (optional),
(iii) one or more addresses (optional),
(iv) parameters (optional), and
(v)   operands (optional).

The data on which instructions operate may also have different formats. Some examples are given in Fig. 1.3.4.

The execution of an instruction stored in memory takes place in a *'machine cycle'*. This consists of a timing *'phase'* during which the *instruction is fetched* from memory followed by a second timing phase during which the *instruction is executed*. The latter phase may be further sub-divided into periods during which (i) operands are fetched (from memory or registers), (ii) the instruction is executed, and finally (iii) the result is stored (in memory or registers). During the 'fetch instruction phase', the current instruction is loaded into the *'instruction register'*, and it remains in this register for the remainder of the machine cycle as it is the function of the instruction register to control the interpretation and execution of the instruction.

The sequence in which instructions stored in memory are executed is controlled by the *'program counter'*. This is a register of the computer which, at the beginning of each machine cycle, holds the *address of the next instruction* to be executed. In the fetch instruction phase of the machine cycle, the contents of the program counter are copied into the memory address register and a read memory cycle is initiated. During this memory cycle, the instruction to be executed is read from memory into the memory data register, from which a copy is transferred to the *instruction register*. As instructions in memory are normally obeyed sequentially, until a break in the sequence is ordered by an instruction, the program counter is incremented (by one) by hardware sometime in the machine cycle. This is usually carried out early in the fetch instruction phase. A break in the normal sequence can be caused by types of instructions described as *jumps*, *branches* and *skips*, etc. The mechanism for this is simply the overwriting of the incremented program counter with a new address which then becomes effective at the beginning of the next machine cycle.

An *'arithmetic logic unit'* is depicted in Fig. 1.3.3. This unit performs arithmetic and logical operations on operands supplied by the memory or *register array*. Results so produced are stored back in memory or the register array.

A reference to the 'bottleneck' caused by the fixed (i.e. limited) *'bandwidth'* of the main memory of a von Neumann-type computer has already been made. It is often stated that this type of computer is *'memory limited'*. To lessen the effect of this feature, some computers are provided with a number of registers (e.g. 8 or 16) in a *register file* or *register array*. Programs optimised for execution time make good use of this small but higher speed form of storage for frequently used data.

Fig. 1.3.3 contains a block labelled *'effective address'*. The three inputs to this block shown in the figure are (i) address (from a field of the instruction register), (ii) addressing mode (from a field of the instruction register), and (iii) index (from the register array). The addressing mode field specifies one of a number of different methods of addressing which is to be used. For *indexed addressing* the contents of a special hardware register called an *index register* are added to the address specified by the instruction to form the *effective address*. This mechanism for *address modification*, which originated from early computers constructed at the University of Manchester, produces significant improvements in coding

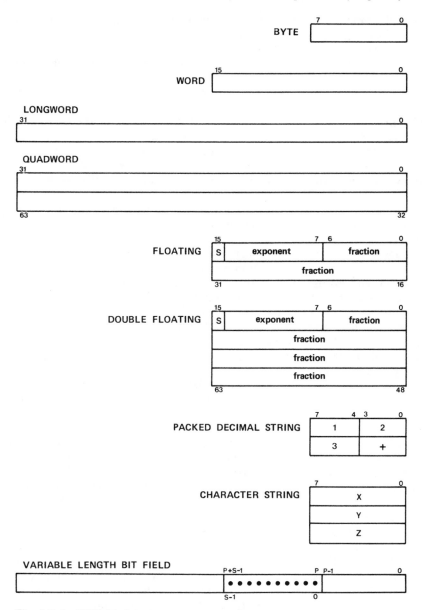

Fig. 1.3.4 VAX-11 data type representations

'program loops'. This program structure occurs so frequently that indexing adds substantially to the performance capability of a computer. Other methods of addressing are listed below with brief descriptions:

Absolute addressing: addressing using the assigned unique numeric address of an
(direct addressing) operand or memory location.
Indexed addressing: generation of an effective address of an operand or memory
location by adding the contents of a specified index register
to a specified (base) address.

Inherent addressing: (implicit addressing)	operands are implied from the operation code of the instruction.
Register addressing: (geometric addressing)	the specification of one of the working registers or other registers of a computer using the appropriate number of bits of the instruction.
Immediate addressing:	the specification of the actual operand as part of the instruction.
Indirect addressing: (deferred addressing)	the specification of the address of the location where the operand address is stored.
Relative addressing:	addressing a memory location relative to the location in which the current instruction is stored.
Relative-to-base addressing:	addressing a memory location relative to the contents of a base register.
Page zero addressing: (abbreviated or truncated addressing)	addressing a location in memory page 0 (which typically consists of locations 0 to 2^n-1 when $n = 8$ or 9).
Current page addressing:	addressing a location of the page in which the current instruction resides.
Autoincrement addressing: (post-increment addressing)	use of the contents of a specified register as the operand address followed by the automatic incrementing of the contents of this register.
Autodecrement addressing: (pre-decrement addressing)	decrementing of the contents of a specified register followed by the use of the resultant contents as the operand address.
Associative addressing: (addressing by content)	addressing a full memory 'cell' by the contents of part of the cell.
Virtual addressing:	the use of a fictitious address space which is automatically mapped into actual (physical) address spaces using hardware memory management devices.

An important program structure is the '*nested subroutine*'. This is illustrated in Fig. 1.3.5(a). The sequence of instructions and program segments represented by this diagram is shown below. In this listing, the symbols M, A, B, C, D and E represent the main program and subroutines A, B, C, D and E respectively. Subscripts define program segments. The words EXECUTE, JUMP SUBROUTINE and RETURN define respectively (i) the execution of a program segment, (ii) the calling of (or jump to) a subroutine and (iii) the end of a subroutine and subsequent return to the calling program/subroutine.

A pair of instructions '*jump-to-subroutine*' (JSR) and '*return-from-subroutine*' (RTS) must be organised so that a '*return link*' stored by a JSR is utilised by a RTS. The return link is the value of the *incremented program counter* when a JSR is being executed. This ensures that following the execution of a subroutine, the computer will resume with the instruction following the JSR. The requirement of the nested subroutine structure is that return links must be stored in a '*last-in-first-out memory*' (*LIFO memory*). The LIFO function may be implemented with a *stack* consisting of consecutive locations in main (RAM) memory. The location at the top of the stack is pointed to (i.e. addressed) by a *stack pointer*. The operation of *pushing* a data element onto the stack involves decrementing the stack pointer and then *storing* the data element in RAM using the address of the stack pointer. The operation of *pulling* a data element off the stack involves *reading* from the location in RAM addressed by the stack pointer and then incrementing the stack pointer.

Fig. 1.3.5(b) illustrates a useful extension of the stack when applied to nested subroutines. One of the working registers, designated R, together with the consecutive locations in RAM pointed to by the stack pointer constitute the LIFO memory for the

→ Nesting depth

```
EXECUTE M₁
JUMP SUBROUTINE A
        EXECUTE A₁
        RETURN
EXECUTE M₂
JUMP SUBROUTINE A
        EXECUTE A₁
        RETURN
EXECUTE M₃
JUMP SUBROUTINE B
        EXECUTE B₁
        JUMP SUBROUTINE C
                EXECUTE C₁
                JUMP SUBROUTINE D
                        EXECUTE D₁
                        RETURN
                EXECUTE C₂
                RETURN
        EXECUTE B₂
        JUMP SUBROUTINE E
                EXECUTE E₁
                RETURN
        EXECUTE B₃
        RETURN
EXECUTE M₄
```

Time

storage of the return links. The register R holds the 'last-in' return link. The advantage of this structure is that it provides an efficient mechanism for a 'called subroutine' to gain access to locations (containing *subroutine parameters*) of the 'calling program'.

The reader is now advised to study Fig. 1.3.5(a) and (b). The requirement of a LIFO memory for return links of nested subroutines should be confirmed.

1.3.2.2 *Micro-programmed control*

The generation of control signals for each instruction type in every timing period of a machine cycle (of a computer) requires a sequential circuit of great complexity. Computer designers confronted with the task of designing such a circuit have devised techniques of performing this task in a systematic way. One of these techniques is 'micro-programmed control'. This technique was originally proposed by Professor M. V. Wilkes and used in early computers constructed at Cambridge University.

The top half of Fig. 1.3.3 represents the organisation of a hypothetical computer. The main data paths are shown but no details are given of the control signals. These, of course, depend on (i) the detailed specification of the instruction set, (ii) details of addressing modes, (iii) memory features and timing, (iv) interface with input/output devices, (v) interface with control console and so on. These details have not been provided; nevertheless, the required types of control signals would, very likely, *include* the following:

    (i) main timing signals,
    (ii) memory timing signals,
    (iii) memory control signals (e.g. specification of type of memory cycle—'read', 'write', 'read-modify-write'),

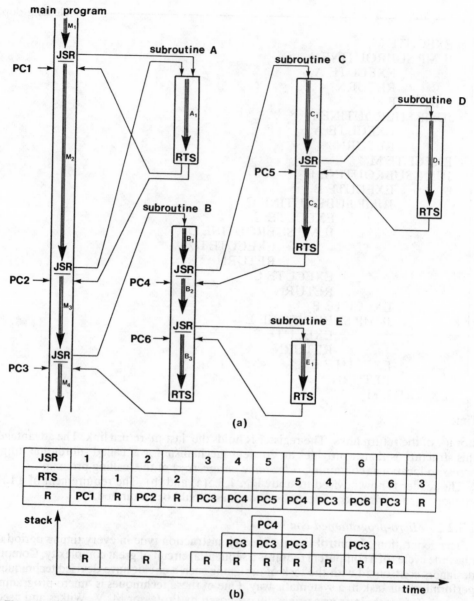

Fig. 1.3.5 Nested subroutines—(a) subroutine linkage, (b) stack contents

(iv)   clocks to each register,
 (v)   data selector control signals specifying parallel inputs to each register,
(vi)   signals specifying serial inputs to some working registers (e.g. for shift instructions),
(vii) control signals for the arithmetic logic unit specifying the type of operation to be performed,
(viii) data selector control signals specifying the parallel inputs to the arithmetic logic unit,
 (ix) signals specifying the inputs to the adder used for indexing,

(x) carry signals,
(xi) signal to increment the program counter,
(xii) signals to overwrite the program counter, and
(xiii) control signals for interface to input/output devices.

The bottom half of Fig. 1.3.3 shows the organisation of a 'read-only control memory' with two associated registers—viz, *control memory address register* (CMAR) and *control memory data register* (CMDR). The control memory holds programs of *micro-instructions*. Each word of control memory represents one micro-instruction which is formatted with two fields. The first field specifies all the required control signals (such as those listed above) for performing the elementary operations (such as transfer, shift, increment, add, etc.) which every hardware unit has been designed to execute in a *micro-instruction cycle*. The second field of a micro-instruction specifies the address of the next micro-instruction. That part of the CMDR corresponding to this latter field is connected to an input of the CMAR. Hence, following the loading of the CMAR with the *starting address* of a program of instructions, a *sequence of control signals* will be generated in successive micro-instruction cycles. There is a defined sequence of control signals (i.e. sequence of micro-instructions) for each type of 'machine-language instruction' (or 'macro-instruction') stored in main (RAM) memory. Hence the invocation of the correct sequence (i.e. the specification of the correct starting address of a micro-program) is controlled by that part of the instruction register corresponding to the operation code.

1.3.2.3 *Bus-structured computer*

A very flexible arrangement of transmitting information between any two of a number of devices is provided by a bus-structured digital system. The term 'bus' in this context refers to a collection of signal lines (i.e. wires) to which a number of devices may be connected. The actual electrical circuits connected to the bus are 'line drivers' and 'line receivers'. As implied by the names used for these circuits, the important characteristic of a bus is that any device connected to the bus may 'drive the bus' (i.e. transmit information to it), while any other device may receive information from the bus.

The organisation of a bus-structured computer was illustrated in Fig. 1.2.1. There are usually three distinct subsections within a bus for (i) data, (ii) address, and (iii) control. For a minicomputer there may be (typically) 16 lines for data, 16 or 18 lines for address and a dozen or so lines for control. Associated with a bus is a hardware unit called a 'priority arbitration unit' which arbitrates on the use of the bus. Any device connected to the bus may request its use by sending 'bus request signals' to the priority arbitration unit along the control lines of the bus. The priority arbitration unit responds with 'bus grant signals' (again along control lines of the bus); this signals the device to begin transmitting or receiving information using the data and address parts of the bus. The arbitration of the use of the bus is usually carried out on a (bus) cycle-by-cycle basis.

There are many advantages in using a bus for the interconnection of the components of a computer. Some of these advantages are summarised by the points listed below:

(i) Modularity: enabling a computer system to be readily assembled from functionally independent sub-assemblies.

(ii) Expandability: (extensibility) enabling a computer system to be readily upgraded while still retaining the major sub-assemblies.

(iii) Flexibility: enabling a computer system to be modified to meet changing requirements.

(iv) Maintainability: improved maintainability (i.e. lower 'mean-time-to-repair') resulting in improved 'availability'.

(v) Interfacing: the adoption of a standard bus simplifies the problem of interfacing a computer with peripheral devices.

    (vi) Interconnection: the bus provides an efficient method of interconnecting units with moderate physical separation.

   (vii) Distributed processing: concurrent operation of components with the use of the
       (concurrent operation)   bus restricted to information interchanges improves processing capability.

  (viii) Direct-memory-access: access to the random-access memory of the system by a peripheral device without the involvement of the central processing unit improves both the rate of data transfer and the CPU throughput.

    (ix) Memory-mapped   data and status registers of peripheral devices are
       input–output: assigned addresses, and hence may be tested, read and written into using memory-addressing instructions.

     (x) Priority interrupts: the priority arbitration unit may also arbitrate on requests to interrupt the current program, and information relating to the starting address of an interrupt service routine may be transmitted over the bus by the peripheral unit initiating the granted request.

    It is seen that the bus-structured computer lends itself to extremely versatile extensions of the stored-program concept. Two of these extensions, 'direct-memory-access' and 'priority interrupts' are briefly described in the following sections.

1.3.3　Interrupts

1.3.3.1　*Priority interrupts*

The stored-program computer, as described in earlier sections, utilises a highly sequential mode of operation. A program consists of a set of instructions which are obeyed sequentially with only one instruction being executed at any time. In a computer system containing many peripheral devices (keyboards, printers, discs, tapes, etc.) there is usually one program (in RAM) for each peripheral device. Each of these programs 'services' a peripheral device performing such tasks as code conversion, data reformatting, error detection, data retrieval and so on. Such a program will be referred to as a *'service routine'*. It is assumed that each peripheral device has a certain *'patience'*, and following a request for service, the central processing unit must execute the appropriate service routine within a certain *'response time'*.

    Service requests from peripheral devices occur randomly in time. They may be sensed and used to initiate appropriate action either by software (i.e. by program) or by hardware. The software approach implies that programs must be structured so that instructions which test the external service request signals must be executed repetitively in such a way that successive testing of each service request is less than the required response time. Because of the complexity of program structures in general, this condition is difficult to meet except in simple applications. Moreover, the 'overhead' measured in processing time lost to repeated testing of external signals makes the approach extremely unattractive.

    The hardware approach implies that digital hardware is provided for the *continuous monitoring of all service request signals*. This function is performed by the priority arbitration unit of a bus-structured computer. The approach also implies that a mechanism is provided for (i) the interruption of the current program and the initiation of a service routine under direction of the priority arbitration unit, and (ii) (following the completion of the service routine) the resumption of the interrupted program. The procedure just described is referred to as an *'interrupt'*.

    If a computer system provides for the allocation of priorities to peripheral devices in

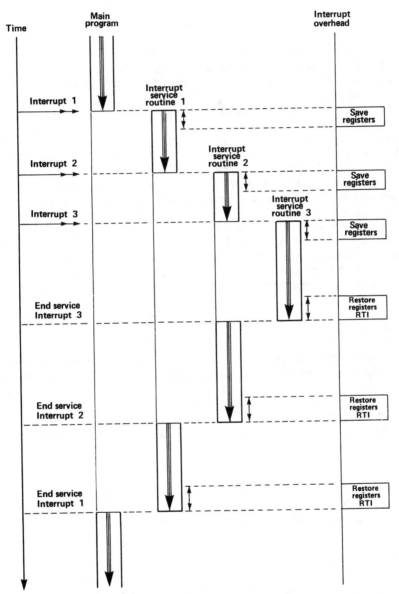

Fig. 1.3.6 Diagram illustrating an interrupt handling sequence in a computer with priority interrupts (in the diagram, interrupt 1 has the lowest priority and interrupt 3 has highest priority)

such a way that a service request from a peripheral device of high priority may interrupt a service routine servicing a peripheral device of lower priority, the computer system is said to have '*priority interrupts*'. It is usual to allocate high priority to peripheral devices with low patience (requiring rapid response) and lower priorities to devices with higher patience.

Following a decision made by the priority arbitration unit to cause a program interruption, the following operations are required:

  (i) wait until the end of execution of the current instruction,
 (ii) store the (incremented) program counter and other computer '*status*' information (so that the computer may resume executing the program following the interruption), and
(iii) set the program counter with the starting address of the appropriate 'interrupt service routine'.

Step (ii) above requires a 'stack' or other form of 'last-in-first-out' memory (LIFO memory) if a system of priority interrupts is to be implemented. Step (iii) above may be implemented in several ways. One common method is to have '*interrupt vectors*' stored in random-access memory. These interrupt vectors are stored in unique locations assigned to each peripheral device, and included in each vector is the starting address of the relevant interrupt service routine.

If an interrupt service routine uses the working registers of the computer, the first part of its code must store the contents of these registers in a stack or LIFO memory before it services the interrupt. Following the servicing of the interrupt, the working registers must be restored, and the last instruction executed must be a 'return-from-interrupt' instruction (RTI). This restores the program counter and other computer status information.

The mechanism described above is illustrated in Fig. 1.3.6. This figure represents the following sequence of events:

  (i) interruption of the main program by interrupt 1,
 (ii) interruption of interrupt service routine 1 by the higher priority interrupt 2,
(iii) interruption of interrupt service routine 2 by the highest priority interrupt 3,
 (iv) return to interrupt service routine 2,
  (v) return to interrupt service routine 1, and
 (vi) return to the main program.

The time required to vector to and return from interrupt service routines, plus the time required by the interrupt service routines to save and restore register contents results in a time overhead of the priority interrupt mechanism. This overhead is also illustrated in Fig. 1.3.6.

In an on-line, real-time environment in which a single computer is used to control a large number of devices of varying patience, it is essential for the computer to have priority interrupts. This feature is one of many extensions of the original stored-program concept.

1.3.3.2 *Re-entrant subroutine*

Subroutine re-entrancy is important in the situation where a number of service routines (and the main program) require the use of the same subroutine. *Without* subroutine re-entrancy each service routine must contain its own copy of the subroutine; *with* subroutine re-entrancy each service routine may call the one and only copy of the subroutine when required. This can result in a significant reduction in memory requirements.

The mechanism for handling subroutine re-entrancy must provide the correct '*return links*' for situations such as that depicted in Fig. 1.3.7(a). The symbols M, A and S refer to the main program, the re-entrant subroutine A, and the service routine respectively.

Subscripts define program segments. The sequence of events depicted is:

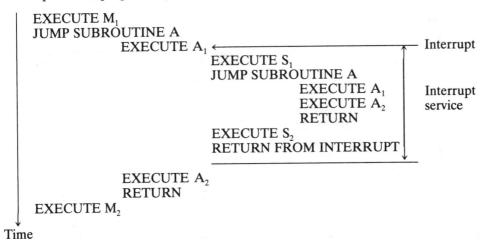

Time

Fig. 1.3.7(b) shows how the LIFO memory characteristic of a *stack* is utilised to handle re-entrancy. The details come from the PDP11 family of computers. Interrupts in the PDP11 cause the values of both the incremented program counter (PC) and the *processor status word* (PS) to be stored on the stack. A *return-from-interrupt* (RTI) causes these values to be pulled from the stack and loaded into the relevant registers. The mechanism for handling subroutines is the same as that described in Section 1.3.2.1. A study of Fig. 1.3.7(a) and (b) is advised.

1.3.4 Memory devices

The classical *memory hierarchy* is depicted in Fig. 1.3.8. The various types of memory devices in this hierarchy vary in *speed, cost/bit* and *capacity*. Earlier sections have described the organisation of the stored-program computer in terms of *registers* and *main memory*. The *secondary memory* is a large memory for *on-line storage of files* representing programs, data, compilers, utility programs, etc. These files are copied when required into main memory under the control of the computer's *operating system*. *Mass memory* in the form of automated file libraries is used for large amounts of collected data, back-up copies of programs, archives of computer operations, etc.

The *cache memory* has an *access time* (i.e. speed) between that of registers and main memory. Its function is to reduce the effective access time of the main memory. Frequently used program and data segments reside in cache for a substantial proportion of the time. The longer access time of main memory is only incurred when the necessary word is not in cache. Special hardware (some involving *associative memories*) manages the operations of the cache and main memory using algorithms which *maximise the 'hit-rate'* of the cache. This is the number of times a word is found in cache expressed as a percentage of the total required number of memory accesses for a specific program.

The function of the *disc cache* is to minimise the effective access times of the magnetic discs of the secondary memory. In addition special hardware can effectively combine main memory and disc units into a *one-level* memory system with a very large 'address space' accessed by a '*virtual address*'.

Fig. 1.3.9 shows the range of access times and costs of computer memories. Projected improvements are also given. The very wide *gap* between the technologies used for main memory (MOS RAM) and secondary memory (moving-head disc) should be noted. Many newer technologies (e.g. bubble memories) have been considered for 'filling the gap'. However discs utilise a very *mature technology* (magnetic recording). Discs have steadily

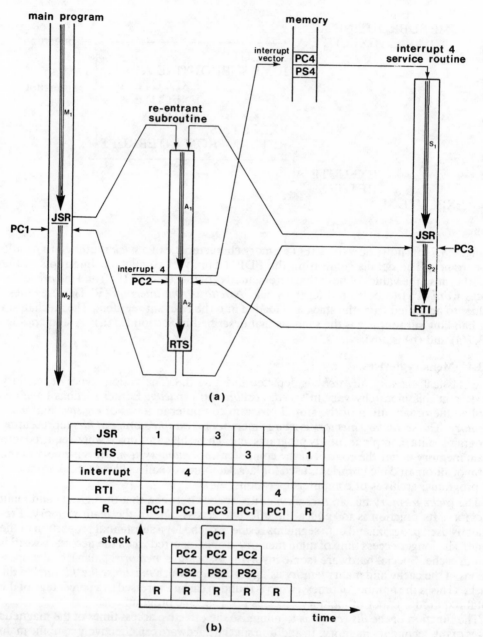

(a)

JSR	1		3		
RTS				3	1
interrupt		4			
RTI					4
R	PC1	PC1	PC3	PC1	PC1	R

		PC1			
stack	PC2	PC2	PC2		
	PS2	PS2	PS2		
	R	R	R	R	R

time

(b)

Fig. 1.3.7 Re-entrant subroutine—(a) linkage between main program, re-entrant subroutine and interrupt service routine, (b) stack contents

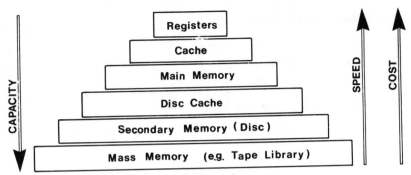

Fig. 1.3.8 The classical memory hierarchy

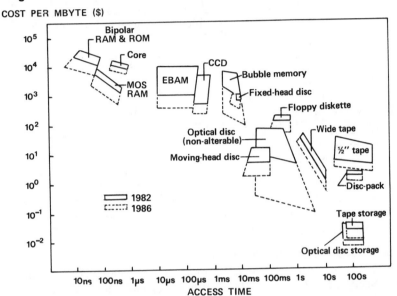

Fig. 1.3.9 Range of access times and costs of computer memories (data from Chi, C. S., 'Advances in Computer Mass Storage Technology', *Computer*, May 1982, pp 60–74)

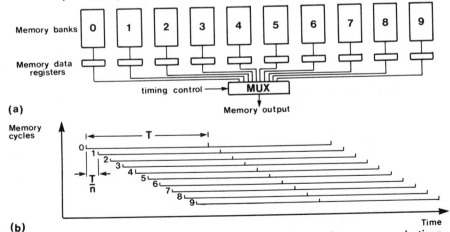

Fig. 1.3.10 Diagram illustrating the potential reduction of memory cycle time from T to T/n for memory banks with interleaved cycles (diagram drawn for $N = 10$)—(a) organisation, (b) memory cycles

improved in performance, and with further developments in *vertical recording* (or *'perpendicular recording'*) an enormous jump in disc capacities is expected. Table 1.3.1. lists the maximum recording densities achievable by various technologies. This provides some indication of potential improvements.

Table 1.3.1   Maximum recording densities achievable by various technologies

TECHNOLOGY	DENSITY		
	bits per inch	tracks per inch	bits per square inch
Longitudinal magnetic recording—oxide-coated disc and thin-film head	15 000	800	12×10^6
Longitudinal magnetic recording—thin-film disc and ferrite head	25 000	1200	30×10^6
Perpendicular magnetic recording	100 000	1200	120×10^6
Optical recording	15 000	15 000	225×10^6

Data from—Taranto, J., 'Thin-film disks drive densities to new heights', *Electronics*, April 21, 1982, pp. 108–111.

1.3.5   Memory organisation and techniques

The *addressing modes* for accessing the main (RAM) memory of a computer were discussed in Section 1.3.2. The functions of memory units in the classical *memory hierarchy* were described in Section 1.3.4. Reference has been made to techniques which involve more than one memory type. A detailed description of these techniques (e.g. use of cache memories and virtual addressing) exceeds the scope of the overview of Chapter 1. This section provides two additional examples of memory organisation and techniques.

Earlier sections have indicated that *memory bandwidth* is a major limiting factor of stored-program computers. One approach for increasing memory bandwidth is that of *memory interleaving*. This is illustrated in Fig. 1.3.10. This diagram shows ten memory banks with data registers feeding a multiplexer (MUX) which generates the memory output. The timing of the memory banks is interleaved as shown in Fig. 1.3.10(b). If the memory cycle time is T ns, then one word is produced from consecutive memory banks every $T/10$ ns. This represents a *potential improvement* in memory bandwidth by a factor of ten.

The second example is *'memory-cycle-stealing'* in *'direct-memory-access'* channels. This feature allows a peripheral device to gain direct access to the random-access memory of the system without the involvement of the central processing unit. The feature is commonly used for transferring blocks of data from random-access memory to peripheral device and vice versa.

An illustration of the mechanism by which a block of data may be transferred from a magnetic disc to the random-access memory of a system is given in Fig. 1.3.11. The disc controller shown in Fig. 1.3.11(a) is a hardware unit for reading data from, and writing data to the disc. The functions performed by the disc controller include (i) head movement, (ii) track selection, (iii) reformatting of data, (iv) addition of check bits, (v) detection of disc errors, (vi) record management using a directory, and so on. We

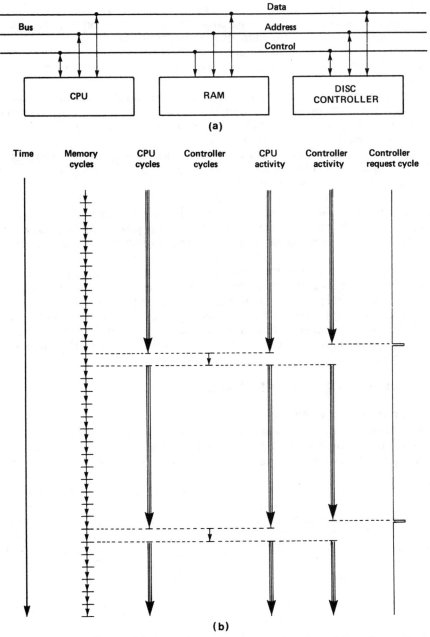

Fig. 1.3.11 Illustration of direct-memory-access transfer of data from disc to RAM—(a) bus-structured system, (b) timing diagram showing the concurrency of CPU activity and disc controller activity

assume that the disc controller contains two registers (a data register and an address register) whose outputs are connected to the data and address lines of the bus.

It is assumed that the process of transferring a block of words from disc to random-access memory consists of the following steps, of which steps (ii)–(v) are repeated a number of times depending on the number of words transferred:

(i) load the address register of the disc controller,

(ii) assemble a word into the data register of the disc controller from data stored on disc,

(iii) store the contents of the data register of the disc controller into the location of the random-access memory specified by the address register of the disc controller,

(iv) increment the contents of the disc controller's address register,

(v) go to step (ii) if not end of block.

At the end of step (ii) above, the disc controller produces a signal requesting a memory cycle. If this request is granted by the priority arbitration unit, step (iii) above will take place. It is to be noted that in step (iii), the data and address information required by the random-access memory is supplied over the data and address lines of the bus from the data and address registers of the disc controller. The registers of the central processing unit are not involved at all in step (iii), and hence the central processing unit may continue uninterrupted or, if waiting for a memory access, resume its operation immediately following the memory cycle 'stolen' or 'snatched' by the disc controller.

Fig. 1.3.11(b) illustrates the process just described using timing diagrams. These clearly show that there can be a significant amount of 'concurrency' in the operations of the disc controller and the central processing unit. In particular, it is possible for the disc controller to carry out steps (iv), (v) and (ii) while the central processing unit is in operation and has control of the bus. It also follows that the disc controller and other such peripheral units can operate at their maximum data transfer rates with only a small demand on the capabilities of the bus.

1.4   THE DESIGN OF DIGITAL SYSTEMS

1.4.1   Integrated circuit technology

During the 1960s great progress was made in improvements to the performance of the silicon bipolar transistor. By the end of the decade the cut-off frequencies of transistors had exceeded 1 GHz, and commercial logic gates were available with propagation delays approaching 1 ns.

During the 1970s rapid progress was made with the level of integration. This ushered in the 'microprocessor era' and resulted in the realisation of the 'single-chip computer'. By the early 1980s the level of integration approached one million devices on a chip.

From the early 1960s to the late 1970s, the number of components per chip in the most advanced integrated circuits had doubled each year. This development, known as 'Moore's Law', (for silicon) is represented by a graph in Fig. 1.4.1. Some of the discoveries and technological innovations which were responsible for this progress in integration level are also shown in Fig. 1.4.1. The classification of integration level by the terms 'small-scale', 'medium-scale', 'large-scale' and 'very-large-scale' is imprecise, and the boundaries shown in Fig. 1.4.1 must be taken as approximate.

During the early 1980s there were further improvements in integration level. However the rate at which these occurred was lower than that which occurred in the previous two decades (as indicated by Moore's Law). Higher integration levels are possible with chips with a *regular structure*, the primary examples of which are the various types of memory chips. Higher integration levels have also been utilised in recent 16-bit microprocessors and 32-bit microprocessors (or '*micromain-frames*'). Trends for memory chips and micro-processors are shown in Fig. 1.4.1.

Silicon integrated circuit technology is a 'mature' technology supported by more than two decades of intensive fundamental research and innovative engineering. It is the dominant integrated circuit technology of today. However technologies based on other semiconductor materials are being developed. One such material is gallium arsenide (GaAs) for which the electron mobility is about six times that for silicon. The promise of

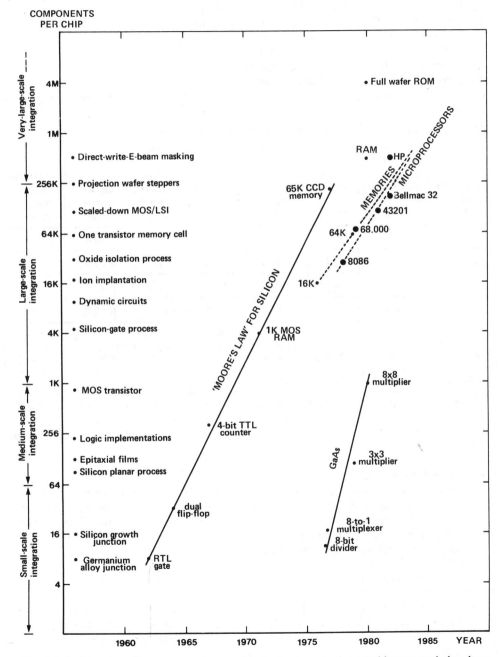

Fig. 1.4.1 Number of components per chip in the most advanced integrated circuit vs year of development

higher speed (and performance) has been one of the driving forces behind the development of GaAs technology. Improvement in the integration level of GaAs devices has also been graphed in Fig. 1.4.1.

Some parameters (relevant to digital systems) which characterise the silicon integrated circuit technology of the early 1980s are as follows:

Packing density (memory) 4000 transistors per mm²
Packing density (logic)   2000 transistors per mm²
Feature size $2\,\mu m$ (approx.)
Gate delay $200\,ps$ (approx.)
Power delay product $0.03\,pJ$ (approx.)
Chip size $0.25\,cm^2$ (approx.)

Further details are given in the summary of semiconductor process technologies in Table 1.4.1.

Table 1.4.1 Summary of semiconductor process technologies

TECHNOLOGY (early 1980s)	Logic complexity (components per 2-input gate)	Packing density (gates per mm²)	Typical propagation delay (ns)	Power–delay product (pico-joules)	Typical supply voltages (volts)	Signal swings (volts)	Guaranteed noise margin (volts)
TTL	12	10–20	6–30	30–150	+5.0	0.2/3.4	0.3–0.4
LS TTL	12	20–40	2–10	10–60	+5.0	0.2/3.4	0.3–0.4
ECL	8	15–20	0.7–2	15–80	−5.2	−0.8/−1.7	0.125
I²L	3–4	75–150	7–50	0.2–2.0	+(0.8–1.0)	0.2/0.8	<0.1
PMOS	3	75–150	30–200	50–500	−(15–20)	0/−15.0	1–2
NMOS	3	100–200	4–25	5–50	+5.0	0.2/3.4	0.5–2.0
CMOS	4	40–90	10–35	2–40	+10.0	0/10.0	3.5–4.5
SOS	4	100–200	0.5–30	+10.0	0/10.0	3.5–4.5

Data from—Hooper, D. E. and Roberts, D. H., 'Silicon Systems', *GEC Journal of Science and Technology*, **48**, No. 2.

1.4.2 Design methodology

Digital systems design embraces all procedures required to produce an '*engineered system*' to satisfy a '*specified need*'. Because of the complexity of such systems, in general, a *hierarchical, structured approach* has proved to be extremely effective. This approach involves the specification of the system to be designed using various *levels of abstraction*. For example, the following three levels may be identified:

1. Behavioural level
2. Functional level
3. Logic/physical level.

Specification at the *behavioural level* deals with overall system performance, performance of major system components and interaction (e.g. via data paths) between major system components, etc. The term '*system design*' is often used to describe this level of the design approach.

The *functional level* deals with the specification of the functions of all 'sub-components' of all major system components for every distinct time period of the system's operation.

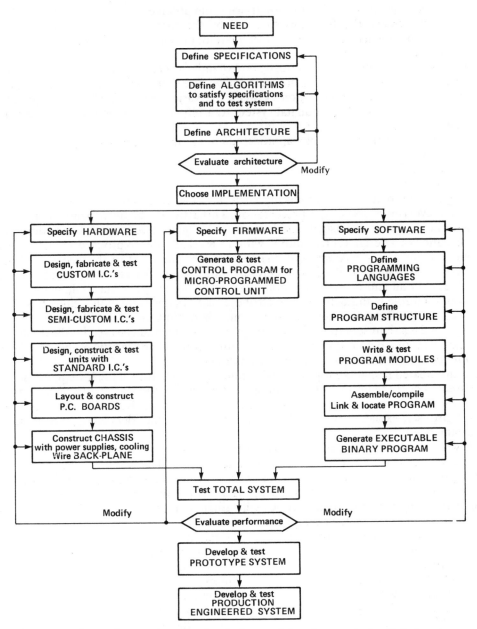

Fig. 1.4.2 General procedure for the design and development of a digital system

'*Register transfer languages*' are often used to assist with the specification and simulation of the system at this level. The term '*functional design*' has also been used to describe this level of the design approach.

The *logic/physical level* is concerned with the interconnection of primitive logic elements to achieve the functions specified by the functional design. The *layout* of electronic components on a printed circuit board or of cells in a VLSI integrated circuit is also of concern at this level.

The levels of design briefly described above handle a very wide range of activities from, for example, the assessment of an architectural feature to the wiring of two components on a printed circuit board. Interaction between the various levels is required in order to transform a stated need for a digital system to a physical realisation of a system which satisfies this need.

Within each level of the design approach there are three basic design activities, viz:
1. Synthesis
2. Optimisation
3. Analysis.

Synthesis is the creative act of producing a new, lower level representation of a design from a higher level (more abstract) representation. This activity is highly dependent on human qualities of 'creativity', 'insight' and 'experience'. *Optimisation* involves the addition or modification of a design representation within a level in order to produce a better design. Suitable *performance measures* (or *metrics*) are a requirement of this activity. Finally, *analysis* is the evaluation of a design representation to indicate where an alternative design (synthesis) or an improved design (optimisation) should be performed. Simulation plays an important role in this activity. The attributes used in the evaluation include functional correctness, performance, cost, testability, maintainability and fault-tolerance.

Fig. 1.4.2 is a representation of a general procedure which can be used for the design and development of a digital system. The procedure has the characteristic of the '*top-down*', *hierarchical, structured approach* briefly described above. Activities at the behavioural level are treated first at the top (of the diagram) while activities at the logic/physical level are treated near the bottom. The diagram contains many 'feedback paths' indicating the highly *iterative* nature of the design procedure. Most of the activities represented by Fig. 1.4.2 are self-explanatory. A close examination of the details of this figure is recommended.

It was stated that the '*synthesis*' part of the design procedure was highly dependent on creativity, insight and experience. What is also involved here is a *knowledge base* consisting of *existing theory* and *current practices*. Much of the knowledge base is classified under the headings of Computer Science, Electrical Engineering, Mathematics, Physics, Computer Engineering, Integrated Circuit Engineering and Materials Science, etc. Examples of more specific headings are:

Computer architecture	Testability
Multi-processing	Electronic circuits
Micro-programming	Transmission line theory
Microprocessors	Filters
Unified switching theory	Communications theory
Numerical analysis	Information theory
Algorithms	Control theory
Operating systems	Signal processing
Software engineering	Image processing
Error correcting codes	Semiconductor physics
Fault-tolerant computing	Technology of integrated circuit
Digital circuits	fabrication
Digital systems	Integrated circuit design

Many of the activities of digital system design have been automated with the use of computer-based aids. These design aids have evolved in step with the increase in chip complexity. Some representative design aids are as follows:

Integration level	Representative design aid
SSI	Oscilloscopes, digital multimeters
MSI	Logic analysers
LSI	Microprocessor development system
VLSI	VLSI development system

Fig. 1.4.3 represents the facilities of a typical VLSI design automation system. These facilities could handle either semi-custom or full custom designs which are generated from a *work station* of a VLSI development system. The output is in the form of magnetic tapes for the mask-making/fabrication process and for integrated circuit testing.

Very large design libraries are involved in the system represented by Fig. 1.4.3. These can be embedded in a *data-base system* managed and organised by a *data-base manager*. The major modules of the system have been classified under the headings:

Design capture
Logic and circuit verification
Physical design capture
Layout verification
Format interchange

The *design capture* section supports the entry of design information at various levels of abstraction—from behavioural descriptions to device descriptions. Data entry and modification may be handled either by a *text editor* or a *graphics editor*. High performance colour-graphics terminals with bit-mapped raster-scanned displays provide efficient methods for handling schematic diagrams. Design documentation takes the form of listings and schematic plots.

The *logic and circuit verification* section supports the verification of logic and circuit designs (also) at various levels of abstraction. Simulators verify performance at the functional, logical, timing, circuit and process levels. One module is used to compare the logic specification with the layout specification.

The *physical design capture* section produces the layout of a chip. A *layout editor* is used for entry of floor-plan and layout modification. Standard cells may be called from a *cell library* and regular structures such as *programmable logic arrays* may be readily generated. Utility programs for *cell placement, cell compaction* and *wire routing* are also available. The layout produced by a plotter may be checked visually.

The *layout verification* section contains a program for checking whether the *design rules* for the integrated circuit fabrication technology have been satisfied. Another program checks whether electrical characteristics satisfy required *electrical rules*. A circuit may be extracted from the layout, and a comparison of the logic specification and the layout specification may be performed.

The *format interchange* section provides the link to other design automation systems, the mask-making process and the fabrication/testing processes. After the chip layout has been verified, data files in various formats are required for mask-making, E-beam direct write on wafer fabrication and chip testing. The data transfer medium for these files is usually magnetic tape.

Fig. 1.4.4 illustrates the steps involved in mask-making, fabrication and packaging of integrated circuits. The *fabrication process* consists of a sequence of steps in which successive layers are *patterned* on a silicon wafer. Patterning is used for layers of silicon

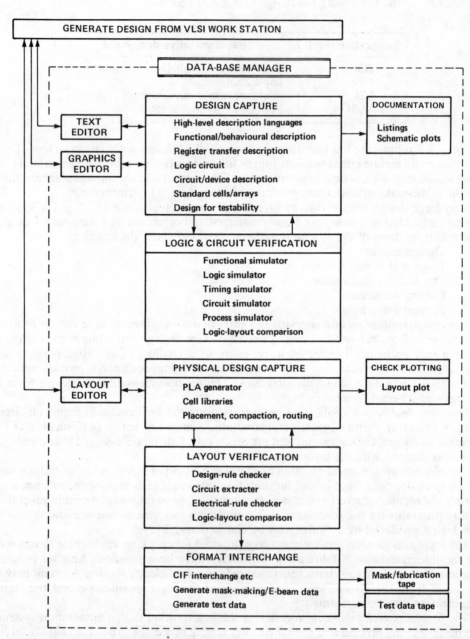

Fig. 1.4.3 VLSI design automation system

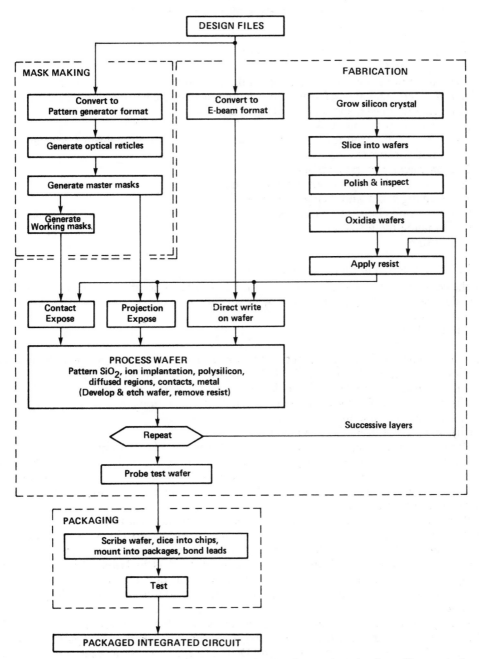

Fig. 1.4.4 Steps involved in mask-making, fabrication and packaging of integrated circuits

dioxide, ion implanted regions, polysilicon, diffused regions, contacts and metalisation, etc. The patterning process consists of:

(i) applying a coating of '*resist*' to the wafer,
(ii) writing directly on the wafer using an E-beam, or exposing the resist through a *mask*,
(iii) developing the resist,
(iv) etching the wafer (and rinsing), and
(v) removing the resist.

The *mask-producing process* consists of the following steps for each layer:

(i) generate optical *reticles* (usually ten times actual size master photographic plates),
(ii) generate master masks (actual size), and
(iii) generate working masks

Working masks are used for 'contact exposure' of the resist on the wafer. Master masks may be used for 'projection exposure'.

The *packaging process* consists of:

(i) testing wafer and identifying faulty chips,
(ii) scribing wafer and dicing into chips,
(iii) mounting chips into packages,
(iv) bonding the leads, and
(v) testing.

1.4.3   Logic design of digital circuits

In the context of *complexity management* in VLSI systems design, it has often been stated that designers should exploit the following attributes:

(i) hierarchy,
(ii) regularity, and
(iii) parameterisation.

Hierarchy is an inherent feature of the '*top-down, standard design approach*' discussed in Section 1.4.2. Hierarchy on the VLSI chip implies a structure in which:

(i) *composite cells* of level 1 are defined in terms of basic *leaf cells*,
(ii) composite cells of level n are defined in terms of composite cells of level m $(m < n)$ and basic leaf cells,
(iii) and a repetition of (ii) to any level.

Regularity is a characteristic of a circuit which contains a large number of identical cells arranged in one-dimensional and two-dimensional arrays. The structure is such that most (if not all) of the connections to a cell are to its *nearest neighbours*, and complex wire routing of interconnections between cells is avoided. Such a structure lends itself to an efficient, compact chip layout.

Parameterisation is a feature of a design automation system which allows a designer to characterise the size (for example) of a regularly structured circuit by one or more parameters. The circuit may be designed and the design verified using a modestly small value of a size parameter. When the parameter is assigned its final (much larger) value, the design automation system will generate the design and documentation (e.g. schematic plots and chip layout) for the final circuit with very little additional effort on the part of the designer.

A diagram which illustrates the concepts discussed above is given in Fig. 1.4.5. The diagram defines a circuit structure of a *carry–save multiplier array*. The inputs to the array are four 4-bit binary integers A, B, C and D. The output is an 8-bit binary integer P such that:

$$P = A \times B + C + D$$

Most of the multiplier array is composed of a regular array of identical *cells*. Each cell

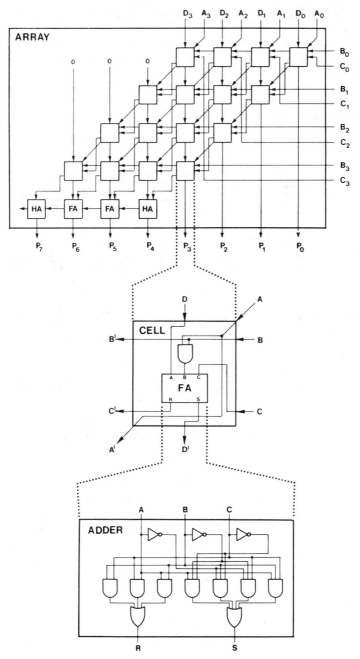

Fig. 1.4.5   Nested block definition of iterative carry-save multiplier array

consists of an AND gate and a *full adder*. Each full adder consists of a number of AND gates, OR gates and INVERTERS (or NOT gates) with interconnections as shown.

In the context of VLSI systems, designers may freely consider structures such as the bi-directional, two-dimensional shift network represented by Fig. 1.4.6. This network is a direct extrapolation of the bi-directional (one-dimensional) shift register which is readily available as a MSI integrated circuit. In the two-dimensional shift network, the data represented by the symbol A (with subscripts) is shifted from top-to-bottom of the network; the B-data is shifted from left-to-right; the C data from bottom-to-top and the D-data from right-to-left. The four shift-modes are controlled by the two mode control signals M and N.

The structure and characteristics of the *arithmetic pipe-line* were described in Section 1.2.6. One arithmetic operation which lends itself very well to a pipe-lined implemention is floating-point addition/subtraction. The organisation of a pipe-lined, floating-point

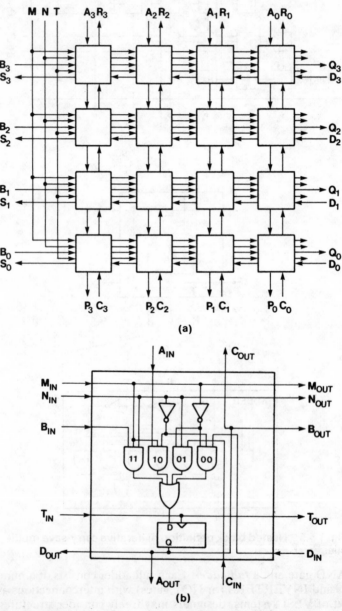

(a)

(b)

Fig. 1.4.6 Bi-directional, two-dimensional shift network—(a) circuit, (b) cell

adder-subtracter is represented by Fig. 1.4.7. The functions performed by the various sections of the pipe-line from the input (latch 0) to the output (latch 6) are as follows:

1. Decode exponents and fractions;
   select fraction to shift;
   determine number of places to shift.
2. Determine sign of result;
   shift fraction to align (binary points).
3. Add/subtract.
4. Normalise fraction part of result.
5. Determine exponent of result (with normalised fraction);
   round fraction.
6. Test for special cases and exceptions;
   generate result in standard format.

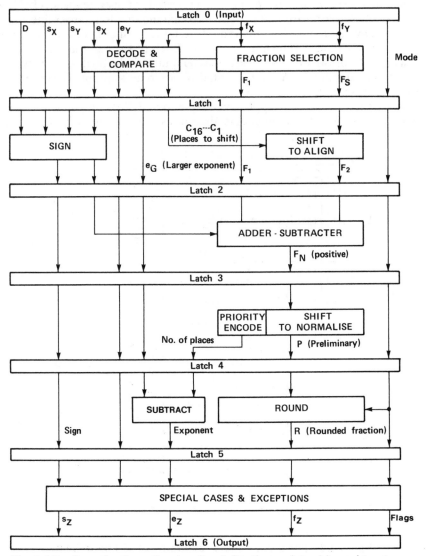

Fig. 1.4.7 Organisation of a pipe-lined, floating-point adder-subtracter

The circuits in each stage of the pipe-line of Fig. 1.4.7 (i.e. circuits between successive latches) are *combinational circuits*. The various *propagation delays* of signals passing through these circuits will determine the frequency at which the latches may be clocked. This defines the speed of the pipe-line.

The functions performed by the various sections of the pipe-line (listed above) define the functions of various (combinational) *hardware* components. These functions include:

   (i) decoders,
  (ii) comparators,
 (iii) data-selectors,
 (iv) combinational shift networks,
  (v) fixed-point adder/subtracters,
 (vi) priority encoders, and
(vii) combinational incrementers.

The function of the *priority encoder* has been selected to illustrate the level of functional complexity of these hardware components. An extendable 8-line-to-3-line priority encoder has been available as a MSI integrated circuit for some time. The functional logic diagram of such a circuit is shown in Fig. 1.4.8. Each of the eight inputs $\bar{I}_0$---$\bar{I}_7$ of this circuit is assigned a priority 0---7. The *asserted* input with the highest priority is encoded into a 3-bit binary number A_2, A_1, A_0 presented at the circuit's output. The other inputs and outputs are used for circuit extension.

The priority encoder has been applied in the pipe-lined, floating-point adder/subtracter of Fig. 1.4.7 to determine the number of leading zeros of an *un-normalised binary fraction*.

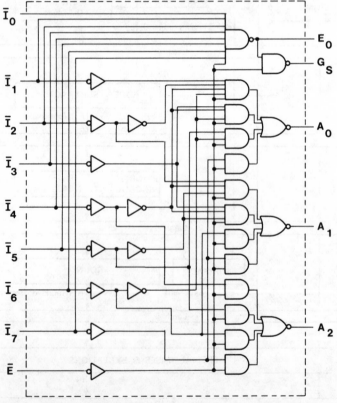

Fig. 1.4.8 Functional logic diagram of 8-line-to-3-line priority encoder SN74148

This number is then used to control a combinational shift network which generates a *normalised binary fraction*.

One decision which must be made early in the design process is whether a *parallel* or a *serial* implementation should be used. The 'trade-off' between *hardware requirements* and *execution times* is illustrated in Fig. 1.4.9. Alternative implementations of a *binary accumulator* are represented. In the parallel implementation of Fig. 1.4.9(a), eight full adders (forming an 8-bit *parallel adder*) are required to produce the 8-bit sum of two 8-bit binary numbers. This 8-bit sum may be clocked into one of the registers (the accumulator register A) using a single clock pulse as shown in Fig. 1.4.9(c). The serial implementation uses a *serial adder* consisting of one full adder and a flip-flop to hold successive *carry*

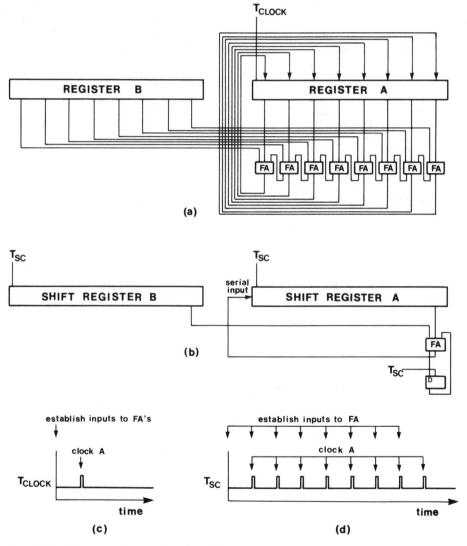

Fig. 1.4.9 Diagram illustrating the differences in hardware requirements and execution times between parallel and serial implementations of a binary accumulator—(a) parallel implementation, (b) serial implementation, (c) timing of parallel implementation, (d) timing of serial implementation

signals. This implementation obviously uses much less hardware than the parallel implementation but the execution time is also much longer because of the requirement of the eight clock pulses as illustrated in Fig. 1.4.9(d).

The use of *parallel structures* (multi-processing) to achieve high performance was discussed in Section 1.2.4. The application of *multi-processing* using *serial arithmetic units* can often result in an efficient design. A very simple illustration is given in Fig. 1.4.10. This figure is a simplified block diagram of an arithmetic unit for solving a *linear difference equation*. This equation takes the form:

$$x\{nT\} = P_0 y\{nT\} + P_1 y\{(n-1)T\} + P_2 y\{(n-2)T\} - Q_1 x\{(n-1)T\} - Q_2 x\{(n-2)T\}$$

In this equation, P_0, P_1, P_2, Q_1 and Q_2 are constants. The output to be computed, $x\{nT\}$, is the value of the output x at sampling instant $t = nT$, where T is the sampling period. The symbols $x\{(n-1)T\}$ and $x\{(n-2)T\}$ define the values of x at $t = (n-1)T$ and $t = (n-2)T$. The input $y\{nT\}$ is the value of the input y at sampling instant $t = nT$. The symbols $y\{(n-1)T\}$ and $y\{(n-2)T\}$ define the value of y at $t = (n-1)T$ and $t = (n-2)T$.

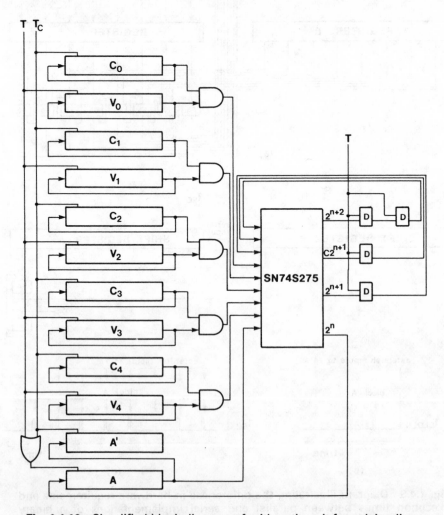

Fig. 1.4.10 Simplified block diagram of arithmetic unit for solving linear difference equations

In the implementation illustrated by Fig. 1.4.10, ten shift registers are used to store the five constants, present and past values of the input y and the past values of the output x. The symbols used in Fig. 1.4.10 are defined as follows:

$$C_0 = P_0 \qquad V_0 = y\{nT\}$$
$$C_1 = P_1 \qquad V_1 = y\{(n-1)T\}$$
$$C_2 = P_2 \qquad V_2 = y\{(n-2)T\}$$
$$C_3 = -Q_1 \qquad V_3 = x\{(n-1)T\}$$
$$C_4 = -Q_2 \qquad V_4 = x\{(n-2)T\}$$

Hence the solution of the difference equation requires the computation of the following expression:

$$C_0 V_0 + C_1 V_1 + C_2 V_2 + C_3 V_3 + C_4 V_4$$

The above expression defines five multiplications and four additions. Fig. 1.4.10 suggests an implementation using a *'serial–serial multiplication'* technique and serial addition. However parallelism is achieved by arranging for *all five multiplications and four additions to proceed simultaneously*. The SN74S275 integrated circuit is described as a *7-bit-slice-Wallace-tree*. It was designed for use in high-speed (parallel–parallel) multiplier circuits. This integrated circuit forms the arithmetic sum of a number of single-bit inputs and represents the sum in a coded form. The computed value of the above expression is formed in two shift registers A and A' of Fig. 1.4.10.

At the end of a sampling period, the following data transfers are required:

$$V_1 \rightarrow \text{register } V_2$$
$$V_0 \rightarrow \text{register } V_1$$
$$\text{Input } y \rightarrow \text{register } V_0$$
$$V_3 \rightarrow \text{register } V_4$$
$$A \rightarrow \text{register } V_3$$

All of the above data transfers may proceed simultaneously.

Signals in a digital system may represent either *data* or *control signals*. Data is *entered, transmitted, stored, processed* and *utilised* in a digital system. *Control signals* cause components of a digital system to perform specified operations, the mode of operation at any time being defined by the asserted combination of the control signals at that time.

A requirement in the digital design process is the specification of the *main data paths* and a suitable mechanism for *control*. This part of the design process determines some of the main architectural features of the system being designed. The *micro-programmed control unit* has been described (in Section 1.3.2.2) as an efficient mechanism for controlling the execution of instructions in a general-purpose computer.

The distinction between *data* and *control* is important even at the circuit level. An example is given in Fig. 1.4.11. The physical circuit given in this figure can perform two totally different functions by interchanging the data and control inputs. In Fig. 1.4.11(a) there are two data inputs A and B, and four control inputs R_3, R_2, R_1 and R_0. The function of the circuit in this case is to generate at its output X one of the sixteen different Boolean functions of the two variables A and B as specified by the combination of the four control inputs. With this function the circuit may be described as a *'flexible logic cell'*. In Fig. 1.4.11(b) there are four data inputs D_3, D_2, D_1 and D_0 (previously control inputs in Fig. 1.4.11(a)), and two control inputs S_1 and S_0. The function of the circuit in this case is to generate at its output X one of the four data inputs as 'selected' by the combination of the two control inputs. With this function the circuit may be described as a *'4-line-to-1-line data-selector'* or *'4-line-to-1-line multiplexer'*.

There are two broad classifications for digital circuits such as those described in this section; *combinational circuit* and *sequential circuit*. A *combinational circuit* is a digital

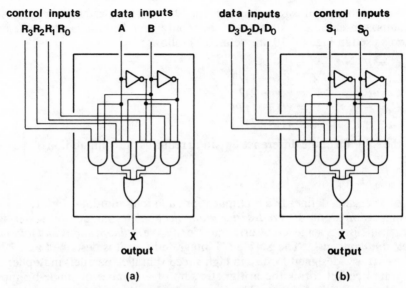

Fig. 1.4.11 Circuit of (a) flexible logic cell for the generation of any Boolean function of two variables A and B, or (b) 4-line-to-1-line multiplexer for selecting one of the four data inputs

circuit in which outputs are specified functions of inputs alone. In such a circuit once the inputs have been established (at steady state values), the outputs would then settle to steady values (which are specified functions of the inputs) during a *settling time* determined by the delays of the logical elements in the circuit. Following a subsequent change of one or more inputs, the outputs would settle to new values once the transients associated with the logical elements in the circuit have decayed to zero. A block diagram of a combinational circuit is shown in Fig. 1.4.12(a).

A *sequential circuit* is a digital circuit which has *internal memory* (or *internal states*). In general the outputs of a sequential circuit are functions of both the digital inputs and the internal states. In addition, other functions of both the digital inputs and the internal states may change the internal states, thus providing the block diagram shown in Fig. 1.4.12(b). Starting from specified internal states, sequences of outputs may be produced from sequences of inputs (and hence the term 'sequential circuit').

Basic elements of both combinational and sequential circuits are *logical gates* of which the *AND-gate, OR-gate* and *NOT-gate* are primary examples. Each AND-gate or OR-gate may have two or more inputs while the NOT-gate has only one input. *All inputs of an AND-gate* must be *asserted* (ACTIVE or TRUE) before its output becomes asserted. *Any asserted input of an OR-gate* will cause its output to become asserted. Finally an asserted input of a NOT-gate will cause its output to become de-asserted, and vice versa.

The symbols used for the AND-gate, OR-gate and NOT-gate are shown in Fig. 1.4.13. The specification of each input as either *data* or *control* provides simple examples of the application of these gates. For the AND-gate, the control inputs B and C allow the data A to pass through the gate to the output P at times when certain conditions are met, and they block the data transfer at other times. For the OR-gate, the data inputs D, E and F could represent, for example, 'alarm condition D', 'alarm condition E' and 'alarm condition F', and it is required that when any one of these three alarm conditions is asserted then the 'master alarm condition Q' should be asserted. The NOT-gate (also called an *inverter*) can be used to produce the *inverse* or *complement* of a control signal which could then be used as a control input of an AND-gate.

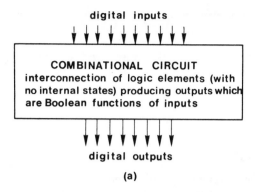

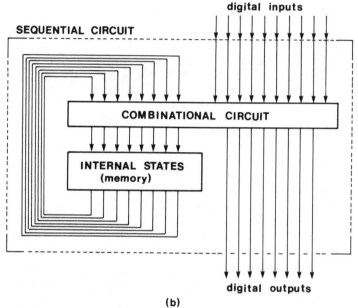

Fig. 1.4.12 Block diagrams of (a) a combinational circuit and (b) a sequential circuit

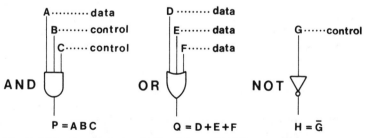

Fig. 1.4.13 Symbols for AND-, OR- and NOT-gates (Inputs shown illustrate applications of these gates)

This completes the '*top-down*' overview of digital systems. We commenced this chapter with a discussion of the applications of very complex systems. We have ended with a description of the basic logical gates.

2 COMBINATIONAL CIRCUITS

Basic theory and techniques for the analysis and synthesis of combinational circuits

2.1 INTRODUCTION

Classical switching theory has been applied to the analysis and synthesis of electromechanical relay circuits ('*contact networks*') and electronic switching circuits ('*gate networks*'). The basic switching elements (the contact and the gate) used in these two types of networks have some fundamental differences. The contact is a bi-directional two-terminal switching element capable of assuming one of two states, on or off. The gate is a uni-directional multiterminal switching element capable of generating an output signal which is a simple Boolean function (e.g. AND, OR) of the input signals. Classical switching theory provides a mathematical framework for describing the *logical behaviour* of these networks.

A *combinational circuit* may be described as an electronic switching circuit (or gate network) in which gate interconnections are such that, when all signals have settled to steady values, circuit outputs are logical (Boolean) functions of circuit inputs.

When the gate interconnections of a combinational circuit are such that each gate output is wired to one or more gate inputs, which implies that there are *no instances of two outputs wired together*, then the classical switching theory enables the logical behaviour of the combinational circuit to be determined from the known behaviour of all component gates and the known gate interconnections. However some integrated circuits allow outputs to be wired together. The '*wired-AND*' and '*wired-OR*' connections require an understanding of the *circuit behaviour* as well as the *logical behaviour* of individual gates before the overall logical behaviour of the composite circuit may be determined. Once this has been done, however, classical switching theory does provide tools for representing the behaviour of the composite circuit. Logical designers who utilise such wired-AND and wired-OR connections may, therefore, consider the composite circuit as a *building block of much greater logical functionality* than that provided by a simple gate.

Designers of digital systems should exploit the high logical functionality which is provided in standard medium-scale and large-scale (MSI/LSI) integrated circuits. To achieve this, a sound understanding of the characteristics of these integrated circuits is required. The analysis of a 4-bit magnitude comparator is given at the end of this chapter as an example.

Classical switching theory recognises only *two logic values, 0 and 1*. However some integrated circuits make extensive use of other values such as a *high-impedance state, Z*. The output of a *tri-state device* may take one of the three values 0, 1 or Z. Another characteristic which is not recognised by classical switching theory is the *effect of load elements* on the logical behaviour of a device. Many VLSI circuits utilise *pull-up/down* load elements which can, under certain conditions, pull a signal up (to logical 1) or down (to logical 0). To overcome the above deficiencies of classical switching theory when applied to some modern devices various '*unified switching theories*' have been utilised. It is beyond the scope of this book to discuss these unified switching theories any further, and we shall restrict our treatment to those systems which can be handled by classical switching theory.

2.2 BOOLEAN ALGEBRA

2.2.1 Application

Boolean Algebra provides a concise and *mathematically precise* method for the specification of combinational circuits. Numbers and variables used in this Algebra can take only one of the values 0 and 1. *Logical (Boolean) functions* of numbers are variables are produced by three basic operators AND, OR and NOT. The outputs of a combinational circuit may be defined as Boolean functions of the circuit inputs. Pre-defined symbols for the basic operators and 'user-defined' symbols for variables (inputs, intermediate values, outputs) are combined to form *Boolean expressions*. These are mathematical definitions of the Boolean functions generated by combinational circuits.

Well chosen symbols in the form of meaningful *mnemonics* are extremely useful for the design, development or maintenance of a digital circuit. The symbol chosen for a signal should reflect the signal's function. Some examples are:

Symbol	Meaning
DATB00	Data bus B line 00
IRQA	Interrupt request line A
CLK0	Clock 0
BCS(L)	Branch condition satisfied (asserted low)

In spite of the above recommendation the symbol used to represent a signal in this book will be restricted to a *single (upper- or lower-case) alphabetical character with any superscript or subscript*. The reason behind this decision is that there is a great advantage in establishing an analogy between some manipulations in Boolean Algebra and corresponding manipulations of classical (real-variable) algebra. To achieve this analogy, the AND operator is described as a *logical product* operator and represented by the symbol 'dot' (.). However this operator symbol may be omitted in all situations where 'implied multiplication' is used in classical algebra. Hence the term AB means 'A AND B' (and not the two-letter symbol AB).

In this book a great emphasis is placed on the specification of combinational circuits using Boolean expressions. With the above restriction on the use of symbols, circuits of some complexity may be described by sets of Boolean equations.

2.2.2 Operators in Boolean Algebra

There are three fundamental operators used in Boolean Algebra, 'AND', 'OR' and 'NOT'. These are represented by the symbols shown in Table 2.2.1.

Table 2.2.1 Symbols used for Boolean operators

OPERATOR	SYMBOL
AND	.
OR	+
NOT	— (bar over symbol)

Hence, symbols (representing Boolean variables) may be combined using the operators to form other Boolean variables which are 'functions' of the initial Boolean variables. For example, starting from symbols A and B representing two Boolean variables, the Boolean functions shown in Table 2.2.2 may be formed.

Table 2.2.2 Boolean functions

BOOLEAN FUNCTION	DESCRIPTION
A.B	A 'AND' B
A+B	A 'OR' B
$\overline{A}$	'NOT' A

In the following sections, the symbol . for the 'AND' operator will be omitted in most instances and will be *implied* whenever the normal conventions for *multiplication* of variables are used. Hence, A.B will be denoted simply as AB, and C.(A+B) will be denoted as C(A+B).

2.2.3 Truth tables

A truth table lists the value of a Boolean function for every possible combination of the Boolean variables. For N variables, there are 2^N combinations of values for these variables. The fundamental operators AND, OR and NOT are defined by the truth tables of Table 2.2.3.

Table 2.2.3 Truth tables of fundamental logic elements

AND				OR				NOT	
A	B	AB		A	B	A+B		A	$\overline{A}$
0	0	0		0	0	0		0	1
0	1	0		0	1	1		1	0
1	0	0		1	0	1			
1	1	1		1	1	1			

Note that AB = 1 only if A = 1 *and* B = 1 (hence the significance of the word 'AND'), while A+B = 1 if A = 1 *or* B = 1 (hence the significance of the word 'OR'). Note also that the OR function is what may be called an 'INCLUSIVE-OR' function as A+B = 1 for the case when *both* A = 1 *and* B = 1. (An 'EXCLUSIVE-OR' function will be defined later.) Finally note that $\overline{A}$ (which as a Boolean variable can have only values 0 or 1) takes on the value of the '*inverse*' or '*complement*' of A if the symbol $\overline{A}$ is to be given the significance of 'NOT A'.

2.2.4 'AND' or 'OR' functions of three or more variables

The AND and OR operators may be used to combine three or more Boolean variables. Hence, the functions ABC and A+B+C may be represented by the truth tables of Table 2.2.4. Examination of this table should consolidate understanding of the concept of the AND and OR functions. However, in general, it will not be necessary to use truth tables to define functions of three or more variables in this way as the full significance of a Boolean function may be obtained by manipulating the Boolean expression representing the function using *Boolean identities* or theorems. In this case, the '*associative law*' of Boolean Algebra applies. This may be represented by the equations:

$$ABC = A(BC) = (AB)C$$

$$A+B+C = A+(B+C) = (A+B)+C$$

Other Boolean identities are listed in the following section (Section 2.2.5).

Table 2.2.4 Truth tables of AND and OR functions of three variables

A	B	C	ABC
0	0	0	0
0	0	1	0
0	1	0	0
0	1	1	0
1	0	0	0
1	0	1	0
1	1	0	0
1	1	1	1

A	B	C	A+B+C
0	0	0	0
0	0	1	1
0	1	0	1
0	1	1	1
1	0	0	1
1	0	1	1
1	1	0	1
1	1	1	1

2.2.5 Boolean identities

Some useful Boolean identities are listed below:

1. $A.0 = 0$
2. $A.1 = A$
3. $A.A = A$
4. $A.\bar{A} = 0$
5. $A+0 = A$
6. $A+1 = 1$
7. $A+A = A$
8. $A+\bar{A} = 1$
9. $\bar{\bar{A}} = A$
10. $A+B = B+A$ ⎫
11. $AB = BA$ ⎬ (Commutative law)
12. $A(BC) = (AB)C$ ⎫
13. $A+(B+C) = (A+B)+C$ ⎬ (Associative law)
14. $A(B+C) = AB+AC$ ⎫
15. $A+BC = (A+B)(A+C)$ ⎬ (Distributive law)
16. $A+AB = A$ ⎫
17. $A(A+B) = A$ ⎬ (Absorption law)
18. $\overline{AB} = \bar{A}+\bar{B}$ ⎫
19. $\overline{A+B} = \overline{AB}$ ⎬ (De Morgan's theorems)

It is to be noted that any of the above identities may be used for the *minimisation* or general manipulation of Boolean expressions. Identity No. 8 ($A+\bar{A} = 1$) is used repeatedly in Karnaugh maps to be treated later. Identity No. 14 is valid in classical algebra and is used in the operation of 'multiplying out to remove brackets'. This identity is important in considerations of 'minimum delay circuits' which will also be treated later. De Morgan's theorems (Identities Nos. 18 and 19) will be useful in the treatment of NOR and NAND circuits. It will be observed that the Boolean identities reflect a certain duality between the AND and OR operators and the Boolean numbers 0 and 1. For example if the following changes are made to any identity: (i) AND replaced by OR, (ii) OR replaced by AND, (iii) 0 replaced by 1, and (iv) 1 replaced by 0, another identity (which is the dual of the original identity) is formed.

Two methods of verifying the identities are suggested: (i) using truth tables and (ii) using manipulations of Boolean expressions. For example, consider Table 2.2.5 which may be used to verify Identity No. 18.

Table 2.2.5   Verification of a Boolean identity

Col. 1	Col. 2	Col. 3	Col. 4	Col. 5	Col. 6	Col. 7
A	B	AB	$\overline{AB}$	$\overline{A}$	$\overline{B}$	$\overline{A}+\overline{B}$
0	0	0	1	1	1	1
0	1	0	1	1	0	1
1	0	0	1	0	1	1
1	1	1	0	0	0	0

Columns 1 and 2 list all combinations of the two variables A and B. Column 3 is obtained from the definition of the AND operator. Column 4 is obtained from Column 3 and the definition of the NOT operator. Similarly, Column 5 is obtained from Column 1, Column 6 from Column 2, and Column 7 from Columns 5 and 6. An examination of Columns 4 and 7 shows that the entries are identical, and hence the Boolean expressions corresponding to these columns are identical. This approach is often very useful for verifying the equivalence of complex Boolean expressions.

To illustrate the second approach suggested, consider Identity No. 15, viz:

$$A+BC = (A+B)\,(A+C)$$

The right-hand-side of this equation may be 'multiplied out' and various terms combined using minimisation and absorption laws. The steps are as follows:

$$
\begin{aligned}
(A+B)\,(A+C) &= AA+AB+AC+BC \\
&= A+AB+AC+BC \\
&= A+AC+BC \\
&= A+BC
\end{aligned}
$$

Some of the identities may be verified using Venn diagrams. This method, which is treated in early texts on logic, will not be covered in this text. However, a development of this method (known as Karnaugh maps) will be presented in later sections.

2.3   APPLICATION OF BOOLEAN ALGEBRA TO COMBINATIONAL LOGIC CIRCUITS

2.3.1   Logic conventions

Logic circuits use two voltage levels (a HIGH level and a LOW level) to represent the two Boolean numbers 1 and 0. For example, in the Series 7400 Transistor-Transistor-Logic (TTL) family, voltage levels of typically 3.4 volts and 0.3 volts are used to represent Boolean values. As it is possible to use the HIGH level to represent either 1 or 0, two logic *conventions* are possible. These are called the *positive logic* convention in which the HIGH level is used to represent Boolean 1 and the *negative logic* convention in which the HIGH level is used to represent Boolean 0 (see Table 2.3.1).

It is obvious that it is desirable that only one of the two conventions should be used in a digital system and if, for some reason, a designer wishes to use both, then full and clear documentation should be provided to avoid confusion.

The positive logic convention is commonly used in digital systems. Moreover many integrated circuit suppliers assume a system of positive logic unless otherwise indicated.

Table 2.3.1 Positive logic and negative logic conventions

CONVENTION	VOLTAGE LEVEL	BOOLEAN NUMBER
Positive logic	HIGH LOW	1 0
Negative logic	HIGH LOW	0 1

This is achieved by appropriately marking (usually with a small circle) all signals which use a negative logic convention or by labelling signals with the term ACTIVE LOW. (For example, the activation of a circuit, e.g. the setting of a flip-flop which requires a LOW signal at an input would require this input to be labelled ACTIVE LOW if this circuit is to be used correctly.)

Using 'H' to denote a HIGH level and 'L' to denote a LOW level, a 'positive logic AND-gate' and a 'positive logic OR-gate' would have input–output relationships defined by the tables shown in Table 2.3.2.

Table 2.3.2 Input–output relationship of positive logic AND gate and positive logic OR-gate

INPUT A	INPUT B	OUTPUT AB		INPUT A	INPUT B	OUTPUT A+B
L	L	L		L	L	L
L	H	L		L	H	H
H	L	L		H	L	H
H	H	H		H	H	H

2.3.2 Logic circuit from Boolean equation

Boolean equations may be used to define digital (or Boolean) signals in terms of other signals. Each of these equations takes the form:

< Boolean variable > = < Boolean expression >

A Boolean expression is formed by combining Boolean variables and numbers using the fundamental operators AND, OR and NOT. As in classical algebra, parentheses may be used and the operators have an assigned priority whenever there is any ambiguity concerning the sequence in which operators are to be processed. In the Boolean algebra used in this book this operator priority is simply that 'AND has precedence over OR'. Hence, for the following equation defining Z in terms of A, B and C:

$Z = A + BC$

the required sequence in processing the operators is (i) B and C should be combined using the (implied) AND operator to form the signal BC, and (ii) A and BC should then be combined using the OR operator. The incorrect sequence would be to combine A and B using the OR operator and then to combine A+B with C using the AND operator. As in classical algebra, parentheses have precedence over all other operators and may be used to alter the sequence in which the operators are processed. Hence, another signal Y could well be defined as:

$Y = (A + B)C$

Logic circuits corresponding to the above Boolean equations defining Z and Y may be readily derived. In these examples, it is assumed that digital signals representing the

Boolean variables A, B and C are available and are used as inputs to the circuits. The circuits are then required to produce signals representing the Boolean variables Z and Y. This may be achieved using the interconnection of AND-gates and OR-gates shown in Fig. 2.3.1.

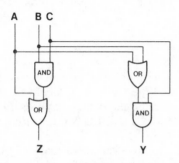

Fig. 2.3.1   Logic circuit from Boolean equation

For a more complex example, consider the Boolean equation:

$$X = A\overline{B} + C[DEF + \overline{G}(H + \overline{LJ + K})]$$

which defines a signal X in terms of input signals A, B, C, D, E, F, G, H, J, K and L. It will be observed that the requirements concerning operator precedence discussed above will be satisfied by the following procedure for producing X from the input signals:

(i)   combine L and J in an AND-gate to produce LJ,

(ii)   combine LJ and K in an OR-gate to produce LJ+K,

(iii)   use LJ+K as input to an inverter to produce $\overline{LJ+K}$,

(iv)   combine H and $\overline{LJ+K}$ in an OR-gate to produce $H + \overline{LJ+K}$,

(v)   use G as input to an inverter to produce $\overline{G}$,

(vi)   combine $\overline{G}$ and $H + \overline{LJ+K}$ in an AND-gate to produce $\overline{G}(H + \overline{LJ+K})$,

(vii)   combine D, E and F in an AND-gate to produce DEF,

(viii)   combine DEF and $\overline{G}(H + \overline{LJ+K})$ in an OR-gate to produce $DEF + \overline{G}(H + \overline{LJ+K})$,

(ix)   combine   C   and $DEF + \overline{G}(H + \overline{LJ+K})$ in   an   AND-gate   to   produce $C[DEF + \overline{G}(H + \overline{LJ+K})]$,

(x)   use B as input to an inverter to produce $\overline{B}$,

(xi)   combine A and $\overline{B}$ in an AND-gate to produce $A\overline{B}$,

(xii)   combine $A\overline{B}$ and $C[DEF + \overline{G}(H + \overline{LJ+K})]$ in an OR-gate to produce X.

It will be observed that expressions in the innermost brackets are treated first. A 'product' is handled using an AND-gate, and a '+' sign involves an OR-gate. Intermediate signals are produced until the output signal may be formed in terms of input and intermediate signals.

A logic circuit for producing the signal X defined by the above equation is shown in Fig. 2.3.2. Note that the signals L and J must pass through eight gates before the output is reached. As all practical circuits will introduce some time delay between their inputs and outputs, and these delays are cumulative in a circuit such as that of Fig. 2.3.2, it may be necessary (in time critical situations) to derive *equivalent switching circuits* which have the same functional relationship between inputs and outputs but which have different circuit implementations. Equivalent switching circuits may be derived from the alternative forms in which Boolean expressions may be structured. These are discussed in the following sections.

2.3.3   Boolean expressions in 'sum-of-products' form

Any Boolean expression (irrespective of complexity) can always be expressed in a 'sum-of-products' form in which the input signals or their inverses are combined to form

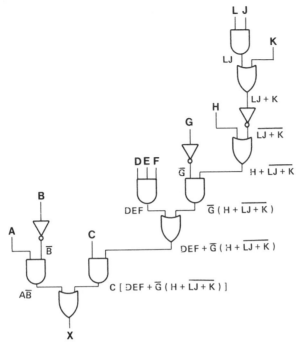

Fig. 2.3.2 Logic circuit corresponding to the Boolean
equation $X = A\overline{B} + C[DEF + \overline{G}(H + \overline{LJ + K})]$

(logical) product terms and the expression is formed as the (logical) sum of these product terms. Examples of Boolean expressions in sum-of-products form are as follows:

(i) $BC + CA + AB$
(ii) $A + B\overline{C} + \overline{C}\overline{D}$
(iii) $\overline{A}\overline{B}C + \overline{A}B\overline{C} + A\overline{B}\overline{C} + ABC$

It is to be noted that the 'product' terms can contain one or more of the variables or their inverses. It is also to be noted that the expressions must not contain parentheses. Expressions which do contain parentheses can always be manipulated into the sum-of-products form by applying appropriate theorems and identities. For example, consider the Boolean expression defining the signal X considered in the last section. This was:

$$X = A\overline{B} + C[DEF + \overline{G}(H + \overline{LJ + K})]$$

By applying de Morgan's theorems in various forms and the identity which allows the operation of 'multiplying out to remove brackets', the steps in the reduction process are as follows:

$$\begin{aligned}
X &= A\overline{B} + CDEF + C\overline{G}H + C\overline{G}\ \overline{LJ + K} \\
&= A\overline{B} + CDEF + C\overline{G}H + C\overline{G}\ (\overline{LJ}\,\overline{K}) \\
&= A\overline{B} + CDEF + C\overline{G}H + C\overline{G}(\overline{L} + \overline{J})\overline{K} \\
&= A\overline{B} + CDEF + C\overline{G}H + C\overline{G}\overline{L}\,\overline{K} + C\overline{G}\overline{J}\,\overline{K}
\end{aligned}$$

The last expression is in the sum-of-products form. A logic circuit corresponding to this expression is shown in Fig. 2.3.3. Note that this circuit contains a number of AND-gates to form the product terms which are then combined in a single OR-gate. A circuit with this structure has been referred to as an *AND-OR circuit*. Note that such a circuit provides a direct implementation of a Boolean expression in the sum-of-products form. It is also to be noted that there are only two gate delays from the input signals (or their complements) and the output signal.

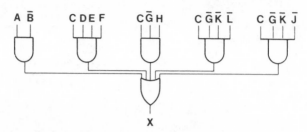

Fig. 2.3.3   AND-OR circuit from Boolean equation in sum-of-products form

2.4   KARNAUGH MAPS

2.4.1   Karnaugh maps representing canonical sum-of-products expressions

Karnaugh maps or K-maps are used for a pictorial representation of a Boolean function of *n* variables. They are useful for functions of up to six variables. Beyond this number K-maps become difficult to interpret.

An earlier section has established that any Boolean expression can always be represented in *sum-of-products form*. Two examples of Boolean functions of three variables A, B and C are:

(i) $R = BC + CA + AB$
(ii) $S = A\overline{B}\,\overline{C} + \overline{A}B\overline{C} + \overline{A}\,\overline{B}C + ABC$

In the second example, each product term contains each of the three variables or their complements. These product terms are described as *canonical product terms*, and the expression is said to be in *canonical sum-of-products form*. In the first example, each term involves only two variables and hence is *not* a canonical product term. However it will now be shown that this expression can be manipulated into an equivalent expression in canonical sum-of-products form, and indeed this is the case for *any Boolean expression*. The manipulation uses the identity $A + \overline{A} = 1$ where A is any Boolean variable. The steps in the manipulation are:

$$R = BC + CA + AB$$
$$= BC(A + \overline{A}) + CA(B + \overline{B}) + AB(C + \overline{C})$$
$$= BCA + BC\overline{A} + CAB + CA\overline{B} + ABC + AB\overline{C}$$
$$= ABC + ABC + ABC + \overline{A}BC + A\overline{B}C + AB\overline{C}$$
$$= ABC + \overline{A}BC + A\overline{B}C + AB\overline{C}$$

For three variables A, B and C, there are eight canonical product terms; $\overline{A}\,\overline{B}\,\overline{C}$, $\overline{A}\,\overline{B}C$, $\overline{A}B\overline{C}$, $\overline{A}BC$, $A\overline{B}\,\overline{C}$, $A\overline{B}C$, $AB\overline{C}$ and ABC. For *n* variables, there are 2^n canonical product terms.

On each K-map of *n* variables, there is an area corresponding to each of the 2^n canonical product terms. As any Boolean expression (of *n* variables) can always be converted to the canonical sum-of-products form, a K-map of *n* variables can always be used to represent this expression by appropriately marking any (including none or all) of the areas corresponding to the canonical product terms.

Karnaugh maps of one to five variables are shown in Fig. 2.4.1. It will be seen that columns and rows of the K-maps are marked with 0s and 1s. These have the following significance. Whenever a column (say) of a variable (say A) is marked with a 0, then the

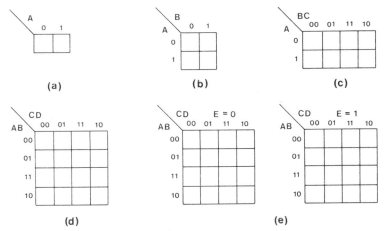

Fig. 2.4.1 Karnaugh maps—(a) one variable, (b) two variables, (c) three variables, (d) four variables, (e) five variables

term $\overline{A}$ will appear in the product term, and conversely when it is marked with a 1, then the term A will appear. To illustrate the significance of the column and row headings, the canonical product terms corresponding to the areas of the K-maps of one, two and three variables are shown on the K-maps of Fig. 2.4.2.

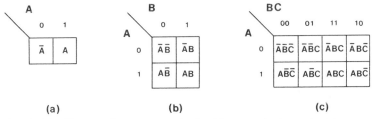

Fig. 2.4.2 Karnaugh maps marked with canonical product terms— (a) one variable, (b) two variables, (c) three variables

Fig. 2.4.3 shows two K-maps of three variables, which represent the two canonical sum-of-products expressions discussed above. These were:

$$R = \overline{A}BC + A\overline{B}C + AB\overline{C} + ABC$$
$$S = A\overline{B}\,\overline{C} + \overline{A}B\overline{C} + \overline{A}\,\overline{B}C + ABC$$

Note that the areas are marked with 1s. The marked areas specify the product terms which appear in the canonical sum-of-products expressions.

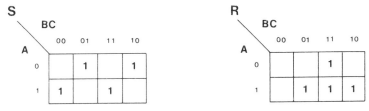

Fig. 2.4.3 Karnaugh maps marked with ones representing canonical sum-of-products expressions

66 *Combinational circuits*

2.4.2 Minimisation using Karnaugh maps

It will be observed from Fig. 2.4.2 that whenever columns (or rows) of K-maps are marked with two binary digits corresponding to two variables (e.g. 00, 01, 11, 10 columns corresponding to variables B and C of the 3-variable map), these digits progress from column to adjacent column (or row to adjacent row) in a Gray code. This code specifies a sequence of a group of digits such that only one digit changes at a time. Hence for the BC columns of the 3-variable map, from column 00 to 01, variable C changes from 0 to 1; from column 01 to column 11, variable B changes from 0 to 1; from column 11 to column 10, variable C changes from 1 to 0 and finally from column 10 to column 00 (the end columns which are to be considered as adjacent), variable B changes from 1 to 0.

The above arrangement enables adjacent areas to be grouped and the combined area can then represent a smaller number of non-canonical product terms. This results in a

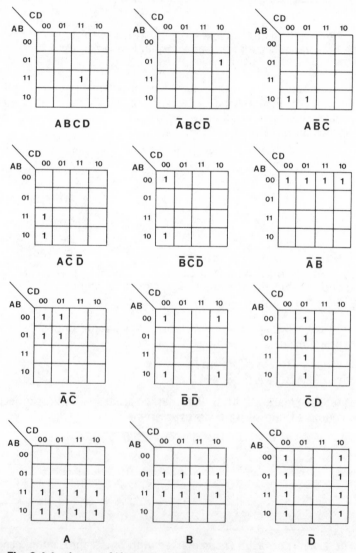

Fig. 2.4.4 Areas of K-maps marked with ones

simplification of Boolean expressions with a consequent minimisation of logic circuit hardware. Note that this minimisation procedure is based on the Boolean identity

$$A + \overline{A} = 1$$

As an example, by grouping the areas corresponding to ABC and $\overline{A}$BC (of a 3-variable map), we have an area corresponding to ABC + $\overline{A}$BC which is equivalent to BC. Further reductions are possible by repeatedly applying the identity. For example, by grouping the areas corresponding to $\overline{A}\,\overline{B}$C, $\overline{A}$BC, $\overline{A}$BC and $\overline{A}$B$\overline{C}$ we have an area corresponding to $\overline{A}\,\overline{B}$C + $\overline{A}$B$\overline{C}$ + $\overline{A}$BC + $\overline{A}$BC which reduces to $\overline{A}$.

The process of minimisation using K-maps involves the identification of product terms corresponding to grouped areas so that a minimised form of a Boolean expression may be obtained. Experience in identifying these product terms is obviously essential. To provide this, a number of examples are presented in Fig. 2.4.4. It is to be observed from these K-maps of four variables that a product term of four variables is represented by one (canonical product term) area; a product term of three variables is represented by two areas; a product term of two variables is represented by four areas and a single variable (or its complement) is represented by eight areas. Hence, to obtain a minimised expression, the objective is to represent all the areas marked with '1' (and only these areas) by a small number of groups with total areas as large as possible. In selecting these groups, an area may be included two or more times because of the 'inclusive' nature of the OR function.

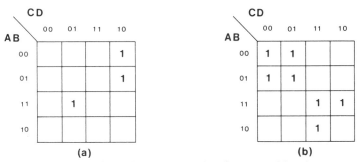

Fig. 2.4.5 Sum-of-products expression from combined area on K-map—(a) K-map of AB$\overline{C}$D + $\overline{A}$CD, (b) K-map of $\overline{A}$C + ABC + ACD

Examples of (non-canonical) sum-of-products expressions obtained from combined areas on K-maps are shown in Fig. 2.4.5. A further example is shown in Fig. 2.4.6. This figure provides two alternative groupings with corresponding Boolean expressions and logic circuits. Clearly the objective is to obtain groupings which are as large as possible.

A further application of K-maps arises when *don't care* conditions exist. For example, in the specification of a Boolean function F in terms of input variables (say A, B, C and D), F may be required to be equal to 1 for some input conditions, and 0 for other conditions. However it may not matter whether F takes on the value of 1 or 0 for some further input conditions, which may then be described as 'don't care' conditions. An example of this situation is shown in Fig. 2.4.7 where the don't-care conditions are represented by the symbol X. Here the function F must be equal to 1 for the four input conditions marked by 1s viz. A$\overline{B}\,\overline{C}\,\overline{D}$, AB$\overline{C}D, ABC\overline{D}$ and A$\overline{B}$C$\overline{D}$. The function must be equal to 0 for the six input conditions marked by 0s and it may be either 1 or 0 for the six input conditions marked by Xs. The objective here is to specify the X conditions so that F is minimised. The pictorial representation of the problem readily provides a solution. If the two Xs outside the dotted outline are made equal to 0 and the four Xs inside the dotted outline are made equal to 1, the K-map will consist of the eight 1s within the dotted outline. This combined

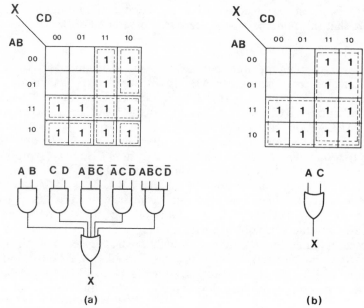

Fig. 2.4.6   Minimisation using K-maps

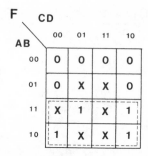

Fig. 2.4.7   Minimisation using 'don't-care' terms

area corresponds to the variable A, and hence the solution is F = A which does not require any circuit at all.

2.4.3   Karnaugh maps representing product-of-sums expressions

Examples of Boolean expressions in 'product-of-sums' form are

(i) $(A+C)(A+D)(B+C)(B+D)$
(ii) $(A+B+C+D)(\bar{A}+B+\bar{C}+\bar{D})$

Both of these expressions are functions of the four variables A, B, C and D. However as each sum term of (ii) contains every variable or its complement, each sum term is called a *canonical sum term* and the expression (ii) is called a *canonical product-of-sums expression*.

The generation of the signal defined by expression (i) above may be achieved using the OR–AND circuit shown in Fig. 2.4.8. As this type of circuit is often useful (especially in handling NOR circuits treated in the next section), a description of how Karnaugh maps may be used to represent product-of-sums expressions will now be presented.

When a K-map is marked with 1s as used in earlier sections, it is assumed that all unmarked areas are 0s. Consequently a K-map could be marked with 0s assuming that all unmarked areas are 1s. This latter procedure results in expressions in product-of-sums form. The procedure is firstly illustrated by an example.

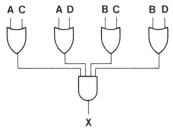

Fig. 2.4.8 Two-level OR-AND circuit from product-of-sums expression

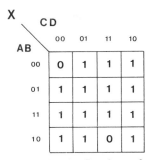

Fig. 2.4.9 Product-of-sums expression from areas of K-map marked with zeros

Consider the K-map of Fig. 2.4.9 which defines a signal X in terms of A, B, C and D. Both 0 and 1 areas are marked. This is to emphasise the point that the defined function X is equal to 1 unless the input conditions specified by the 0 areas hold. There are two 0 areas corresponding to the input conditions $\overline{A}\overline{B}\overline{C}\overline{D}$ and $A\overline{B}CD$. Hence:

$$X = \overline{\overline{A}\overline{B}\overline{C}\overline{D}} \ \overline{A\overline{B}CD}$$
$$= (A+B+C+D)(\overline{A}+B+\overline{C}+\overline{D})$$

This latter expression is of the product-of-sums form.

Minimisation can also be achieved using K-maps marked with 0s. Again experience with identifying terms corresponding to combined areas is necessary. Some examples are presented in Fig. 2.4.10.

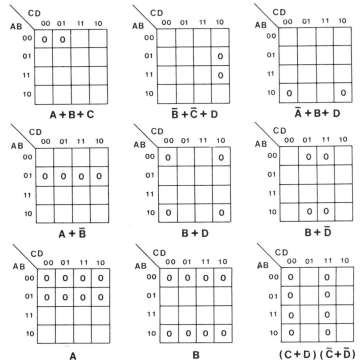

Fig. 2.4.10 Areas of K-maps marked with zeros

To derive the minimal product-of-sums expression from a K-map marked with 0s, it is necessary to include every 0 (and to exclude every 1) in areas which are as large as possible. An example is given in Fig. 2.4.11. This is the K-map of the expression $(A+C)(A+D)(B+C)(B+D)$. In this example the $(A+C)$ term corresponds with the four areas marked α; the $(A+D)$ term corresponds with the four areas marked β; the $(B+C)$ term corresponds with the four areas marked γ and the $(B+D)$ term corresponds with the four areas marked δ. Note that some 0 areas may be treated more than once to achieve a minimised expression.

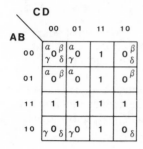

Fig. 2.4.11 Product-of-sums expression from combined area of K-map marked with zeros

2.4.4 Procedure for converting sum-of-products expression to product-of-sums expression and vice versa

Karnaugh maps may be used to convert a sum-of-products expression to an equivalent product-of-sums expression and vice versa. The procedure for the conversion of a sum-of-products expression involves the two steps:

(i) mark a K-map with ones corresponding to all product terms,
(ii) from unmarked areas (assumed marked with zeros) write down the sum terms.

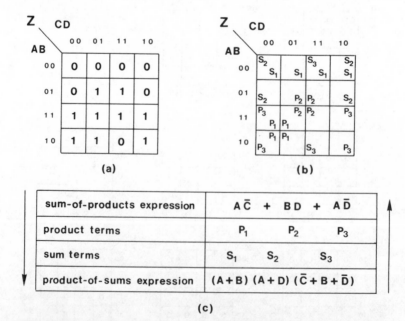

Fig. 2.4.12 Illustration of procedure for converting sum-of-products expression to product-of-sums expression and vice-versa— (a) K-map, (b) sum and product terms, (c) equivalent expressions

The corresponding procedure for the conversion of a product-of-sums expression involves the steps:

(i) mark a K-map with zeros corresponding to all sum terms,

(ii) from unmarked areas (assumed marked with ones) write down the product terms.

The above procedures are illustrated in Fig. 2.4.12. The expressions used in this example are:

$$\begin{aligned} Z &= A\overline{C} + BD + A\overline{D} \\ &= P_1 + P_2 + P_3 \\ &= (A+B)(A+D)(\overline{C}+B+\overline{D}) \\ &= \quad S_1 \qquad S_2 \qquad S_3 \end{aligned}$$

The areas of the K-map corresponding to the above product terms and sum terms are identified in Fig. 2.4.12(b).

2.5 'NOR' AND 'NAND' CIRCUITS

2.5.1 'Universal' logic elements

The truth tables of NOR- and NAND-gates with two inputs are shown in Fig. 2.5.1. The symbols used for these gates are also shown. It will be observed that the NOR-gate is equivalent to an OR-gate followed by an inverter (NOT-gate). It is to be noted that the inverter part is represented by the small circle to which the output is connected. Similarly the NAND-gate is equivalent to an AND-gate followed by an inverter, and the symbol for a NAND-gate is that of an AND-gate combined with a small circle to represent the inverter.

A	B	$\overline{AB}$
0	0	1
0	1	1
1	0	1
1	1	0

A	B	$\overline{A+B}$
0	0	1
0	1	0
1	0	0
1	1	0

Fig. 2.5.1 Truth tables and symbols of NOR- and NAND-gates

Each of the NOR- and NAND-gates is a 'universal logic element' in the sense that circuits comprising either type alone can be constructed to carry out the fundamental operations of AND, OR and NOT.

Fig. 2.5.2 shows how NOR- and NAND-gates may be used as universal elements. Firstly, note how an inverter may be constructed using two-input NOR- and NAND-gates. Both of the inputs can be connected together and the truth tables of Fig. 2.5.1 clearly show that the gates so connected provide the inverter function. Alternatively the second (unused) input of a two-input (positive logic) NOR-gate may be connected to the LOW voltage level, and the second (unused) input of a two-input (positive logic) NAND-gate may be connected to the HIGH voltage level to provide the inverter function. Note that if NOR- and NAND-gates with more than two inputs are used as inverters, all unused inputs should be correctly terminated (i.e., connected to HIGH or LOW voltage levels) in the interest of maintaining good noise immunity.

Note from Fig. 2.5.2 that the OR function may be obtained by connecting a NOR-gate to an inverter, and that the AND function may be obtained by connecting a NAND-gate to an inverter.

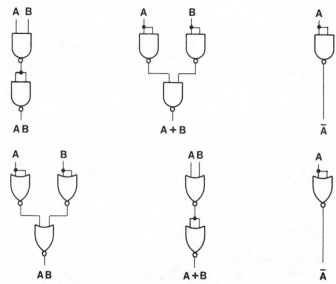

Fig. 2.5.2   NOR- and NAND-gates as 'universal' elements

The remaining cases, i.e., that of producing the AND function using NOR-gates and the OR function using NAND-gates require the application of de Morgan's theorems which, for two variables, are as follows:

$$\overline{AB} = \overline{A} + \overline{B} \text{ or } AB = \overline{\overline{A} + \overline{B}}$$

$$\overline{A + B} = \overline{A}\,\overline{B} \text{ or } A + B = \overline{\overline{A}\,\overline{B}}$$

The first of the above relationships shows that the function AB may be produced by a NOR-gate with inputs $\overline{A}$ and $\overline{B}$, and that the function $A + B$ may be produced by a NAND-gate with inputs $\overline{A}$ and $\overline{B}$. The required circuit arrangements are shown in Fig. 2.5.2.

When it is required to produce the AND or OR functions of more than two variables, similar circuit arrangements are used. These are based on de Morgan's theorems for more than two variables. For three variables, de Morgan's theorems are:

$$\overline{ABC} = \overline{A} + \overline{B} + \overline{C}$$
$$\overline{A + B + C} = \overline{A}\,\overline{B}\,\overline{C}$$

Further extension to four or more variables is obvious.

It has been shown that either the NOR- or the NAND-gate is a universal logic element, and hence the combinational part of a digital system may be constructed entirely of only one circuit type. This approach was, in fact, used in some early digital systems constructed of discrete semiconductor components. As a large percentage (approaching 70%–80%) of the digital system contained only one circuit type, high reliability and easy maintainability were obtained.

There was another reason for the widespread use of NOR- and NAND-gates in digital systems constructed of discrete semiconductor components. The inverter was usually implemented as a transistor inverter circuit, and hence not only could the circuit drive many other circuits (i.e., having high 'fan-out'), but also the output voltage (representing Boolean 0 or 1) was fully regenerated, being defined by the supply voltages of the circuit. This latter feature meant that circuits could be cascaded to any level without any fear of a cumulative voltage shift which was a major problem with circuits constructed of passive elements (e.g., diode–resistor gates).

Most integrated circuit families now provide NOR- and NAND-gates with various package configurations. The semiconductor technology used often results in a predominance of the number of packages using one type of gate. However, both types of gates are frequently required in the interests of circuit minimisation.

2.5.2 NAND and NOR circuits from Boolean expression

Earlier sections have described how logic circuits containing AND-, OR- and NOT-gates may be readily derived from Boolean expressions. A direct substitution of AND-, OR- and NOT-gates by the NOR or NAND equivalents of Fig. 2.5.2 might suggest that the number of NOR- or NAND-gates to implement a given Boolean expression would be much greater than the total number of AND-, OR- and NOT-gates required for the same expression. This is not necessarily so. The reasons for this are that (i) complements of input signals are often available (e.g., outputs from bi-stable circuits, treated later), and (ii) the inverse of a signal, and not the signal itself, is required to drive the next level of cascaded circuits. Hence, many of the inverters required by the circuit substitutions suggested by Fig. 2.5.2 would not be required.

Earlier sections have described how Boolean expressions in sum-of-products form may be readily implemented as AND–OR circuits, and those in product-of-sums form may be readily implemented as OR–AND circuits. Both of these types of circuits may be described as 'two-level circuits' as input signals and their complements must pass through two levels of gates before output signals are formed. The 'settling time' of these circuits, i.e., the period from the time the input signals and their complements are established and the time the output signals settle to their correct values, corresponds to two gate delays.

This section will describe further types of circuits using NAND and NOR circuits alone which may be readily derived from Boolean expressions in either sum-of-products or product-of-sums form. These types of circuits are:

  (i) two-level NAND circuit derived from a Boolean expression in sum-of-products form,
 (ii) three-level NOR circuit derived from a Boolean expression in sum-of-products form,
(iii) two-level NOR circuit derived from a Boolean expression in product-of-sums form, and
(iv) three-level NAND circuit derived from a Boolean expression in product-of-sums form.

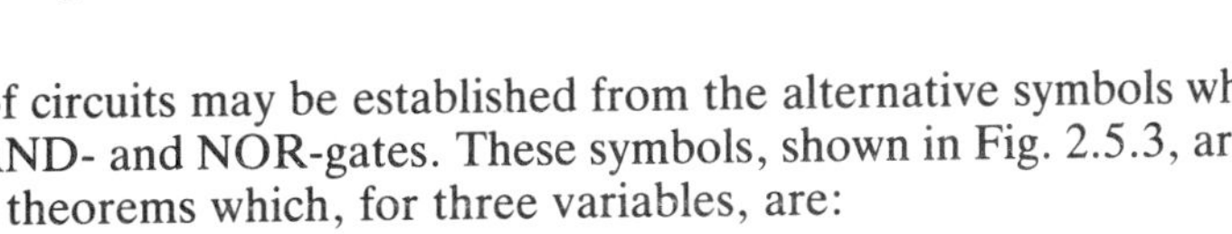

Fig. 2.5.3 Alternative symbols for NOR- and NAND-gates

These types of circuits may be established from the alternative symbols which may be used for the NAND- and NOR-gates. These symbols, shown in Fig. 2.5.3, are suggested by de Morgan's theorems which, for three variables, are:

$$\overline{ABC} = \overline{A} + \overline{B} + \overline{C}$$
$$\overline{A+B+C} = \overline{A}\,\overline{B}\,\overline{C}$$

Hence, the NAND-gate is functionally equivalent to an OR-gate driven by the inverses of all input signals; and the NOR-gate is functionally equivalent to an AND-gate driven by the inverses of all input signals. In the alternative symbols, the small circles shown at the inputs of the OR- and AND-gates represent inverters which produce the required inverses of all input signals.

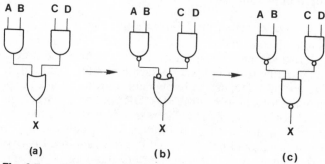

Fig. 2.5.4   Derivation of two-level NAND circuits

The steps involved in establishing the four new types of circuits listed above are shown in Figs. 2.5.4, 2.5.5, 2.5.6 and 2.5.7. The Boolean expression in sum-of-products form used in Figs. 2.5.4. and 2.5.5 is $AB+CD$. This expression is firstly represented by the two-level AND–OR circuit of Fig. 2.5.4(a). Two inverters in series are then introduced into each of the intermediate signal lines as shown in Fig. 2.5.4(b). These inverters (represented by the small circles) do not alter the functional relationship between input and output signals. Finally, it is observed that the alternative symbol for the NAND-gate is used for one of the gates in Fig. 2.5.4(b). This is replaced by the standard symbol for the NAND-gate in Fig. 2.5.4(c). This figure (Fig. 2.5.4(c)) shows the structure of the two-level NAND circuit which may be readily derived from a sum-of-products expression. Note that the input signals to NAND-gates in the first level of Fig. 2.5.4(c) are the same as the signals to the AND-gates of Fig. 2.5.4(a). Note also that the two-level NAND circuit of Fig. 2.5.4(c) has the same 'structure' as that of the AND–OR circuit of Fig. 2.5.4(a), and may be obtained by a direct substitution of each gate of Fig. 2.5.4(a) by a NAND-gate.

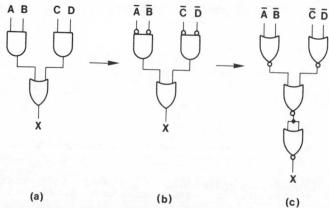

Fig. 2.5.5   Derivation of three-level NOR circuit

Fig. 2.5.5 shows the steps involved in the derivation of the three-level NOR circuit from a sum-of-products expression. Starting from the AND–OR circuit of Fig. 2.5.5(a), inverters are introduced into every input line as shown in Fig. 2.5.5(b). However, in order to maintain the same output signal, it is necessary to complement every input signal. Hence the A input to the AND-gate of Fig. 2.5.5(a) is replaced by the $\overline{A}$ input to the inverter which then drives the AND-gate of Fig. 2.5.5(b). It will now be observed that the first level gates of Fig. 2.5.5(b) are represented by the standard symbol for the NOR-gate in Fig. 2.5.5(c), and the OR-gate of Fig. 2.5.5(b) is replaced by the NOR-gate followed by the inverter gate of Fig. 2.5.5(c). This figure (Fig. 2.5.5(c)) shows the structure of the three-level NOR circuit which may be readily derived from a sum-of-products expression. Note that this structure is essentially the same as that of the AND–OR circuit of Fig. 2.5.5(a) with the exception of the inverter gate in level 3 of Fig. 2.5.5(c). Note, however, that the input signals to the first level NOR-gates of Fig. 2.5.5(c) are the complements of the signals to the AND-gates of Fig. 2.5.5(a).

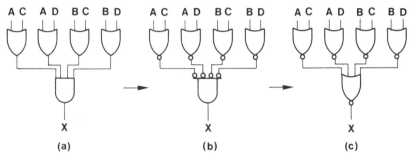

Fig. 2.5.6 Derivation of two-level NOR circuit

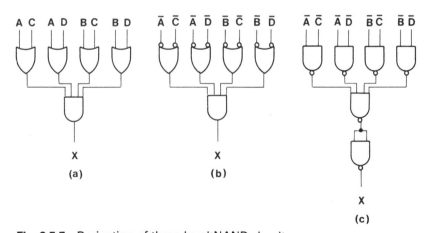

Fig. 2.5.7 Derivation of three-level NAND circuit

The Boolean expression in product-of-sums form used in Fig. 2.5.6 and Fig. 2.5.7 is $(A+C)(A+D)(B+C)(B+D)$. The derivation of the required NOR and NAND circuits shown finally in Fig. 2.5.6(c) and Fig. 2.5.7(c) is based on the OR–AND circuit of Fig. 2.5.6(a) and Fig. 2.5.7(a), which comes directly from the above product-of-sums expression. The details of the derivation, which follow very closely that described in earlier paragraphs, are left to the reader.

The reader may also wish to verify the Boolean identity:

$$(A+C)(A+D)(B+C)(B+D) = AB+CD$$

This may be achieved by considering the Karnaugh map of Fig. 2.4.11. The sum-of-products expression may be obtained by considering the areas of the Karnaugh map marked with 1s, and the product-of-sums expression may be obtained from the areas marked with 0s. Because of this identity, the four circuits of Figs. 2.5.4(c), 2.5.5(c), 2.5.6(c) and 2.5.7(c) are equivalent, i.e. they have identical functional relationships between input and output signals. In this case, the circuit of Fig. 2.5.4(c) seems to have slight advantages over the others using the criteria of (i) minimum number of gates and (ii) minimum delay between input and output signals. However, there may well be other cases or specific circuit limitations which will cause a designer to choose other circuit arrangements. In any event it is a decided advantage to be aware of the equivalent circuits which are possible using NAND and NOR circuits.

2.6 ALL POSSIBLE BOOLEAN FUNCTIONS OF TWO OR MORE VARIABLES

2.6.1 Boolean functions of two variables

There are sixteen different Boolean functions of two variables A and B. These are listed in columns 5 and 6 of Table 2.6.1. Each of the functions may be obtained by selecting none, any one, any two, any three or all four of the canonical product terms $\overline{A}\overline{B}$, $\overline{A}B$, $A\overline{B}$ and AB. This description of how the various Boolean functions may be obtained suggests the circuit shown in Fig. 2.6.1. This circuit will generate at its output X any one of the sixteen

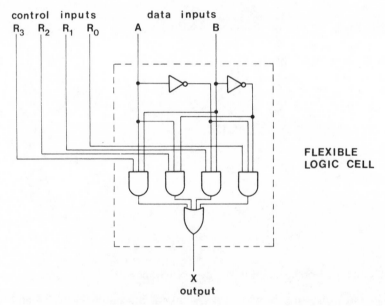

Fig. 2.6.1 Circuit for the generation of any Boolean function of two variables A and B

possible Boolean functions of two variables A and B as specified by four control signals R_3, R_2, R_1 and R_0. These control signals 'gate' the canonical product terms to the OR-gate which produces the output X. By allowing R_3, R_2, R_1 and R_0 to take on successive values in binary sequence from 0000 to 1111 respectively, Table 2.6.1 is produced.

The '*function table*' shown in Table 2.6.1 represents another convenient method for the representation of a complex Boolean function. In this example the output is a function of

Table 2.6.1 Function table of a circuit for the generation of any Boolean function of two variables A and B

R_3	R_2	R_1	R_0	Function	Name
0	0	0	0	0	ZERO
0	0	0	1	$\overline{A}\,\overline{B} = \overline{A+B}$	NOR
0	0	1	0	$\overline{A}B$	
0	0	1	1	$\overline{A}$	NOT A
0	1	0	0	$A\overline{B}$	
0	1	0	1	$\overline{B}$	NOT B
0	1	1	0	$A\overline{B}+\overline{A}B$	EXCLUSIVE OR
0	1	1	1	$\overline{A}+\overline{B} = \overline{AB}$	NAND
1	0	0	0	AB	AND
1	0	0	1	$AB+\overline{A}\,\overline{B}$	EQUIVALENCE
1	0	1	0	B	B
1	0	1	1	$\overline{A}+B$	
1	1	0	0	A	A
1	1	0	1	$A+\overline{B}$	
1	1	1	0	$A+B$	INCLUSIVE OR
1	1	1	1	1	ONE

the six variables R_3, R_2, R_1, R_0, A and B, the first four of which are considered as 'control' inputs and the last two as 'data' inputs. The function table is to be interpreted as follows:
  (i) the first line specifies that when $R_3 = 0$, $R_2 = 0$, $R_1 = 0$ and $R_0 = 0$ then $X = 0$,
  (ii) the second line specifies that when $R_3 = 0$, $R_2 = 0$, $R_1 = 0$ and $R_0 = 1$ then $X = \overline{A}\,\overline{B}$
    and so on.
The function table may be more descriptive than a truth table in which entries are restricted to 0 and 1 (and perhaps X for the don't care conditions). This is so as the entries in the form of Boolean expressions clearly define the output as meaningful functions of data signals. Further examples will be given later in the description of the functions of 'arithmetic-logic-units' which are provided in many families of medium- to large-scale integrated circuits.

2.6.2 Example of the application of K-maps to the minimisation of a Boolean function of six variables

The interpretation of the function table (Table 2.6.1) described in the last section enables a Boolean expression for the output X to be written in terms of the six input variables. This expression is:

$$X = \overline{R}_3\overline{R}_2\overline{R}_1R_0\overline{A}\,\overline{B}+\overline{R}_3\overline{R}_2R_1\overline{R}_0\overline{A}B+\overline{R}_3\overline{R}_2R_1R_0\overline{A}$$
$$+\overline{R}_3R_2\overline{R}_1\overline{R}_0A\overline{B}+\overline{R}_3R_2\overline{R}_1R_0\overline{B}+\overline{R}_3R_2R_1\overline{R}_0(A\overline{B}+\overline{A}B)$$
$$+\overline{R}_3R_2R_1R_0(\overline{A}+\overline{B})+R_3\overline{R}_2\overline{R}_1\overline{R}_0AB+R_3\overline{R}_2\overline{R}_1R_0(AB+\overline{A}\,\overline{B})$$
$$+R_3\overline{R}_2R_1\overline{R}_0B+R_3\overline{R}_2R_1R_0(\overline{A}+B)+R_3R_2\overline{R}_1\overline{R}_0A$$
$$+R_3R_2\overline{R}_1R_0(A+\overline{B})+R_3R_2R_1\overline{R}_0(A+B)+R_3R_2R_1R_0$$

It is quite instructive to apply a K-map of six variables to the minimisation of this expression for X. This map is shown in Fig. 2.6.2. It will be observed that areas on this map are marked, not by the usual 1s corresponding to terms in a sum-of-products expression, but by numbers 1 to 15 inclusive. These numbers should be treated as functionally equivalent to the usual 1s. However, they provide the additional information of which term in the above complex expression for X caused the inclusion of the marked canonical product term. The numbers used are the 'decoded' values of R_3, R_2, R_1 and R_0 with these

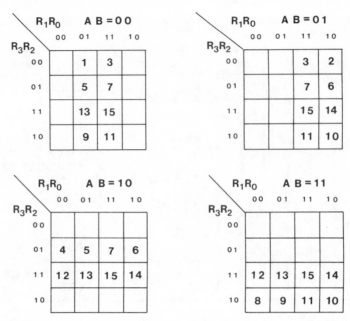

Fig. 2.6.2   K-map for the minimisation of a function of six variables

variables being given weightings of 8, 4, 2 and 1 respectively. For example, for the term $\overline{R}_3\overline{R}_2\overline{R}_1R_0\overline{A}\,\overline{B}$, the number used is 1 and the single area in the map for $A = 0$ and $B = 0$ is marked. Again for the term $R_3R_2\overline{R}_1R_0(A+\overline{B})$, the number used is 13 and the areas in the three maps (i) for $A = 1$ and $B = 0$, (ii) for $A = 1$ and $B = 1$ and (iii) for $A = 0$ and $B = 0$ are marked.

When the above procedure is completed for all terms, the resultant map is as shown in Fig. 2.6.2. The corresponding minimised expression for X is:

$$X = R_3AB+R_2A\overline{B}+R_1\overline{A}B+R_0\overline{A}\,\overline{B}$$

The expression is consistent with Fig. 2.6.1 from which the function table of Table 2.6.1 was initially derived.

2.6.3   The EXCLUSIVE-OR function

Earlier sections have described the development of Boolean algebra based on the AND, OR and NOT operators. This algebra proved extremely suitable for the treatment of combinational circuits in general and was quite satisfactory for handling circuits composed of NAND- and NOR-gates.

Another gate which has found very wide application is the EXCLUSIVE-OR gate. The EXCLUSIVE-OR function can, of course, be defined in terms of the fundamental operators (as shown in Table 2.6.1). However, its early development by digital system designers and its continued usefulness justify the introduction of a *special symbol* for the EXCLUSIVE-OR operator. This symbol is $\oplus$ and the operator is defined by the following equation:

$$A \oplus B = A\overline{B}+\overline{A}B$$

The symbol used for the EXCLUSIVE-OR gate is shown in Fig. 2.6.3(a). It is to be noted that the EXCLUSIVE-OR gate has two and only two inputs. Hence, when three or more signals are to be combined using the EXCLUSIVE-OR operator, such as in the term $A \oplus B \oplus C$, a cascading of EXCLUSIVE-OR gates is required. For example, the term $A \oplus B \oplus C$ will be taken as $(A \oplus B) \oplus C$ (or possibly $A \oplus (B \oplus C)$ as the EXCLUSIVE-OR operator obeys the associative law) and its implementation will be as in Fig. 2.6.3(b).

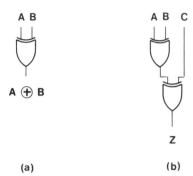

A B

A ⊕ B

(a)

A B C

Z

(b)

Fig. 2.6.3 Exclusive-OR gate—(a) symbol, (b) application to Boolean function $(A \oplus B) \oplus C$

Applications of the EXCLUSIVE-OR gate include (i) construction of 'half adders' and 'full adders', (ii) use in 'comparison circuits', (iii) use in 'true/complement' gates and (iv) use in 'parity generators' and 'parity detectors'. The last of these applications will be described to illustrate the usefulness of the gate.

In some digital systems involving the storage or transmission of a fixed number of bits of information, an extra bit (the parity bit) is used as a check bit. The parity bit can be generated so that the system has either 'odd parity' or 'even parity', this characteristic being chosen by the system designer. In an odd parity system, the *total number of ones* in the parity bit and information bits must be an *odd* number. The corruption of any one bit (i.e. by changing from 0 to 1 or from 1 to 0) can be detected by the parity detection circuit which signals an error condition. The organisation of parity circuits for the storage or transmission of five data bits is shown in Fig. 2.6.4.

We shall consider two alternative methods of constructing a parity detection circuit for an odd parity system in which five information bits and one parity bit are transmitted to that part of the system containing the parity detection circuit. Let the information bits be designated A, B, C, D and E, and the parity bits be designated P. The first method uses EXCLUSIVE-OR gates and is represented by the circuit of Fig. 2.6.5. Note that this circuit utilises only five EXCLUSIVE-OR gates to produce the signal Z which is equal to 1 when the parity of the input signals A, B, C, D, E and P is odd, i.e. when the total number of ones in the signals A, B, C, D, E and P is an odd number. Consider the intermediate signals V, W, X and Y of Fig. 2.6.5. Firstly consider the EXCLUSIVE-OR gate with inputs A and B. The output V is a 1 only if A and B are different (as $V = \bar{A}B + A\bar{B}$). This represents the condition that 'the parity of A and B is odd'. We shall describe V as a signal *representing the parity of A and B*. Similarly W represents the parity of C and D, and Y represents the parity of E and P. Now consider the EXCLUSIVE-OR gate with inputs V and W. The output X is a 1 only if V and W are different, i.e. if the parity of A and B is odd and the parity of C and D is even, or vice versa. Hence, X is a 1 only if A, B, C and D have odd parity, i.e. X represents the parity of A, B, C and D. Similar reasoning shows that Z represents the parity of A, B, C, D, E and P.

For the second method we shall use a K-map of the six variables A, B, C, D, E and P. We shall mark each of the 64 areas corresponding to the canonical products terms with a 1 when the parity of the input signals is odd. We shall then examine the map to determine any useful groupings of areas so that a minimised Boolean expression for the output signal Z may be determined. This map is shown in Fig. 2.6.6. Note the so-called 'checkerboard

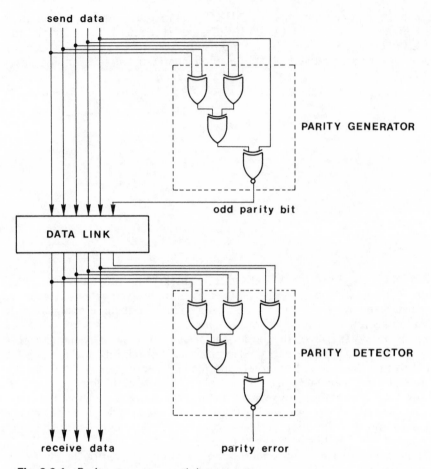

Fig. 2.6.4 Parity generator and detector

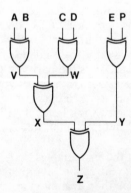

Fig. 2.6.5 Parity detection circuit using exclusive-OR gates

pattern' of 1s. Note also that there are no adjacent 1s and hence no groupings of areas are possible. Hence no minimisation is possible and the Boolean expression for Z would be the logical sum of the 32 canonical product terms marked with 1s in Fig. 2.6.6. If an implementation using a two level NAND circuit is required, this circuit would contain 32 NAND-gates each with 6 inputs and one NAND-gate with 32 inputs !! There is usually a limitation on the number of inputs to a gate which can be provided in any logic circuit family. This limitation which is imposed by electrical characteristics of the digital circuits themselves or by physical constraints of packaging will be referred to as the '*fan-in*' of a circuit. However, even if fan-in problems could be overcome, the implementation using this approach would be grossly uneconomic in the light of the alternative solution using EXCLUSIVE-OR gates.

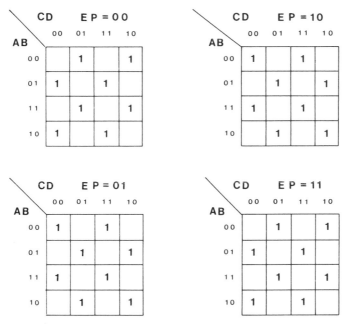

Fig. 2.6.6 K-map of circuit to detect odd parity in signals A, B, C, D, E, and P

2.6.4 Boolean functions of three or more variables

The circuit given in Fig. 2.6.1 for the generation of any Boolean function of two variables may be extended to three or more variables. A circuit for three variables is shown in Fig. 2.6.7. In this circuit, R_7, R_6, . . ., R_0 are eight control signals which gate signals corresponding to the canonical product terms of the input signals A, B and C to the output.

Following an examination of Fig. 2.6.1 and Fig. 2.6.7, it may be deduced that for n variables, 2^n control signals are used to gate the 2^n canonical product terms. As there are 2^{2^n} combinations of these control signals, there are 2^{2^n} different Boolean functions. For $n = 3$, this number is 256, and for larger values of n this number increases very rapidly as shown in Table 2.6.2.

The circuits of Fig. 2.6.1 and Fig. 2.6.7 have been described as '*flexible logic cells*' with the adjective '*flexible*' referring to the characteristic that any such cell's outputs may be made equal to any Boolean function of the cell's inputs by appropriately setting the cell's control input signals. This concept has certainly been implemented in 'arithmetic-logic-

82   *Combinational circuits*

Table 2.6.2   Number of Boolean functions of *n* variables

Number of variables n	Number of Boolean functions 2^{2^n}
1	4
2	16
3	256
4	65 536
5	4 294 967 296
6	18 446 744 073 709 551 616

units' provided in many integrated circuit families. However, this implementation is only for $n = 2$, i.e. functions of only two variables are produced. More general applications, e.g. by interconnecting flexible logic cells in cascade or in two-dimensional *arrays* have been researched but will not be further described in this section.

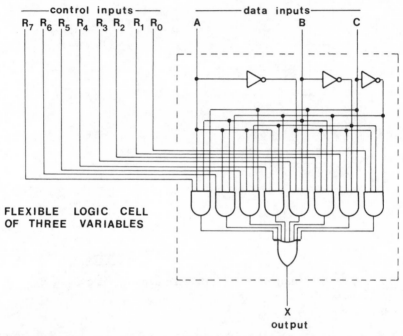

Fig. 2.6.7   Circuit for the generation of any Boolean function of three variables

2.7   LOGIC CIRCUITS FOR THE ADDITION OF TWO BINARY NUMBERS

2.7.1   Representation of binary numbers

A number of Boolean signals may be used to represent a binary number. These signals define binary digits which are associated with *weightings equal to integral powers of two*, and the number represented is the arithmetic sum of these digits with these assigned weightings. For example the signals A_3, A_2, A_1 and A_0 may represent a *positive binary integer* if the weightings are 2^3, 2^2, 2^1 and 2^0 respectively. Hence the integer represented would be:

$$A_3 2^3 + A_2 2^2 + A_1 2^1 + A_0 2^0$$

where the symbol + represents arithmetic addition and the digits A_3, A_2, A_1 and A_0 have arithmetic values of either 1 or 0 corresponding to their Boolean values.

Binary *'fractions'* may be represented by assigning weightings which are negative integral powers of two. Numbers which may be either positive or negative may be represented by the use of an additional *'sign bit'*. Several alternative conventions and methods may be used for the representation of binary integers and fractions which may have either sign. Some of these will be described in later sections. This section will be restricted to positive binary integers with the representation described above as this will be sufficient to illustrate how logic circuits may be constructed to perform binary arithmetic addition.

2.7.2 Half adders and full adders

Consider the circuit requirements of adding two four-bit positive binary integers A and B represented by (A_3, A_2, A_1 and A_0), and (B_3, B_2, B_1 and B_0) respectively. The *binary digits* (*abbreviated to 'bits'*) with the lowest weighting are A_0 and B_0. These may be summed using a circuit known as a *'half adder'*. This circuit is shown in Fig. 2.7.1 and the truth table defining circuit outputs in terms of inputs is given in Table 2.7.1.

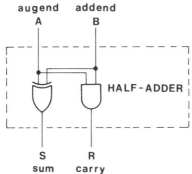

Fig. 2.7.1 Logic circuit of half adder

The Boolean expressions for the SUM output S and the CARRY output R are given by:

$$S = A \oplus B$$
$$R = AB$$

Table 2.7.1 Truth table of half adder

INPUTS	A	0	1	0	1
	B	0	0	1	1
OUTPUTS	S(SUM)	0	1	1	0
	R(CARRY)	0	0	0	1

The half adder with inputs A_0 and B_0 will have SUM and CARRY outputs S_0 and R_0 respectively. The S_0 bit becomes the least significant bit of the result but R_0 (which must be given the next higher weighting) must be incorporated in the addition of the pair of inputs with the next higher weighting viz. A_1 and B_1. This may be achieved in two ways, the first of which is shown in Fig. 2.7.2. The circuit of Fig. 2.7.2 uses two half adders represented by the rectangular blocks marked HA. One of these produces the intermediate SUM and CARRY signals S' and R' from A_1 and B_1. The second then combines S' and R_0 to form the output SUM bit S_1 and another intermediate CARRY signal R". As either half adder may produce carry signals, the intermediate carry signals R′ and R″ must be combined in an OR gate to produce the output carry bit R_1.

The circuit of Fig. 2.7.2 has three inputs which are to be arithmetically summed, and two outputs with the significance of SUM and CARRY bits. Such a circuit is called a '*full adder*'. The second method (referred to above) therefore involves the design of a full adder circuit from these basic requirements.

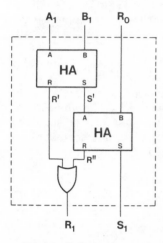

Fig. 2.7.2   Circuit for the addition of three binary digits using half adders

We shall designate the three inputs of a full adder by A, B and C, and the SUM and CARRY outputs by S and R. The truth table defining these outputs is shown in Table 2.7.2. Columns in this truth table must be considered quite independently of one another. For example we could firstly consider the condition A = 1, B = 1 and C = 0. The rules of binary addition require that the SUM digit should be equal to 0 and that there should be a carry, i.e. the CARRY digit should be equal to 1. Secondly for the condition A = 1, B = 1 and C = 1, we require both the SUM and CARRY digits to be equal to 1. This is repeated until all SUM and CARRY entries of the truth table of Table 2.7.2 have been completed.

Table 2.7.2   Truth table of full adder

INPUTS	A	0	1	0	1	0	1	0	1
	B	0	0	1	1	0	0	1	1
	C	0	0	0	0	1	1	1	1
OUTPUTS	S(SUM)	0	1	1	0	1	0	0	1
	R(CARRY)	0	0	0	1	0	1	1	1

The Boolean expressions for the SUM and CARRY outputs of a full adder may be obtained by scanning the rows of the truth table of Table 2.7.2 which define the SUM and CARRY bits. Whenever a 1 occurs, a product term specified by the values of A, B and C is added to the expression. For example the SUM bit S equals 1 for the inputs A = 1, B = 0 and C = 0; hence the term $A\overline{B}\overline{C}$ is added to the expression for S. The complete expressions for the SUM bit S and the CARRY bit R are:

$$S = A\overline{B}\overline{C} + \overline{A}B\overline{C} + \overline{A}\,\overline{B}C + ABC$$
$$R = \overline{A}BC + A\overline{B}C + AB\overline{C} + ABC$$

It may be shown that the above expression for S cannot be minimised but that the expression for R may be reduced to:

$$R = BC + CA + AB$$

An implementation of the full adder using two-level NAND circuits is shown in Fig. 2.7.3.

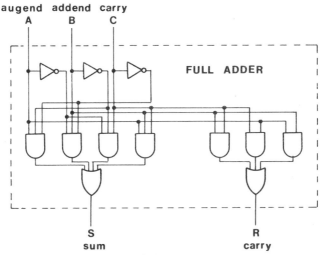

Fig. 2.7.3 Logic circuit of full adder

2.7.3 Ripple-carry parallel adder

A '*parallel adder*' is a combinational circuit which has inputs representing all bits of two numbers and which has outputs representing the sum of these numbers. As a combinational circuit, all inputs are applied to the circuit simultaneously, and once internal transients have decayed to zero, the outputs are established at values specified by the required functional relationship between inputs and outputs.

A 'ripple-carry' parallel adder is a parallel adder which utilises full adder circuits (or their equivalents) and which is structured so that the CARRY output of one full adder stage is connected to the C input (i.e. CARRY input) of the full adder stage with the next higher weighting.

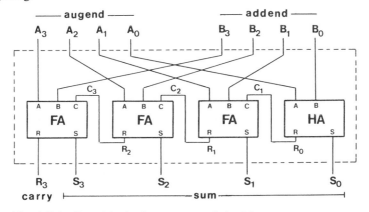

Fig. 2.7.4 Four-bit ripple-carry parallel adder

A four-bit ripple-carry parallel adder is shown in Fig. 2.7.4. This circuit has eight inputs: A_3, A_2, A_1 and A_0 representing a four-bit integer A, and B_3, B_2, B_1 and B_0 representing another four-bit integer B. It has five outputs: S_3, S_2, S_1 and S_0 representing a four-bit sum S and a CARRY output R_3 which can be used as a CARRY input to further adder stages or which can be considered as a fifth (most-significant) SUM digit.

The significance of the term 'ripple-carry' is that a CARRY signal (R_0) which may be generated in the least-significant stage must *ripple through* all full adder stages before all output signals are established. With this circuit structure the circuit delays of each full adder stage are cumulative, and this accumulated ('*worst-case*') delay which applies only to the last of the outputs to settle following an input change must be taken as the delay of the total parallel adder circuit. Other circuit configurations of parallel adders designed for high speed (in particular the 'carry-lookahead adder') will be described in later sections.

In spite of the discussion of circuit delays given in the last paragraph, it must be stressed that the ripple-carry parallel adder is a *combinational* circuit and as such it is possible to derive Boolean expressions for *all* outputs in terms of all inputs with the elimination of all intermediate or internal signals (such as C_3, C_2 and C_1 of Fig. 2.7.4). However, a circuit such as that of Fig. 2.7.4 clearly defines the functional relationship between inputs and outputs, and in many applications, it is not necessary to obtain Boolean expressions for outputs in terms of inputs alone.

It is useful to consider a circuit such as that of Fig. 2.7.4 as a '*multi-input/multi-output*' circuit. Once the input-output relationship of such a circuit is clearly understood by a designer, it becomes a '*building block*' of much greater complexity than the basic logic gates. This building block approach must of course be taken by designers when using commercially available medium/large-scale integrated circuits. Further examples of multi-input/multi-output circuits are given in the next section.

2.8 EXAMPLES OF MULTI-INPUT/MULTI-OUTPUT CIRCUITS

2.8.1 Decoders

A decoder is a combinational circuit which generates at its outputs all of the 2^n canonical product terms of the n signals connected to its inputs. As the canonical product terms are *mutually exclusive* and the logical sum of all of the 2^n terms is equal to Boolean 1, one and only one output of a decoder is 'selected' for any combination of input signals. If the decoder is implemented as a set of 2^n *AND-gates each with n inputs*, the selected output will go HIGH while all others remain LOW. However, if it is implemented as a set of 2^n NAND-gates each with n inputs, the selected output will go LOW while all others remain HIGH. A general block diagram of a decoder is shown in Fig. 2.8.1.

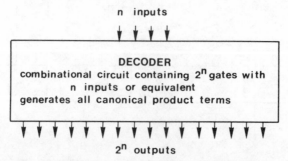

Fig. 2.8.1 General block diagram of an n-line-to-2^n-line decoder

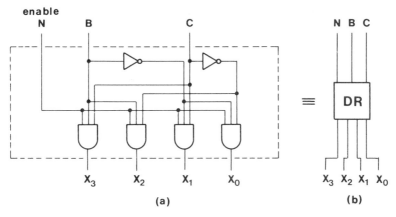

Fig. 2.8.2 Two-line-to-four-line decoder with enable—(a) circuit,
(b) symbol used in Fig. 2.8.3

The gates of a decoder are often provided with another input which is common on all
gates and brought to the decoder input. This is the *enable* input which allows decoders to
be used in '*tree-structured*' arrangements. An example is given in Fig. 2.8.2 and Fig. 2.8.3.
A 2-line-to-4-line decoder with enable input is shown in Fig. 2.8.2. The defining equations
are:

$$X_0 = N\overline{B}\,\overline{C}$$
$$X_1 = N\overline{B}C$$
$$X_2 = NB\overline{C}$$
$$X_3 = NBC$$

Fig. 2.8.3 then shows how a 5-line-to-32-line decoder may be constructed using ten 2-line-
to-4-line decoders. In this figure, the five inputs are A, B, C, D and E with associated
weightings 2^4, 2^3, 2^2, 2^1 and 2^0. The 32 outputs are designated X_{31}, X_{30}, ... X_1, X_0. Note how
the input A, which has the highest weighting has been connected to the enable input of one
of the 2-line-to-4-line decoders in the 'first level' of the tree, while the signal $\overline{A}$ has been
connected to the enable input of the other decoder in this level. These two decoders are

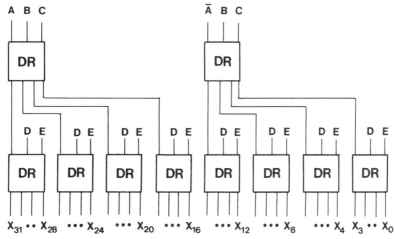

Fig. 2.8.3 Circuit of a tree-structured five-line-to-thirty-two-line
decoder

then functionally equivalent to a 3-line-to-8-line decoder. Note also how the outputs of the decoders in the first level are connected to the enable inputs of decoders in the second level.

Some MSI/LSI (medium-scale to large-scale) integrated circuits are described as '*decoder/demultiplexers*'. The concept of a decoder we have already described. The concept of a *demultiplexer* is a circuit which enables a data signal to be channelled to a number of outputs. It may be seen that the decoder with enable input (e.g. the circuit of Fig. 2.8.2) may be used for such an application. The enable input (or another similarly connected input) may be used as the data signal which may then be channelled to any one of the outputs under control of the select inputs. For example, in the circuit of Fig. 2.8.2, when $B = 0$ and $C = 0$ the data input N will be channelled to X_0 (with all other outputs remaining equal to 0); and when $B = 0$ and $C = 1$, N will be channelled to X_1 and so on.

2.8.2   Magnitude comparator

Fig. 2.8.4 is a functional circuit diagram of a 4-bit magnitude comparator which is available as a MSI/LSI integrated circuit. The analysis of this circuit will now be developed as a final example in this chapter of how useful Boolean algebra is for the analysis and design of combinational logic circuits.

The circuit of Fig. 2.8.4 has eleven inputs and three outputs. Four of the inputs A_3, A_2, A_1 and A_0 represent a number A and another four B_3, B_2, B_1 and B_0 represent a number B. The most significant bits are A_3 and B_3, and the least significant are A_0 and B_0. Another three inputs I_E, I_G and I_L are used for 'circuit extension' to be described later. The three outputs X_E, X_G and X_L specify whether (i) A is equal to B, (ii) A is greater than B, or (iii) A is less than B. When no circuit extension is required I_E, I_G and I_L must be set to 1, 0 and 0

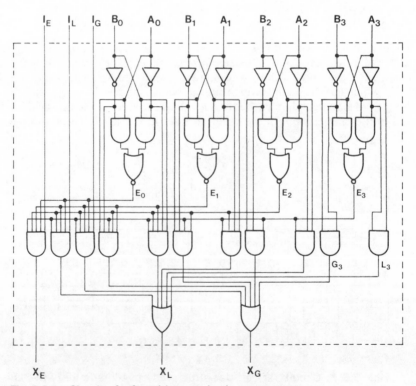

Fig. 2.8.4   Circuit of a four-bit magnitude comparator

respectively. Under these conditions, the outputs for the three magnitude relations stated above are given by Table 2.8.1.

Table 2.8.1 Outputs of magnitude comparator for the condition $I_E = 1$, $I_G = 0$ and $I_L = 0$

CONDITION	X_E	X_G	X_L
A = B	1	0	0
A > B	0	1	0
A < B	0	0	1

The analysis of the circuit of Fig. 2.8.4 begins by identifying the significance of the intermediate signals E_3, E_2, E_1 and E_0. For our immediate requirements these will be called 'equals functions' (as the term 'equivalence' was used in an earlier section), and are defined by:

$$E_n = \overline{A}_n\overline{B}_n + A_nB_n \qquad (n = 3, 2, 1, 0)$$

Hence, $E_n = 1$ when A_n and B_n are the same.

We shall also define 'greater than functions' G_n and 'less than functions' L_n as follows:

$$G_n = A_n\overline{B}_n \qquad (n = 3, 2, 1, 0)$$
$$L_n = \overline{A}_nB_n \qquad (n = 3, 2, 1, 0)$$

Hence, $G_n = 1$ when $A_n = 1$ and $B_n = 0$, and therefore, for all other bits being equal, A would be greater than B. Similarly $L_n = 1$ when $A_n = 0$ and $B_n = 1$, and for all other bits being equal, A would be less than B. Only G_3 and L_3 appear as outputs of gates in the circuit of Fig. 2.8.4. However, it may be seen readily that these functions for other values of *n* are represented by pairs of signals to AND-gates.

Having identified how the above functions have been implemented in the circuit of Fig. 2.8.4, Boolean expressions for the outputs X_E, X_G and X_L may be derived as follows:

$$X_E = E_3E_2E_1E_0I_E$$
$$X_G = G_3 + E_3G_2 + E_3E_2G_1 + E_3E_2E_1G_0 + E_3E_2E_1E_0I_G$$
$$X_L = L_3 + E_3L_2 + E_3E_2L_1 + E_3E_2E_1L_0 + E_3E_2E_1E_0I_L$$

We shall firstly consider the input conditions for no 'circuit extension' viz. $I_E = 1$, $I_G = 0$ and $I_L = 0$. For these conditions it may be seen firstly that $X_E = 1$ only if $E_3 = 1$, $E_2 = 1$, $E_1 = 1$ and $E_0 = 1$, i.e., every bit of A is the same as the corresponding bit of B.

Consider next the expression for X_G (the 'greater than output'). This contains a number of terms representing conditions which produce $X_G = 1$. The first is simply G_3 (the 'greater than function' for $n = 3$), and as bit 3 is the most significant bit, the condition $G_3 = 1$ requires X_G to be equal to 1 irrespective of the relationship between other less significant bits. The second term E_3G_2 covers the condition when the most significant bits are equal and when the condition $G_2 = 1$ requires X_G to be equal to 1 irrespective of the relationship between other less significant bits. The third term $E_3E_2G_1$ covers the condition when the two most significant bits are equal, and the fourth term $E_3E_2E_1G_0$ covers the condition when the three most significant bits are equal.

The expression for X_L may be derived by reasoning analogous to that given in the last paragraph.

Note that the inputs I_E, I_G and I_L required for 'circuit extension' are combined with $E_3E_2E_1E_0$ to form product terms in the expressions for X_E, X_G and X_L. The condition $E_3E_2E_1E_0 = 1$ specifies that all four corresponding bits of A and B are the same, and hence the X_E, X_G and X_L will depend on the I_E, I_G and I_L inputs. These inputs may be connected to the X_E, X_G and X_L outputs of another 4-bit magnitude comparator whose inputs are the *next less significant* group of four bits of the numbers A and B. This arrangement is shown in Fig. 2.8.5 which provides a circuit of an 8-bit *magnitude comparator*.

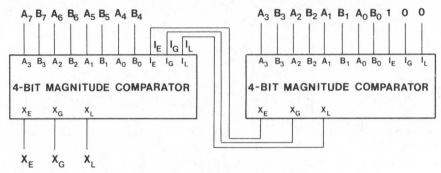

Fig. 2.8.5   Circuit of an eight-bit magnitude comparator

Using the symbols and conditions shown in Fig. 2.8.5, the Boolean equations defining the outputs are:

$$E_n = \overline{A}_n\overline{B}_n + A_nB_n \quad (n = 7, 6, 5, 4, 3, 2, 1, 0)$$
$$G_n = A_n\overline{B}_n \quad (n = 7, 6, 5, 4, 3, 2, 1, 0)$$
$$L_n = \overline{A}_nB_n \quad (n = 7, 6, 5, 4, 3, 2, 1, 0)$$
$$X_E = E_7E_6E_5E_4I_E$$
$$X_G = G_7 + E_7G_6 + E_7E_6G_5 + E_7E_6E_5G_4 + E_7E_6E_5E_4I_G$$
$$X_L = L_7 + E_7L_6 + E_7E_6L_5 + E_7E_6E_5L_4 + E_7E_6E_5E_4I_L$$
$$I_E = E_3E_2E_1E_0$$
$$I_G = G_3 + E_3G_2 + E_3E_2G_1 + E_3E_2E_1G_0$$
$$I_L = L_3 + E_3L_2 + E_3E_2L_1 + E_3E_2E_1L_0$$

Following the reasoning given in earlier paragraphs it may be verified quite readily that the two 4-bit magnitude comparators with the interconnections shown in Fig. 2.8.5 may be used to compare two 8-bit numbers. Further circuit extensions to compare numbers with a larger number of bits is obvious.

The analysis of the 4-bit magnitude comparator given above is a good example of the usefulness of Boolean algebra for handling complex combinational circuits. The Boolean expressions provide not only a clear indication of the algorithms involved but also a functional logic circuit diagram from which the circuit may be constructed.

2.9   QUESTIONS

2.9.1   Logic circuit from Boolean equation

Draw a logic diagram of a circuit which produces a signal Z from signals A, B, C, D, E, F and G when Z is defined by the Boolean equation:

$$Z = A\overline{B}(C+D) + \overline{A}B[D + \overline{E}(CF + \overline{G})]$$

This circuit can take a number of forms. It is suggested that you draw the diagrams of the following:

(i) A circuit containing AND-, OR- and NOT-gates defined by the above Boolean equation without removal of brackets, assuming that the inverses of the signals A, B, C, D, E, F and G are *not* available.

(ii) A circuit containing AND-, OR- and NOT-gates defined by the 'sum-of-products' form of the Boolean expression for Z, assuming that the inverses of the signals A, B, C, D, E, F and G are available.

2.9.2 Circuits with minimum gate delays from Boolean equations

Four signals W, X, Y and Z are defined in terms of signals, A, B, C, D, E, F and G by the Boolean equations:

$$W = C+D$$
$$X = CF+\bar{G}$$
$$Y = D+\bar{E}X$$
$$Z = A\bar{B}W+\bar{A}BY$$

Draw the logic diagrams of circuits which will produce the signals W, X, Y and Z with the minimum gate delays between any of the input signals, A, B, C, D, E, F and G (and their inverses) and any of the output signals W, X, Y and Z.

2.9.3 NOR and NAND logic circuit from Boolean equation

The signal X is defined in terms of the signals A, B, C and D by the Boolean equation:

$$X = \bar{A}\bar{C}+D+\bar{A}B$$

Draw logic diagrams of the circuit for producing the signal X in the following forms:
   (i) a circuit containing NAND-gates only derived from the above 'sum-of-products' expression for X
   (ii) a circuit containing NOR-gates only derived from the above 'sum-of-products' expression for X
   (iii) a circuit containing NAND-gates only derived from an equivalent 'product-of-sums' expression for X
   (iv) a circuit containing NOR-gates only derived from an equivalent 'product-of-sums' expression for X.

2.9.4 Minimisation of Boolean expression

Minimise the following Boolean expressions:
   (i) $XY+\bar{X}Y\bar{Z}+YZ$
   (ii) $\bar{B}C+B\bar{C}+\bar{A}B+AB$
   (iii) $AB+BC\bar{D}+\bar{B}+AD$
   (iv) $\bar{A}\bar{B}CD+AB+C\bar{D}+AD+\bar{B}\bar{D}$
   (v) $\bar{A}BCD+A\bar{D}+\bar{B}CD+\bar{A}\bar{B}\bar{C}D+AB\bar{C}+\bar{B}\bar{D}+\bar{A}B\bar{D}$
   (vi) $\bar{A}BD+AD\bar{W}+AB\bar{C}D+BCW+B\bar{C}\bar{D}W+BD\bar{W}$

2.9.5 Conversion of Boolean expression into sum-of-products form

Convert the following Boolean expressions into 'sum-of-products' form:

   (i) $\overline{AB\bar{C}}(A+B)$

   (ii) $\overline{EF+\bar{E}FA\bar{B}\bar{C}}$

2.9.6 Boolean expression from logic circuit

Obtain a Boolean expression in the 'sum-of-products' form for the output Z of the following circuit in terms of the inputs A, B, C, D, E and F.

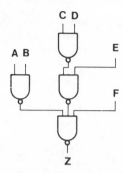

Fig. 2.9.1   Logic circuit for question of Section 2.9.6

2.9.7   Boolean expressions from logic circuits

Obtain Boolean expressions in the 'sum-of-products' form for the outputs Y and Z of the following circuit in terms of the inputs A, B, C, D, E and F.

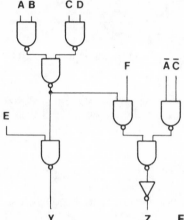

Fig. 2.9.2   Logic circuit for question of Section 2.9.7

2.9.8   Karnaugh map marked with 'ONES'

Write down a minimised Boolean expression for the signal Z defined by the following Karnaugh map:

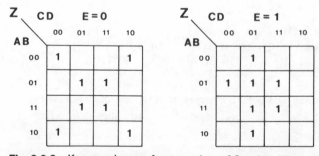

Fig. 2.9.3   Karnaugh map for question of Section 2.9.8

2.9.9   Karnaugh map marked with 'ZEROS'

Write down a minimised Boolean expression for the signal Z in the 'product-of-sums' form represented by the following Karnaugh map marked with zeros.

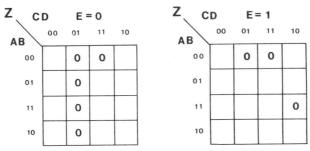

Fig. 2.9.4 Karnaugh map for question of Section 2.9.9

2.9.10 Minimisation using 'don't care' conditions

The following Karnaugh map defines a signal Z in terms of signals A, B, C, D and E. The areas marked with X correspond to 'don't care' conditions. Define the values which the Xs should take to minimise the expression for Z. Write down the minimised expression.

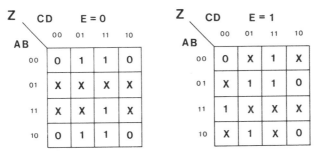

Fig. 2.9.5 Karnaugh map for question of Section 2.9.10

2.9.11 Circuit from Karnaugh map

The following Karnaugh map defines a function Z of six variables A, B, C, D, E and F.

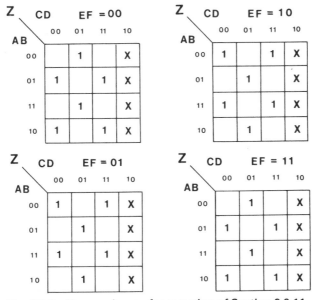

Fig. 2.9.6 Karnaugh map for question of Section 2.9.11

  (i) Specify the values of all the X entries representing 'don't care' conditions so that a circuit containing a minimum number of gates can be obtained for producing the signal Z from the input signals A, B, C, D, E and F. Sketch this circuit.

 (ii) If all the X entries are zero, derive a circuit for producing the signal Z. It is suggested that this should be carried out by modifying the circuit derived in (i).

2.9.12   Circuit containing NAND-gates with limited number of inputs

Derive circuits containing only NAND-gates with a maximum of four inputs for the production of the two signals Y and Z defined by the following Boolean equations:

$$Y = ABCDEF + ABCGH + ABCJKL + MN + PQR + ST$$
$$Z = ABCDEFGH$$

2.9.13   Circuit containing NAND- and NOR-gates with limited number of inputs

Using only NAND- and NOR-gates with a maximum of eight inputs, derive a circuit containing a minimum number of gates for producing a signal Z defined by the Boolean equation:

$$Z = ABCDEFGHJKLMNPQR$$

Table 2.9.1   BCD-to-Gray-code conversion

INPUTS				OUTPUTS			
B_3	B_2	B_1	B_0	G_3	G_2	G_1	G_0
0	0	0	0	0	0	0	0
0	0	0	1	0	0	0	1
0	0	1	0	0	0	1	1
0	0	1	1	0	0	1	0
0	1	0	0	0	1	1	0
0	1	0	1	0	1	1	1
0	1	1	0	0	1	0	1
0	1	1	1	0	1	0	0
1	0	0	0	1	1	0	0
1	0	0	1	1	1	0	1
1	0	1	0	X	X	X	X
1	0	1	1	X	X	X	X
1	1	0	0	X	X	X	X
1	1	0	1	X	X	X	X
1	1	1	0	X	X	X	X
1	1	1	1	X	X	X	X

2.9.14 Minimisation using don't care conditions: BCD-to-Gray-code conversion

Table 2.9.1 defines four outputs G_3, G_2, G_1 and G_0 of a combinational circuit in terms of four inputs B_3, B_2, B_1 and B_0. The first ten combinations of the inputs represent the decimal digits 0---9 in BCD (binary-coded-decimal). The corresponding combinations of the outputs represent the decimal digits in Gray code. The remaining six combinations of inputs are 'can't happen' combinations, and hence the corresponding outputs are defined by the X entries in the table as 'don't care' conditions.

Derive minimised Boolean expressions for the outputs G_3, G_2, G_1 and G_0 in terms of the inputs B_3, B_2, B_1 and B_0.

2.9.15 Logic circuit from Boolean equation: an example from the design of an early computer

The logical design of the LGP-30 general-purpose computer (Frankel 1957) was represented by about 42 Boolean equations. One of the most complex of these equations is reproduced below. It defined a signal A'' in terms of other signals each of which was represented by a single alphabetic character (lower- or upper-case) with or without a numeric subscript. Derive a logic circuit (say using NAND-gates only) for the generation of the signal A'' from the other signals.

$$A'' = A\overline{H}[\overline{F}+\overline{G}+Q_1\overline{Q}_2\overline{Q}_3+\overline{Q}_2(Q_3+\overline{Q}_4)+\overline{Q}_1Q_2(Q_3+Q_4)\overline{t}]$$
$$+FG\overline{H}[\overline{Q}_2\overline{Q}_3Q_4(\overline{Q}_1+A)V+Q_1Q_2Q_3b+\overline{Q}_1\overline{Q}_2\overline{Q}_3\overline{Q}_4p]$$
$$+Hb(\overline{t}+P_1+\overline{F}G)$$

3 SEQUENTIAL CIRCUITS

Techniques for the analysis and synthesis of circuits containing flip-flops

3.1 INTRODUCTION

A general block diagram of a *sequential circuit* was given in Fig. 1.4.12(b). This type of circuit has *internal states* defined by memory circuits. The main characteristics of a sequential circuit are element interconnections which produce:

(i) *outputs* defined by Boolean functions of present internal states and present inputs, and

(ii) *new internal states* defined by Boolean functions of present internal states and present inputs.

The memory circuits defining internal states of most of the sequential circuits described in this chapter take the form of '*bi-stable circuits*' or '*flip-flops*'. These are circuits which have two stable states and whose inputs may be used to set the circuit into one of these states or perhaps (for some types of flip-flops) to change the circuit's state.

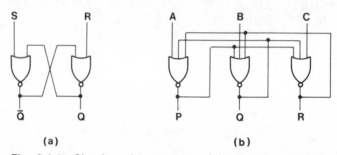

(a)   (b)

Fig. 3.1.1 Circuits with memory—(a) bi-stable circuit (or flip-flop) formed by cross-coupling two NOR-gates, and (b) circuit of three stable gates

A circuit with stable states may be constructed by interconnecting logic gates (or combinational circuits in general) in such a way that there are *feedback connections* from gate outputs through other gates to gate inputs. Two examples are given in Fig. 3.1.1. The first of these which is a bi-stable circuit formed by 'cross-coupling' two NOR-gates, has inputs S and R, and outputs Q and $\overline{Q}$. It may be verified that the two outputs are complementary when S and R are 00, 01 or 10, but are both forced to 0 for the combination S = 1 and R = 1. This last combination is usually avoided when the state of the circuit is sensed. It may also be verified that for the input combination S = 0 and R = 0, the circuit may be in either of the two states:

State 0 defined by Q = 0 and $\overline{Q}$ = 1

State 1 defined by Q = 1 and $\overline{Q}$ = 0.

For the input combination S = 1 and R = 0, the circuit will be 'set' into State 1 (or will not change if it is already in this state), and it will remain in this state even when the inputs change to S = 0 and R = 0. Similarly for the input combination S = 0 and R = 1 the circuit will be set into State 0 and it will remain in this state when the inputs change back to S = 0 and R = 0.

The circuit of Fig. 3.1.1(b) is a circuit with three stable states. These are defined by:

State 1: P = 1, Q = 0, R = 0
State 2: P = 0, Q = 1, R = 0
State 3: P = 0, Q = 0, R = 1

The three input combinations (for A, B and C) of 011, 101 and 110 set the circuit into States 1, 2 and 3 respectively. The input combination 000 does not change the circuit's state, and all other combinations are usually avoided.

Two examples have been given in Fig. 3.1.1 of circuits with feedback connections which have the characteristic of having 'memory' or 'internal states'. It is, however, to be pointed out that the existence of feedback connections is *not a sufficient condition* for the circuit to have memory. This is demonstrated by the circuit of Fig. 3.1.2 which is a combinational circuit despite the feedback connections.

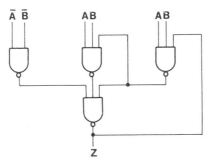

Fig. 3.1.2 A circuit with feedback connections but with no memory (i.e. a combinational circuit)

A further possibility is that feedback connections produce *indeterminate circuit outputs* as illustrated by the circuit connections shown in Fig. 3.1.3. When the input A of this circuit is equal to 0, it is not possible to predict the values of the outputs X, Y and Z using the *steady-state analysis* of the circuit provided by Boolean Algebra. The outputs of the physical circuit defined by Fig. 3.1.3 are found to oscillate and the period of oscillation is determined by the delays of the gates. Such a circuit has, in fact, a very useful application for the generation of multi-phase clocks.

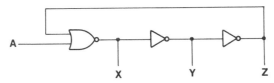

Fig. 3.1.3 A circuit with feedback connections producing indeterminate outputs

Procedures for the analysis and synthesis of sequential circuits are based on a classification of sequential circuits as either *clocked, synchronous sequential circuits* or *asynchronous sequential circuits*.

In a *clocked, synchronous sequential circuit*, the time during which the circuit remains in a particular state is pre-determined by an external, clock signal. The inputs to memory circuits (e.g. flip-flops) may change values many times depending on the propagation delays of the circuit elements which produce these inputs, but a clock senses these inputs only after they have settled to steady-state values.

In an *asynchronous sequential circuit* the time during which the circuit remains in a particular state is dependent, in general, on the levels of all circuit inputs and on the propagation delays of all circuit elements. In this case the circuit's behaviour may depend on the sequence in which inputs change, and it may be necessary to identify certain *'unstable states'* through which the circuit must pass before entering a desired stable state. Design procedures are required to eliminate undesirable circuit behaviour known as *'races'* and *'hazards'* caused by variations in the propagation delays of circuit elements.

The procedures for the analysis and synthesis of both types of sequential circuit are well established. Some systematic procedures for the analysis and synthesis of asynchronous sequential circuits make extensive use of tables or maps. As such they are applicable only to circuits with a modest number of internal states. These procedures will not be discussed any further in this chapter. A presentation of procedures for the analysis and synthesis of clocked, synchronous sequential circuits follows. We start by describing the characteristics of various types of flip-flops.

3.2   FLIP-FLOPS

3.2.1   The R–S flip-flop

The circuit of Fig. 3.1.1(a) may be described as an R–S flip-flop. The characters R and S refer to the terms 'reset' and 'set', and are used to label the inputs of the flip-flop. The term 'reset' is used when an input places the flip-flop into the 'zero state', and the term 'set' is used when an input places the flip-flop into the 'one state'.

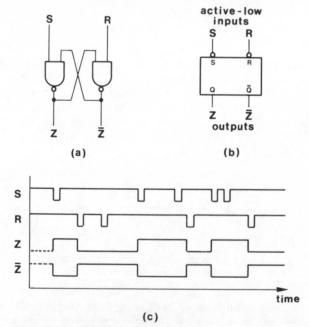

Fig. 3.2.1   R–S flip-flop formed by cross-coupling two NAND-gates—(a) circuit, (b) symbol, (c) waveforms illustrating input–output relationship

An R–S flip-flop can also be formed by cross-coupling two NAND-gates as shown in Fig. 3.2.1(a). A symbol for this type of flip-flop is shown in Fig. 3.2.1(b). The two inputs R and

S are normally HIGH, and activate the circuit when LOW; hence these inputs may be labelled 'active low' inputs. The outputs of the circuit are Z and $\overline{Z}$. When $R = S = 1$ (HIGH), the flip-flop may be in either one of two stable states defined by $Z = 1, \overline{Z} = 0$ and $Z = 0, \overline{Z} = 1$. Note that the circuit is symmetrical, and we may arbitrarily define S, R, Z and $\overline{Z}$. When $Z = 1$, we can say that the flip-flop has been 'set'. When $Z = 0$, we can say that the flip-flop has been reset.

Suppose that the flip-flop has been reset (i.e. $Z = 0$), and then consider what happens when the inputs change to $S = 0, R = 1$. It is quite clear (from the characteristics of NAND-gates) that the outputs change to $Z = 1, \overline{Z} = 0$. Hence the flip-flop switches to the set state. When the inputs change again to $S = 1, R = 1$, the flip-flop will remain in the set state. If the inputs change again to $S = 0, R = 1$, the inputs will require the flip-flop to be in the set state. The flip-flop is already in the set state and hence no change of state takes place.

Table 3.2.1 Function table of R–S flip-flop formed by cross-coupling two NAND-gates

INPUTS		OUTPUT	OPERATION
R	S	Z	
0	1	0	Reset flip-flop
1	0	1	Set flip-flop
1	1	Z	No change
0	0	?	Avoided

It is to be noted from Table 3.2.1 and Fig. 3.2.1(a) that the input condition $S = 0, R = 0$ is usually avoided as the resultant state is indeterminate and depends on which input first returns to 'one'.

The timing waveforms of Fig. 3.2.1(c) illustrate the function of the R–S flip-flop formed by cross-coupling two NAND-gates. It is suggested that the reader should confirm that the waveforms for Z and $\overline{Z}$ are correctly derived from the given waveforms for R and S.

3.2.2 Clocks for R–S flip-flops

From the previous description of the R–S flip-flop formed by cross-coupling two NAND-gates, it is clear that the flip-flop is a memory element capable of storing one binary digit (bit) of information. It may be necessary to transfer information in a digital system from one flip-flop to another or from the output of a combinational circuit to a flip-flop, etc. This is accomplished by a 'clock' which is a timing signal defining the precise instant when the transfer is to take place. The clock may be normally LOW and will go HIGH to define this instant, or vice versa. Some circuit arrangements may require more than one clock.

Fig. 3.2.2(a), (b) shows an arrangement which uses two clocks—a reset clock and a set clock (with the reset clock just preceding the set clock). Information represented by two positive logic signals A and B (which may come from combinational circuits) is to be transferred (or set) into two R–S flip-flops with outputs Z_2 and Z_1. In Fig. 3.2.2(a) it is assumed that the R–S flip-flops are constructed of cross-coupled NAND-gates. Hence ACTIVE LOW signals are required at the S and R inputs. These may be obtained by using an inverter to *invert* the normally low T_{RESET} clock and providing $\overline{T}_{RESET}$ at the R inputs of the flip-flop. It is also convenient to use NAND-gates to 'gate' the positive-logic input signals A and B with the positive-logic clock T_{SET}. Note that irrespective of the initial settings of the flip-flops, on the rising edge of T_{RESET} (see Fig. 3.2.2(b)) both flip-flops will be reset (i.e. $Z_2 = 0$ and $Z_1 = 0$). Now if $A = 0$, the S input of the Z_2 flip-flop will remain HIGH even when T_{SET} goes HIGH and hence the Z_2 flip-flop will not be set (activated) by

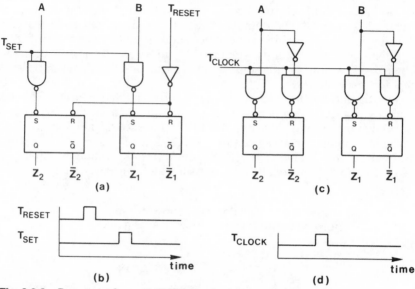

Fig. 3.2.2 Data transfer to R–S flip-flops—(a) first circuit using 'reset' and 'set' clocks, (b) clock waveforms for first circuit, (c) second circuit using single clock, (d) clock waveform for second circuit

the S input. The flip-flop will remain reset (with $Z_2 = 0$) as required by the input condition $A = 0$. However, if $A = 1$, the flip-flop will change to the SET state (with $Z_2 = 1$) on the rising edge of T_{SET}.

Fig. 3.2.2(c), (d) shows an arrangement which uses a single clock T_{CLOCK}. Irrespective of the initial states of the flip-flops, on the rising edge of T_{CLOCK}, the flip-flops will be activated into (or will remain in) the states determined by the input signals A and B (i.e. with $Z_2 = A$ and $Z_1 = B$). Note that the inverse signals $\overline{A}$ and $\overline{B}$ are required, and that inverters are required if these signals are not available (e.g. from flip-flop outputs).

3.2.3 The D-type flip-flop

The functional equivalent of a type of flip-flop known as a D-type flip-flop is shown in Fig. 3.2.3(a). Note that Fig. 3.2.3(a) is essentially the same as the circuits of Fig. 3.2.2(c) except for the addition of 'transient storage gates'. These may be implemented in a number of ways but may be considered as passive integrating networks (constructed of resistors and capacitors in a D-type flip-flop made of discrete semiconductor components). The function of the transient storage gates is to hold (i.e. store) the input signals to the two NAND-gates of Fig. 3.2.3(a) for a period which guarantees the reliable operation of the constituent R–S flip-flop initiated by the rising edge of the clock T_{CLOCK}. By providing transient storage, the flip-flop will still operate reliably even if the D input signals start to change at the rising edge of T_{CLOCK}. This characteristic enables us to cascade D-type flip-flops and obtain predictable performance.

Note that after the rising edge of T_{CLOCK} (of Fig. 3.2.3(a)) the output Q will start to settle to a state defined by the D input signal which existed *before* the rising edge. In summary:

$$Q_{\text{AFTER CLOCK}} = D_{\text{BEFORE CLOCK}}$$

Hence the D-type flip-flop can be considered as a unit with a *delay* of one clock period. Timing waveforms illustrating the function of the D-type flip-flop are shown in Fig. 3.2.3(d). The reader is again asked to verify that the output waveform $Z_1 (= Q)$ is correctly derived from the given input waveform D and the clock T_{CLOCK}.

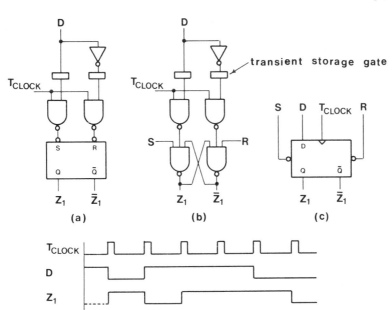

Fig. 3.2.3 D-type flip-flop—(a) functional equivalent, (b) functional equivalent with additional 'set' and 'reset' inputs, (c) symbol, (d) waveforms illustrating input–output relationship

A circuit of the functional equivalent of a 'D-type flip-flop with additional R and S inputs'is shown in Fig. 3.2.3(b). This is essentially the same as the circuit of Fig. 3.2.3(a) with the exception that R (reset) and S (set) inputs are provided to the cross-coupled three-input NAND-gates. These inputs are normally HIGH (i.e. active LOW) and are used to reset or set the flip-flop at times which are independent of the clock input. As far as the R and S inputs are concerned, the outputs Q and $\overline{Q}$ are determined in exactly the same way as described for the R–S flip-flop in Section 3.2.2. A symbol for a 'D-type flip-flop with additional R and S inputs' is shown in Fig. 3.2.3(c). Note the use of the small circles to indicate the active-LOW signals. The R and S inputs are not clocked, and hence may be described as '*asynchronous*' inputs. The terms CLEAR (for R) and PRESET (for S) are commonly used.

3.2.4 The master-slave J–K flip-flop
One of the restrictions of the R–S flip-flop is that one of the four combinations of the R–S inputs is not used. This restriction is removed with the J–K flip-flop, and one of the input

Table 3.2.2 Function table of J–K flip-flop

INPUTS		OUTPUTS		OPERATION
J	K	Q_{n+1}	$\overline{Q}_{n+1}$	
0	0	Q_n	$\overline{Q}_n$	No change
0	1	0	1	Reset flip-flop
1	0	1	0	Set flip-flop
1	1	$\overline{Q}_n$	Q_n	Change state

combinations causes the flip-flop to 'toggle', i.e. to change state. Table 3.2.2 defines the functions of the J–K flip-flop. In this table Q_n and $\overline{Q}_n$ represent the outputs of the flip-flop just prior to the clock pulse, and Q_{n+1} and $\overline{Q}_{n+1}$ represent the outputs after the clock pulse. A symbol for the flip-flop is shown in Fig. 3.2.4(b). Note that there is a CLOCK input which controls when the J and K inputs are sensed, and when the flip-flop outputs change.

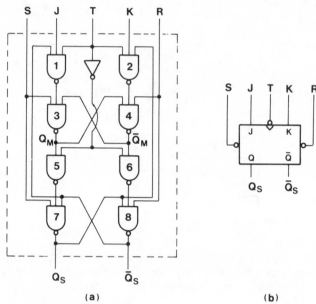

(a)   (b)

Fig. 3.2.4 Master-slave J–K flip-flop—(a) functional circuit equivalent, (b) symbol

The function of the 'transient storage gate' to overcome problems of cascaded flip-flops (and of circuits with feedback connections) was described for the D-type flip-flop. Another method of storing signals temporarily to ensure reliable switching of flip-flops is to store these signals on other flip-flops. What is suggested by the last statement is the duplication of every flip-flop and the use of a two-phase system of interleaved clocks. This arrangement is shown in Fig. 3.2.5(a). This diagram represents a digital system containing flip-flops with feedback connections and/or flip-flop cascading. It is to be inferred from this diagram that the flip-flops with the 'phase one clock' have inputs which are static for the duration of the T_1 clock (and for some time after), and that the flip-flops with the 'phase two clock' have inputs which are static for the duration of the T_2 clock (and for some time after). Hence the problems associated with cascaded flip-flops and/or circuits with feedback connections have been overcome, and all flip-flops in such a system would be expected to function reliably.

To facilitate the construction of digital systems using the 'two-phase clock' arrangement of Fig. 3.2.5(a) integrated circuit manufacturers have provided *master-slave flip-flops*. The arrangement of Fig. 3.2.5(a) is then replaced by that of Fig. 3.2.5(b) which uses a single clock T whose rising edge carries out the same function as the T_1 clock of Fig. 3.2.5(a) and whose falling edge carries out the same function as the T_2 clock.

The circuit of the functional equivalent of a master-slave J–K flip-flop is shown in Fig. 3.2.4(a). Note that there are two cross-coupled NAND-gates forming the master flip-flop Q_M and another two forming the slave flip-flop Q_S. There is only one clock input T, but the circuit is arranged so that clocking of the master flip-flop takes place at the rising edge of T

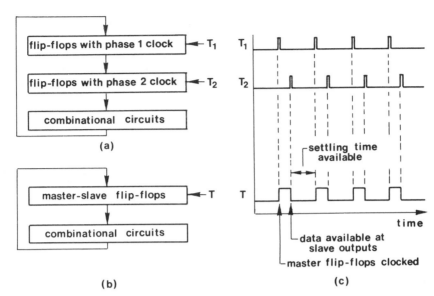

Fig. 3.2.5 Timing of synchronous circuits—(a) system with two-phase clocks, (b) system containing master-slave flip-flops, (c) timing details

and clocking of the slave flip-flop takes place at the falling edge of T. Note that the master flip-flop is used for 'transient storage', and that only the slave flip-flop outputs Q_S and $\overline{Q}_S$ are brought to pins on the integrated circuit package. The timing arrangements of the master-slave flip-flop are summarised by Fig. 3.2.5(c).

To verify that the circuit of Fig. 3.2.4(a) carries out the function of a J–K flip-flop as specified by Table 3.2.2, the NAND-gates of Fig. 3.2.4(a) have been numbered and an analysis of the function of each gate can be described. It may be seen readily that gates 3 and 4 form the master flip-flop, and that gates 7 and 8 form the slave flip-flop. Gates 1 and 2 gate the J and K inputs into the master flip-flop, and gates 5 and 6 gate the master into the slave. When T = 1, the T input to gates 1 and 2 allows the master flip-flop to be set according to the J and K inputs and the slave outputs Q_S and $\overline{Q}_S$. At the same time the $\overline{T}$ input to gates 5 and 6 does not allow the slave flip-flop to change. It may be verified that for the JK input combination of 00, the master flip-flop is left unchanged. Again for the JK input combination of 10, the output of gate 1 will go to 0 only if $\overline{Q}_S = 1$ (i.e. if the slave flip-flop is in the zero state). However, just prior to T going to 1, the slave flip-flop was set according to the state of the master flip-flop. Hence the output of gate 1 will go to 0 only if the master flip-flop is in the 'zero state'. The output of gate 1 will therefore set the master flip-flop to the one state. For the JK input combination of 10, the output of gate 1 will not go to 0 if $\overline{Q}_S = 0$, i.e. $Q_S = 1$. However, in this case the master flip-flop is already in the 'one state', and hence no change is required.

A similar analysis of gate 2 will show that the JK input combination of 01 will reset the master flip-flop to the 'zero state' or will leave the master flip-flop unchanged in the 'zero state'. For the JK input combination of 11 with $\overline{Q}_S = 1$, the output of gate 1 will go to 0 and will therefore *change* the master flip-flop from the 'zero state' to the 'one state'. Again for the JK input combination of 11 with $Q_S = 1$, the output of gate 2 will go to 0 and will therefore *change* the master flip-flop from the 'one state' to the 'zero state'.

We have now verified that the master flip-flop will operate as specified by Table 3.2.2 when T goes to 1. When T goes to 0, the $\overline{T}$ input to gates 5 and 6 will allow the output of the master flip-flop to be set into the slave. This verifies the information transfer times indicated in Fig. 3.2.5(c).

The circuit of Fig. 3.2.4(a) also shows R and S inputs which are provided to the cross-coupled NAND-gates of both the master and slave flip-flops. These inputs are active LOW inputs which are not clocked and therefore may be used either to reset or set both flip-flops at times independent of the clock input T. A symbol for a master-slave J–K flip-flop with additional R and S inputs is shown in Fig. 3.2.4(b). The R and S inputs are commonly referred to as asynchronous CLEAR and PRESET inputs respectively.

3.2.5 Master-slave R–S flip-flop

Consider Fig. 3.2.4(a) with the connections from $\overline{Q}_S$ to gate 1 and from Q_S to gate 2 removed. The modified circuit is functionally equivalent to a master-slave R–S flip-flop. The symbols J, K, S and R of Fig. 3.2.4 may be replaced by the symbols S, R, S_{PRESET} and R_{CLEAR} respectively. This gives the symbol for the master-slave R–S flip-flop shown in Fig. 3.2.6. The function table of the master-slave R–S flip-flop is given in Table 3.2.3.

Table 3.2.3 Function table of master-slave R–S flip-flop

INPUTS		OUTPUTS		OPERATION
S	R	Q_{n+1}	$\overline{Q}_{n+1}$	
0	0	Q_n	$\overline{Q}_n$	No change
0	1	0	1	Reset flip-flop
1	0	1	0	Set flip-flop
1	1	?	?	Indeterminable

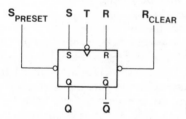

Fig. 3.2.6 Symbol for master-slave R–S flip-flop

3.3 SHIFT-REGISTERS

3.3.1 Circuits of shift-registers

A shift-register may be formed by cascading D-type flip-flops or J–K flip-flops as in Fig. 3.3.1(a) and (b). Each flip-flop is a memory element holding one bit of information, and hence the complete register may be considered to hold a pattern of bits with bit positions having significance, e.g. in the representation of a binary number. The flip-flop interconnections are such that the common clock applied to all flip-flops shifts the bit pattern by one position for every clock pulse applied. If the bit pattern has the significance of a sequence of zeros and ones on a straight line drawn from left to right, and the flip-flop interconnections are such that the bit pattern moves one bit position to the right for every clock pulse, then a *right shift-register* is formed. It is this type of shift-register which is represented by Fig. 3.3.1(a) and (b).

Note that for the case of Fig. 3.3.1(a) which uses D-type flip-flops, the Q output of each flip-flop is connected to the D input of the adjacent flip-flop on the right. The 'serial input' of the shift-register is entered into the D input of the left-most flip-flop and the 'serial

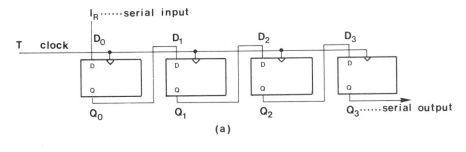

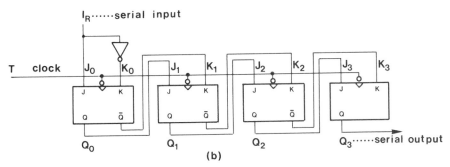

Fig. 3.3.1 Shift-register circuit—(a) using D-type flip-flops, (b) using J–K flip-flops

output' of the shift-register comes from the Q output of the right-most flip-flop. A clock signal is applied to the clock inputs of all flip-flops and hence synchronises the shift operations.

For the case of Fig. 3.3.1(b), which uses J–K flip-flops, the Q and $\overline{Q}$ outputs of each flip-flop are connected to the J and K inputs respectively of the adjacent flip-flop on the right. The serial input is entered into the J input of the left-most flip-flop while the complement of the serial input is entered into the K input of this flip-flop. The serial output of the shift register comes from the Q output of the right-most flip-flop, and the complement of the serial output may, of course, be obtained from the $\overline{Q}$ output of this flip-flop. The clock signal applied to all clock inputs synchronises the shift operations. As described in the former section, this clock causes the shifted information to be stored in the master flip-flops on the rising edge of the clock, and then causes this shifted information to appear at the (slave flip-flop) outputs on the falling edge of the clock.

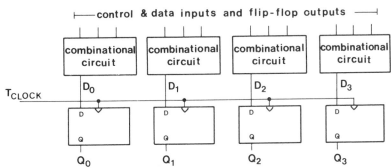

Fig. 3.3.2 General circuit diagram for derivation of shift-register circuits

If the flip-flop interconnections are such that the bit pattern moves one bit position to the left for every clock pulse, then a *left shift-register* is formed. Moreover, a shift-register may be designed to operate in one of several modes defined by control signals. An approach to the design of such a register is shown in Fig. 3.3.2. The 'combinational circuits' define the inputs to each stage of the shift-register, and would in general have as inputs all the control signals, any of the flip-flop outputs and any other data input signals. As a first example, consider the specification of the combinational circuits for a four-bit *bi-directional shift-register* which operates as a left shift-register when a control signal F equals zero, and which operates as a right shift-register when F equals one. A function table defining the flip-flop inputs for this example is given in Table 3.3.1.

Table 3.3.1 Function table defining flip-flop inputs for a bi-directional shift-register

OPERATION	CONTROL F	FLIP-FLOP INPUTS			
		D_0	D_1	D_2	D_3
RIGHT SHIFT	1	I_R	Q_0	Q_1	Q_2
LEFT SHIFT	0	Q_1	Q_2	Q_3	I_L

In Table 3.3.1, I_L is the serial input for a left shift operation and I_R is the serial input for a right shift operation. The Boolean equations defining the flip-flop inputs may be readily derived from the table as follows:

$$D_0 = FI_R + \bar{F}Q_1$$
$$D_1 = FQ_0 + \bar{F}Q_2$$
$$D_2 = FQ_1 + \bar{F}Q_3$$
$$D_3 = FQ_2 + \bar{F}I_L$$

A circuit of a bi-directional shift-register defined by these equations is given in Fig. 3.3.3.

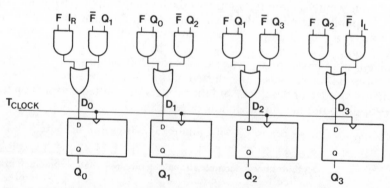

Fig. 3.3.3 Circuit of bi-directional shift-register

When shift-registers are used in digital systems, one characteristic which is frequently required is the ability to 'load' the register in parallel. This is referred to as '*broadside loading of a shift-register*' or alternatively the shift-register is described as one with '*parallel load inputs*'. Such a shift-register would contain one additional input for each stage (i.e. flip-flop) in the shift-register as well as an additional control input which specifies when broadside loading is to take place (and when normal shifting operations are to take place). A shift-register with parallel load inputs can be designed with a single clock input. For such a shift-register, when the control (mode) inputs specify broadside loading, a single clock pulse will load all stages of the register as specified by the pre-established parallel load inputs. However, when the control inputs specify shift operations, the normal shift procedure of one bit position shifted for each clock pulse is obtained. A function table defining the flip-flop inputs of a bi-directional shift-register with parallel load inputs is given in Table 3.3.2.

Table 3.3.2 Function table defining flip-flop inputs for a bi-directional shift-register with parallel load inputs

OPERATION	CONTROL		FLIP-FLOP INPUTS			
	F_0	F_1	D_0	D_1	D_2	D_3
RIGHT SHIFT	1	1	I_R	Q_0	Q_1	Q_2
PARALLEL LOAD	0	X	A_0	A_1	A_2	A_3
LEFT SHIFT	1	0	Q_1	Q_2	Q_3	I_L

In Table 3.3.2, A_0, A_1, A_2, A_3 are the parallel load inputs, and the control signal differentiating the broadside loading operation from the shifting operation is F_0. The control input F_1 specifies shift direction, and the X in the table represents a 'don't care' term. All other entries are as in the earlier table for the bi-directional shift-register without parallel load inputs (Table 3.3.1).

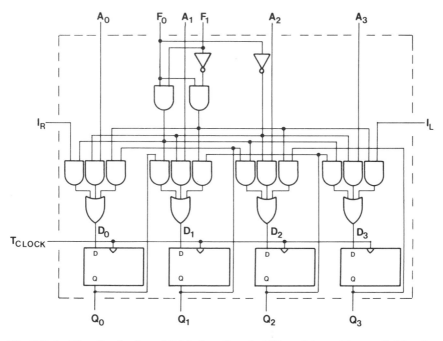

Fig. 3.3.4 Circuit of a four-bit bi-directional shift-register with parallel-load inputs and parallel outputs

From the above table, Boolean equations defining the flip-flop inputs may be derived as follows:

$$D_0 = F_0F_1I_R + \overline{F}_0A_0 + F_0\overline{F}_1Q_1$$
$$D_1 = F_0F_1Q_0 + \overline{F}_0A_1 + F_0\overline{F}_1Q_2$$
$$D_2 = F_0F_1Q_1 + \overline{F}_0A_2 + F_0\overline{F}_1Q_3$$
$$D_3 = F_0F_1Q_2 + \overline{F}_0A_3 + F_0\overline{F}_1I_L$$

A circuit of a bi-directional shift-register with parallel load inputs defined by the above equations is shown in Fig. 3.3.4. The dotted outline of Fig. 3.3.4 defines internal interconnections and output 'pins' of a shift-register 'package'. It is to be noted that all flip-flop outputs are taken to the 'package' outputs. The circuit of Fig. 3.3.4 may then be described as a 'four-bit bi-directional shift-register with parallel load inputs and parallel outputs'. The symbol for this circuit which is used in following diagrams is shown in Fig. 3.3.5.

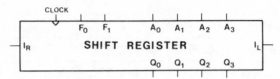

Fig. 3.3.5 Symbol used for a four-bit bi-directional shift-register with parallel-load inputs and parallel outputs (circuit of Fig. 3.3.4)

It is to be pointed out that not all integrated circuit shift-register packages provide 'parallel outputs' as there is a limitation imposed by the number of 'pins' to the package (which are required for voltages and input/output connections). However, there are many applications which do not require parallel outputs (nor parallel load inputs), and for these applications all input/output operations are made using the shift-register's serial inputs and serial outputs. Some applications of shift-registers are described in the following sections.

3.3.2   Shift-registers with feedback connections

Two applications of shift-registers with feedback connections are shown in Fig. 3.3.6 and Fig. 3.3.7. The circuit connections of Fig. 3.3.6 produce what is known as a '*ring counter*'. It will be observed that the four-bit bi-directional shift-register of Fig. 3.3.6(a) is used as a right shift-register, and that the serial output (Q_3) is connected to the serial input (I_R). The timing waveforms of Fig. 3.3.6(b) show that the 'mode control input' F_0 is such that the first pulse of the clock input T is used to 'parallel load' the bit pattern 1000 into the four flip-flops Q_0, Q_1, Q_2, Q_3 respectively. The second and subsequent pulses of the clock input T cause a '*cyclic shift*' of the pattern in the shift-register. This produces the waveforms shown in Fig. 3.3.6(b). The waveforms for Q_0, Q_1, Q_2 and Q_3 of Fig. 3.3.6(b) may be considered as 'four-phase timing waveforms'. These have application in the design of timing circuits for some digital systems.

In the circuit of Fig. 3.3.7(a), the output of an exclusive-OR gate with inputs Q_2 and Q_3 is used as the serial input of the shift-register. The timing waveforms for F_0 and T of Fig. 3.3.7(b) show that the mode control input F_0 is such that a bit pattern 1111 is loaded into the four flip-flops of the shift-register by the first pulse of T, and subsequent pulses of T cause right shift operations to take place. The circuit of Fig. 3.3.7(a) is a member of an interesting class of shift-register circuits, for which an extensive theory and a variety of applications have evolved. They are called '*pseudo-random binary sequence generators*', since the successive states have many of the properties of a fully random quantity. An

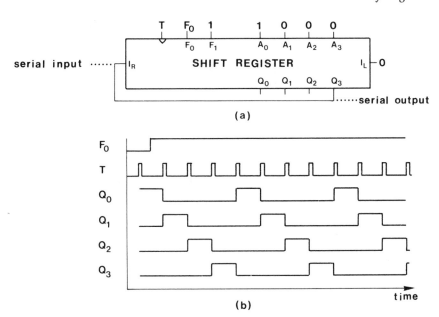

Fig. 3.3.6 Ring counter—(a) circuit, (b) waveforms

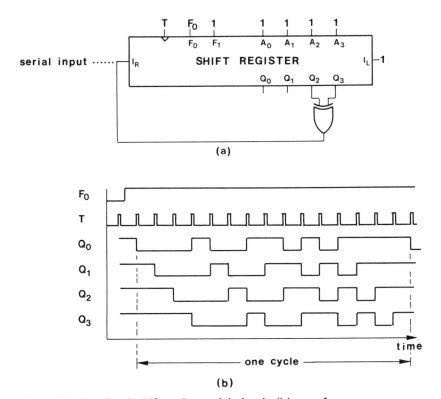

Fig. 3.3.7 Feedback shift-register—(a) circuit, (b) waveforms

n-stage circuit has $2^n - 1$ states with only the 'all-zero' state being omitted. The 'all-one' state is a convenient starting condition.

If the flip-flops Q_0, Q_1, Q_2 and Q_3 of Fig. 3.3.7(a) are given weights 8, 4, 2 and 1 respectively, the waveforms of Fig. 3.3.7(b) show that the sequence of states starting from state 15 (all-ones) is as follows:

$$15, 7, 3, 1, 8, 4, 2, 9, 12, 6, 11, 5, 10, 13, 14, 15, \text{---}.$$

It is quite an instructive exercise to deduce the waveforms of Q_0, Q_1, Q_2 and Q_3 from the given waveforms for F_0 and T in Fig. 3.3.7(b).

3.3.3 Serial addition using shift-registers

A shift-register may be used to store a binary number and then to present the bits of this number '*serially*' to a *serial arithmetic unit*. A serial addition unit for the addition of two numbers would accept corresponding bits of the two numbers (a pair of bits at a time) in the sequence of least-significant bits first and progressing to the most-significant bits. The

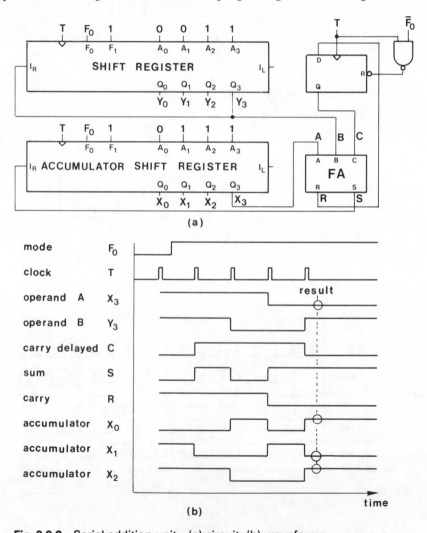

(a)

(b)

Fig. 3.3.8 Serial addition unit—(a) circuit, (b) waveforms

reason for progression in this sequence is that the 'carry bit' for one stage of the addition process may be determined and then used after a one bit delay in the next more significant stage of the process.

A circuit for the serial addition of two four-bit positive integers is shown in Fig. 3.3.8(a). Two four-bit shift-registers with outputs Y_0, Y_1, Y_2, Y_3 and X_0, X_1, X_2, X_3 may be considered to hold two positive integers Y and X in the range 0 to 15 when the flip-flop weightings are 8, 4, 2, 1 respectively. The circuit connections of Fig. 3.3.8(a) and the waveforms of Fig. 3.3.8(b) show that the bit patterns 0011 and 0111 (representing integer three and integer seven) are loaded into the two shift-registers by the first pulse of the clock input T. The next four pulses of T then cause these patterns to be shifted right and to be presented as inputs to the full adder represented by the block marked FA in Fig. 3.3.8(a). A D-type flip-flop is used to delay the carry output (R) of the full adder and to present the delayed carry signal to the full adder input. Note that this 'carry flip-flop' must be initially reset to zero. This is achieved by the signal $T_{\bar{F}_0}$ (i.e. by the first pulse of T) which is connected to the active-low R input of the D-type flip-flop.

It is to be observed from Fig. 3.3.8(a) that the 'sum output' of the full adder is connected to the serial input of the X shift-register. Hence, after the four shift pulses have been applied to the shift-register, this register should hold the sum of the two original integers (i.e. the pattern 1010 representing integer ten for our example). It is also to be observed that the serial output Y_3 of the Y shift-register is connected to the serial input of this register, and hence after four shift pulses have been applied (causing four cyclic shift operations), this register is regenerated to its initial state following the parallel load operation (i.e. to the state 0011).

From the above general description of the circuit of Fig. 3.3.8(a), it is a very instructive exercise to verify that the waveforms for A, B, C, S, R, X_0, X_1 and X_2 of Fig. 3.3.8(b) have been correctly derived from the given waveforms for F_0 and T and from the circuit interconnections given in Fig. 3.3.8(a).

3.3.4 Further applications of shift-registers

Shift-registers have many applications. These include the arithmetic operations of addition, subtraction, multiplication and division implemented using serial operations. These will be described in later chapters. Other serial operations include (i) comparison of two numbers, (ii) parity detection or generation, (iii) testing for number patterns, (iv) gated information transfer and (v) bit reversal. Using the parallel load and parallel output characteristics of some commercially available shift-registers, designs of (i) parallel-to-serial converters, (ii) serial-to-parallel converters and (iii) pattern generators may be readily produced.

3.3.5 Microprocessor rotate and shift operations

Most digital computers can perform '*rotate*' and '*shift*' operations. At this point in our development of design methods using shift-registers, it is instructive to consider what these operations are and how they may be implemented in hardware. We use as examples some *rotate* and *shift* operations available in many 8-bit microprocessors. These operations are illustrated in Fig. 3.3.9.

This figure shows an 8-bit shift-register A_7--A_0 and a 'carry flip-flop'. The sequence of dots (.) represents the initial contents of stages A_6--A_1. The remaining symbols C, S and L are as follows:

C : initial contents of carry flip-flop
S : initial contents of most-significant bit of shift-register (i.e. sign bit)
L : initial contents of least-significant bit of shift-register

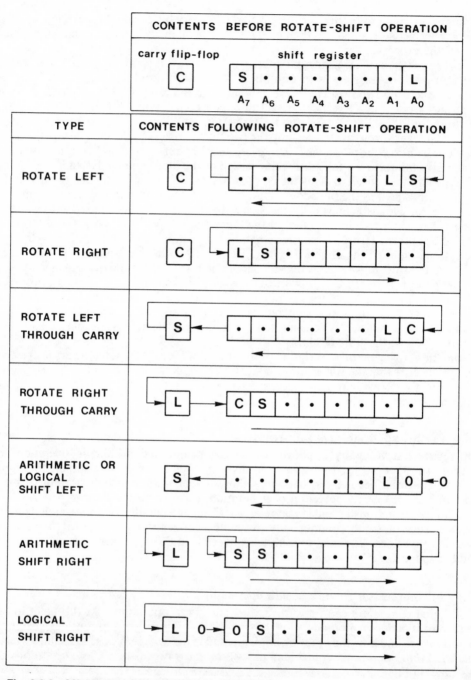

Fig. 3.3.9   Microprocessor rotate/shift operations

Fig. 3.3.9 shows the contents of the carry flip-flop and the shift-register following each of seven different rotate or shift operations. In each of these operations a bit pattern is shifted *one place* to the right or to the left. This corresponds to the application of a single clock pulse to a bi-directional shift-register. The different rotate or shift operations are produced by causing different data to be used for the serial inputs of the shift-register and for the data input of the carry flip-flop.

For the 'rotate left' operation (of Fig. 3.3.9), the shift-register functions as an '8-bit, cyclic, left shift-register'. This operation causes the bit pattern initially in A_6--A_1 to be shifted into A_7--A_2; L is shifted into A_1 and S into A_0. The carry flip-flop (C) remains unchanged. For the 'rotate right' operation, the shift-register functions as an '8-bit, cyclic, right shift-register'. For the 'rotate left through carry' operation, the carry flip-flop and the shift-register function as a '9-bit, cyclic, left shift-register'; and for the 'rotate right through carry' operation, the carry flip-flop and the shift-register function as a '9-bit, cyclic, right shift-register'. For the 'arithmetic/logical shift left' operation, zero is used as the serial input to A_0. For the 'logical shift right' operation, zero is used as the serial input to A_7. The duplication of the sign bit for the 'arithmetic shift right' operation is required by the *'two's complement'* notation.

3.4 BINARY COUNTERS

3.4.1 Binary counter types

Binary counters are circuits containing flip-flops which have assigned weightings of integral powers of two and which have interconnections such that an input clock pulse causes the number (i.e. 'count') represented by the flip-flops to change in a binary sequence. An *'up-counter'* or 'forward counter' is produced when the count is increased by one for each input clock pulse. A *'down counter'* or 'reverse counter' is produced when the count is decreased by one for each input clock pulse. An *'up-down-counter'* or 'reversible counter'

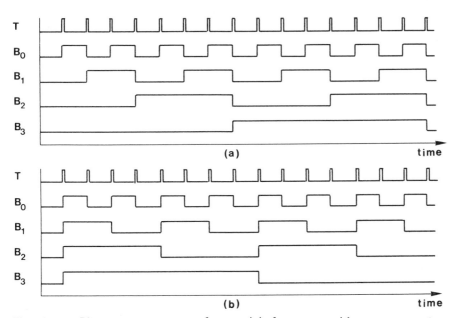

Fig. 3.4.1 Binary counter waveforms—(a) four-stage, binary up-counter, (b) four-stage, binary down-counter

is produced when the counter circuit has a control input (or perhaps two control inputs) which specify whether the count is to be increased or decreased by the input clock pulse.

Waveforms of a four-stage, binary up-counter and a four-stage, binary down-counter are shown in Fig. 3.4.1(a) and (b) respectively. In these figures, T is the waveform of the input clock, and B_0, B_1, B_2, B_3 are the waveforms of the flip-flops (or counter 'stages') with weightings 1, 2, 4, 8 respectively. Note that the 'count' represented by the binary number B_3, B_2, B_1, B_0 for the up-counter *cycles* through the cyclic binary sequence 0000, 0001, 0010, 0011, ----, 1110, 1111, 0000, ----. Note also that the counter stages B_3, B_2, B_1, B_0 for the down-counter cycle through the sequence 0000, 1111, 1110, 1101, ----, 0001, 0000.

The flip-flops of a binary counter may be interconnected to provide either an *asynchronous* or a *synchronous* mode of operation. In an *asynchronous counter* (frequently called a *ripple counter*), the input clock is connected only to the first (i.e. least-significant) counter stage, and the output of each stage is connected to the clock input of the next more significant stage (i.e. each stage is used to 'drive' the next more significant stage). This type of counter is the simpler of the two types (i.e. asynchronous and synchronous) of counter under discussion, and requires fewer gates. However, as circuits are never ideal, and there is always a (small but nevertheless finite) delay between edges of input and output signals, there may be a 'rippling' action as a signal passes through all stages of the counter circuit. Hence, the output of the most-significant stage may be delayed by an amount corresponding to the cumulative delays of all stages. This may be a problem in high-speed operation of a counter containing many stages when combinations of states of the counter stages are sensed and are used to set flip-flops which then initiate some action. When there is a possibility that delays of a ripple counter could cause incorrect circuit operation, one immediate solution is to use a synchronous counter.

In a *synchronous counter* the input clock is connected to *all* counter stages, and hence all stages change state at times defined by the input clock. Therefore time differences between edges of the counter waveforms are *not* produced by the cumulative delays through counter stages (as in a ripple counter) and can only result from the small differences in switching times of the individual (flip-flop) stages. In the design of a synchronous counter it is necessary to provide combinational circuits which define the conditions which will allow the state of each flip-flop stage to be changed by the input clock.

The *implementation* of the different types of binary counters discussed above may be achieved using various types of flip-flops. However, the J–K flip-flop appears to be the most versatile for this application because of the ability to change the state of this type of flip-flop by an input combination. Examples of circuits of asynchronous and synchronous counters are given in following sections.

3.4.2   Asynchronous binary counters

A circuit of a four-stage, asynchronous, binary up-counter containing four positive-edge-triggered D-type flip-flops is shown in Fig. 3.4.2. Note that: (i) the clock input T is connected only to the least-significant (highest frequency) stage B_0, (ii) the $\overline{Q}$ output of each flip-flop is connected to the D input of the same flip-flop, and (iii) the $\overline{Q}$ output of each flip-flop is connected to the clock input of the next more significant flip-flop.

An earlier description of the characteristics of the D-type flip-flop established that feedback connections (as well as connections for cascading flip-flops) were allowed and would produce reliable circuit operation. The feedback connection from the $\overline{Q}$ output to D input of each flip-flop causes each flip-flop to act as a single stage binary counter with each state change being initiated by a rising edge of the clock input. This may be verified as follows: (i) if a flip-flop is in the '0' state, the $\overline{Q}$ output will be equal to '1' and hence (because of the feedback connection), the flip-flop will be set into the '1' state by the next

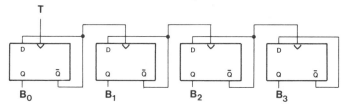

Fig. 3.4.2 Circuit of a ripple binary up-counter using D-type flip-flops

rising edge of the clock input, and conversely, (ii) if a flip-flop is in the '1' state, the $\overline{Q}$ output will be equal to '0' and hence (because of the feedback connection) the flip-flop will be set into the '0' state by the next rising edge of the clock input.

From the above description of the operation of each stage of the counter, the reader should verify that the circuit of Fig. 3.4.2 produces the waveforms of Fig. 3.4.1(a). The reader should also verify that an asynchronous, down-counter may be produced by connecting the Q output (and not the $\overline{Q}$ output as in Fig. 3.4.2) to the clock input of the next more significant stage, and that the waveforms produced would then be as in Fig. 3.4.1(b).

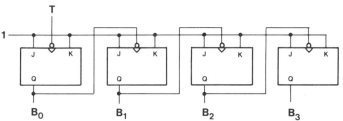

Fig. 3.4.3 Circuit of a ripple binary up-counter using master-slave J–K flip-flops

A circuit of a four-stage, asynchronous, binary up-counter containing four master-slave J–K flip-flops is shown in Fig. 3.4.3. Note that (i) the clock input T is connected only to the least-significant (highest frequency) stage B_0, (ii) the J and K inputs of each flip-flop are both connected to '1', and (iii) the Q output of each flip-flop is connected to the clock input of the next more significant flip-flop.

An earlier description of the characteristics of the master-slave J–K flip-flop established that when both the J and K inputs were connected to '1' the master flip-flop changed state on the rising edge of the clock input and that this new changed state was transferred to the slave flip-flop on the falling edge of the clock input. Although the outputs of the master flip-flop are not usually brought to output pins of a commercially available integrated circuit package, it is instructive to derive waveforms for both the master and slave flip-flops of the circuit of Fig. 3.4.3. These waveforms, shown in Fig. 3.4.4 in which the master flip-flop waveforms are M_0, M_1, M_2 M_3 and the slave flip-flop waveforms are B_0, B_1, B_2, B_3, should be verified by the reader.

The reader should also verify that a down-counter (with waveforms as in Fig. 3.4.1(b)) may be produced by connecting the $\overline{Q}$ output (and not the Q output as in Fig. 3.4.3) to the clock input of the next more significant master-slave J–K flip-flop.

3.4.3 Synchronous binary counters

A general block diagram illustrating a useful approach to the design of synchronous binary counters using master-slave J–K flip-flops is shown in Fig. 3.4.5. Note that: (i) the clock

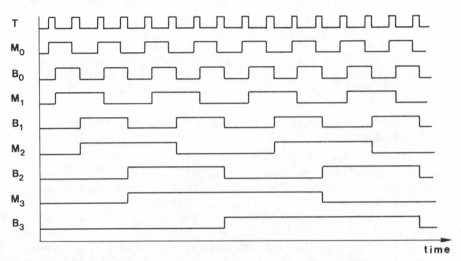

Fig. 3.4.4 Waveforms of the master flip-flops and the slave flip-flops in a ripple binary up-counter using master-slave J–K flip-flops

input T is connected to the clock input of all flip-flops, (ii) the J and K inputs of each flip-flop are joined, and (iii) the J and K inputs of each flip-flop are determined by circuits which sense the 'conditions for counter operation'. These circuits are combinational circuits whose inputs may be the outputs of any stage of the counter and possibly any control signals which define the mode of operation of the counter. These circuits determine whether each of the flip-flops is to have its *state changed by the next clock input*.

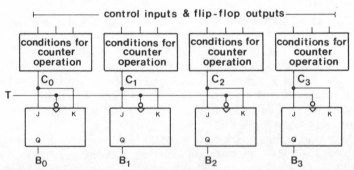

Fig. 3.4.5 General circuit diagram of a synchronous counter using master-slave J–K flip-flops

In Fig. 3.4.5 the combinational circuits determining the 'conditions for counter operations' are designated C_0, C_1, C_2, C_3 with the subscripts corresponding to the flip-flop outputs B_0, B_1, B_2, B_3 respectively. Table 3.4.1 defines C_0, C_1, C_2, C_3 for (i) a binary up-counter, (ii) a binary down-counter and (iii) a binary up-down-counter.

The reader should verify that the first row of the above table (i.e. conditions for a binary up-counter) has been correctly derived from Fig. 3.4.1(a), and that the second row (i.e. conditions for a binary down-counter) has been correctly derived from Fig. 3.4.1(b).

A circuit corresponding to the first row of the above table (i.e. conditions for a binary up-counter) is shown in Fig. 3.4.6. It is suggested that the reader should derive the circuit

Table 3.4.1 Table specifying J–K inputs of master-slave J–K flip-flops used in binary counter circuits represented by Fig. 3.4.5. (The meaning of the signals F and R is described in the text.)

COUNTER TYPE	C_0	C_1	C_2	C_3
BINARY UP-COUNTER	1	B_0	B_0B_1	$B_0B_1B_2$
BINARY DOWN-COUNTER	1	$\bar{B}_0$	$\bar{B}_0\bar{B}_1$	$\bar{B}_0\bar{B}_1\bar{B}_2$
BINARY UP-DOWN-COUNTER	F+R	$FB_0+R\bar{B}_0$	$FB_0B_1+R\bar{B}_0\bar{B}_1$	$FB_0B_1B_2+R\bar{B}_0\bar{B}_1\bar{B}_2$

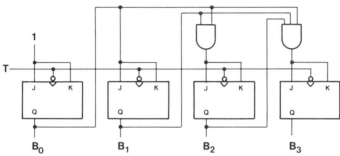

Fig. 3.4.6 Circuit of a four-stage, synchronous, binary up-counter using master-slave J–K flip-flops

corresponding to the second row of the table (i.e. conditions for a binary down-counter).

In the third row of the above table, the variables F and R are used. These are input control signals which specify when the counter is to operate as an up-counter (with a count in the Forward direction) and when it is to operate as a down-counter (with a count in the Reverse direction). It is to be noted that when F = 1 and R = 0, the conditions for counter operation C_0, C_1, C_2, C_3 correspond exactly with those specified for an up-counter, and when R = 1 and F = 0, these conditions correspond exactly with those specified for a down-counter.

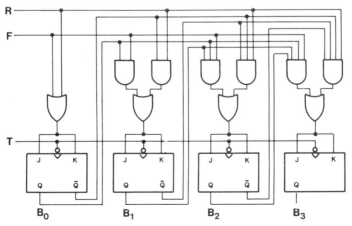

Fig. 3.4.7 Circuit of a four-stage, synchronous, binary up-down-counter using master-slave J–K flip-flops

A circuit corresponding to the third row of the above table (i.e. conditions for a binary up-down-counter) is shown in Fig. 3.4.7. It may be verified that (i) the control inputs $F = 0$, $R = 0$ cause the circuit to operate in an inactive mode, where clock pulses are ignored, (ii) the control inputs $F = 1$, $R = 0$ cause the circuit to operate as an up-counter, (iii) the control inputs $F = 0$, $R = 1$ cause the circuit to operate as a down-counter, and (iv) the control inputs $F = 1$, $R = 1$ cause all flip-flops to change state with every input clock pulse. When only the up-counter and down-counter modes are required, one of the mode control inputs may be eliminated by making $R = \bar{F}$.

The general block diagram of Fig. 3.4.5 has application to the design of other types of counters. This diagram is used in the design of a decade counter in the next section.

3.5   DECADE COUNTERS

3.5.1   Synchronous BCD decade up-counter

A *decade counter* has ten possible states designated $0, 1, \ldots, 9$. A *decade up-counter* is stepped through the forward sequence $0, 1, 2, \ldots, 9, 0, 1, \ldots$ by the input clock (while a decade down-counter would be stepped through the reverse sequence $0, 9, 8, \ldots, 1, 0, 9, \ldots$). A *binary-coded-decimal decade counter or BCD decade counter* contains four flip-flops with assigned weightings 8, 4, 2, and 1 which are used to represent the ten states of a decade counter in binary code. Hence, a *BCD decade up-counter* with outputs B_3, B_2, B_1, B_0 (and corresponding weightings 8, 4, 2, 1) would be stepped through the forward, binary sequence 0000, 0001, 0010, ----, 1000, 1001, 0000, ----. Waveforms of this type of counter are shown in Fig. 3.5.1. In a *synchronous BCD decade up-counter*, the clock input T (shown in Fig. 3.5.2) is applied to all four flip-flops of the counter producing the waveforms as shown.

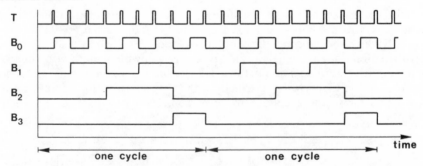

Fig. 3.5.1   Waveforms of a synchronous BCD counter using master-slave J–K flip-flops

The general block diagram of Fig. 3.4.5 can be used to design a synchronous BCD decade up-counter. The 'conditions for counter operation' C_0, C_1, C_2, C_3 defined in Fig. 3.4.5 may be derived for the waveforms of Fig. 3.5.1 as follows:

$$C_0 = 1$$
$$C_1 = B_0\bar{B}_3$$
$$C_2 = B_0B_1$$
$$C_3 = B_0B_1B_2 + B_0\bar{B}_1\bar{B}_2B_3$$

The circuit defined by these equations is shown in Fig. 3.5.2.

3.5.2   Asynchronous BCD decade up-counter

Economical circuits for BCD counters can be obtained by utilising (i) the characteristics of

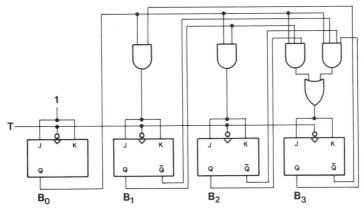

Fig. 3.5.2 Circuit of a synchronous BCD counter using master-slave J–K flip-flops

J–K flip-flops defined by all combinations of the J and K inputs, and (ii) a 'ripple' or 'asynchronous' interconnection of flip-flops.

An examination of Fig. 3.5.1 shows that B_1 changes state whenever B_0 drops from 1 to 0 except when $B_3 = 1$. Hence, B_0 should be used as the clock input of the B_1 flip-flop and $\overline{B}_3$ should be connected to the J and K inputs of the B_1 flip-flop. Further, B_2 changes every time B_1 drops from 1 to 0, and hence B_1 should be connected to the clock input of the B_2 flip-flop while the J and K inputs of this flip-flop should be both connected to '1'. Finally, to derive the B_3 waveform, B_0 should be connected to the clock input of the B_3 flip-flop, and then conditions should be derived for 'setting' and 'resetting' this flip-flop. These conditions may be derived from the waveforms of Fig. 3.5.1 and the characteristic of the master-slave J–K flip-flop represented by Table 3.2.2. It may be verified that the correct setting and resetting of the B_3 flip-flop are obtained if the signal $B_1 B_2$ is connected to the J input and the signal $\overline{B}_2$ is connected to the K input of this flip-flop. The $B_1 B_2$ term requires a two-input NOR-gate for its generation. Hence, the complete asynchronous BCD decade up-counter can be implemented using four master-slave J–K flip-flops and a single two-input NOR-gate. A circuit of this type of counter is shown in Fig. 3.5.3.

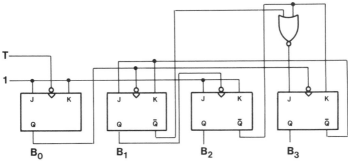

Fig. 3.5.3 Circuit of an asynchronous BCD decade up-counter containing four master-slave J–K flip-flops and a single two-input NOR-gate

3.5.3 Alternative designs of decade counters

The decade counters described in this section utilise ten of the sixteen possible states of the four flip-flops. It was assumed that the flip-flops could be initially set to one of the ten 'used' states and no consideration of the 'unused' states was carried out. When inadvertent setting of the flip-flops of a BCD decade counter is possible, consideration of the transitions through the unused states and desirably back to the used states is necessary. An instructive exercise would be to predict the behaviour of the counters described in this section when they are initially set to any of the unused states.

An alternative approach to the design of decade counters will be given in the next section which will describe an approach with more general application to other sequential circuits.

3.6   DESIGN OF STATE TRANSITION LOGIC OF SEQUENTIAL CIRCUITS

3.6.1   Brief description of method using J–K flip-flops

The synchronous counters described in preceding sections are examples of '*clocked sequential circuits*' or '*synchronous sequential circuits*'. These are sequential circuits in which all flip-flops are synchronised by a single input clock signal. Systematic design procedures are available for specifying the logic which controls the state transitions in this type of circuit. Once this has been carried out, the outputs of the sequential circuit may be specified as Boolean functions of the states and the inputs (using all the techniques available for combinational circuits), thus completing the design.

One procedure for the design of the state transition logic of circuits containing master-slave J–K flip-flops involves the following steps:

STEP 1   From the number (N) of circuit states, specify the minimum number (n) of flip-flops required such that;
$$2^n \geqslant N.$$

STEP 2   Specify the flip-flop states which define the circuit states (i.e. specify the flip-flop code combinations for all circuit states).

STEP 3   Draw a state transition diagram with flip-flop states shown at the nodes of the diagram and state transitions represented by arrows.

STEP 4   For each circuit state, record the flip-flop transitions required by the indicated state transitions.

STEP 5   Specify the inputs of each flip-flop in turn by firstly recording (on a table or K-map) the inputs required by the transitions from each circuit state.

STEP 6   Minimise the expressions obtained for the flip-flop inputs and implement these using available gates.

Step 1 above suggests using the minimum number of flip-flops to represent the circuit states. This, of course, is desirable, but for some applications there is a possibility that *overall* circuit minimisation can be achieved by using more flip-flops than the minimum specified by the number of circuit states. The extreme approach of using one flip-flop for each circuit state will be discussed in a later chapter.

Step 2 should be carried out with the objectives of (a) using the flip-flop outputs as the required outputs of the sequential circuits as far as possible, and (b) minimising the logic which controls state transitions. For the case of the BCD decade counter, it is obvious that an economical design can be achieved if the flip-flop outputs can provide the 'weight 8', 'weight 4', 'weight 2' and 'weight 1' outputs of the counter. However, for many applications the optimum specification of flip-flop states which define circuit states is not at all obvious, and this step in the procedure which is an attempt to achieve overall circuit minimisation by correct *specification* of flip-flop states depends heavily on experience. When no logical or intuitive methods of carrying out this step are suggested by considerations of circuit minimisation, an *arbitrary* specification of flip-flop states which define circuit states may be used.

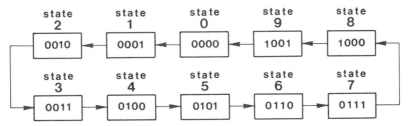

Fig. 3.6.1   State transition diagram specifying flip-flop states and state transitions for a BCD decade counter

Step 3 specifies the use of a *state transition diagram* which can take the form shown in Fig. 3.6.1. This diagram specifies the flip-flop states B_3, B_2, B_1, B_0 and the state transitions for a BCD decade counter. The design of this counter will be described in the next section.

Step 4 transforms the information held in the state transition diagram into a form which will allow a systematic co-ordination of conditions covering all transitions (i.e. changes) of each flip-flop. This step can conveniently be accomplished by using a table in which the flip-flop transitions from each state are listed. For example, the transition from 'state 0' to 'state 1' of Fig. 3.6.1 requires B_3 to remain in the 0 state, B_2 to remain in the 0 state, B_1 to remain in the 0 state and B_0 to change from 0 to 1. Again, the transition from 'state 1' to 'state 2' of Fig. 3.6.1 requires B_3 to remain in the 0 state, B_2 to remain in the 0 state, B_1 to change from 0 to 1 and B_0 to change from 1 to 0. Obviously there are four possibilities for the flip-flop transitions. These are shown in Table 3.6.1 together with symbols used for these transitions.

Table 3.6.1   Table of flip-flop transitions and symbols

FLIP-FLOP TRANSITION	SYMBOL
Remain unchanged in 0 state	$0 \rightarrow 0$
Change from 0 to 1 state	$0 \rightarrow 1$
Remain unchanged in 1 state	$1 \rightarrow 1$
Change from 1 to 0 state	$1 \rightarrow 0$

Step 5 is based on the input–output characteristic of the type of flip-flop chosen for the sequential circuit. For a J–K flip-flop the required flip-flop inputs are summarised by Table 3.6.2.

Table 3.6.2   Inputs to a J–K flip-flop to provide the four possible flip-flop state transitions

FLIP-FLOP TRANSITION	FLIP-FLOP INPUTS	
	J	K
$0 \rightarrow 0$	0	X
$0 \rightarrow 1$	1	X
$1 \rightarrow 1$	X	0
$1 \rightarrow 0$	X	1

Step 6 utilises the techniques described in Chapter 2 for the design of combinational circuits and has the objective of producing a minimised circuit.

3.6.2   The design of a BCD decade counter

The state transition diagram of a BCD decade counter (ignoring the unused states) is shown in Fig. 3.6.1. The information contained in this diagram may be transferred to a table such as that shown in Table 3.6.3. Each circuit state is represented by entries in a line of the table, and transitions are assumed *from* the state represented by one line *to* the state represented by the next line, and *from* the state represented by the last line *to* the state represented by the first line.

Table 3.6.3   Flip-flop transitions and inputs for a BCD decade counter

STATE				REQUIRED FLIP-FLOP TRANSITIONS			REQUIRED FLIP-FLOP INPUTS					
B_3	B_2	B_1	B_0	B_3	B_2	B_1	J_3	K_3	J_2	K_2	J_1	K_1
0	0	0	0	$0\to0$	$0\to0$	$0\to0$	0	X	0	X	0	X
0	0	0	1	$0\to0$	$0\to0$	$0\to1$	0	X	0	X	1	X
0	0	1	0	$0\to0$	$0\to0$	$1\to1$	0	X	0	X	X	0
0	0	1	1	$0\to0$	$0\to1$	$1\to0$	0	X	1	X	X	1
0	1	0	0	$0\to0$	$1\to1$	$0\to0$	0	X	X	0	0	X
0	1	0	1	$0\to0$	$1\to1$	$0\to1$	0	X	X	0	1	X
0	1	1	0	$0\to0$	$1\to1$	$1\to1$	0	X	X	0	X	0
0	1	1	1	$0\to1$	$1\to0$	$1\to0$	1	X	X	1	X	1
1	0	0	0	$1\to1$	$0\to0$	$0\to0$	X	0	0	X	0	X
1	0	0	1	$1\to0$	$0\to0$	$0\to0$	X	1	0	X	0	X

From an examination of the entries in the B_0 column of Table 3.6.3 it is obvious that the B_0 flip-flop must change state for every input clock pulse. This can be achieved by making $J_0 = K_0 = 1$. The required transitions of the B_3, B_2 and B_1 flip-flops are shown in Table 3.6.3. The corresponding J and K inputs (defined by Table 3.6.2) are also shown in this table. From this information K-maps for the J and K inputs of the B_3, B_2 and B_1 flip-flops may be drawn. These are shown in Fig. 3.6.2. Boolean expressions for the J and K inputs may then be derived using the techniques described in Chapter 2.

Note that there are only ten entries in each K-map of Fig. 3.6.2. These entries correspond to the ten 'used' states of the flip-flops B_3, B_2, B_1 and B_0. If it is assumed that the circuit can never enter one of the six 'unused' states, the remaining six entries of each K-map of Fig. 3.6.2 can be assumed to be Xs (i.e. don't care conditions). On this basis, minimised expressions for the J and K inputs may be derived as follows:

$$J_3 = B_2B_1B_0 \qquad K_3 = B_0$$
$$J_2 = B_1B_0 \qquad K_2 = B_1B_0$$
$$J_1 = \overline{B}_3B_0 \qquad K_1 = \overline{B}_3B_0$$

It may be observed that a further minimisation of the expression for K_1 (to $K_1 = B_0$) is

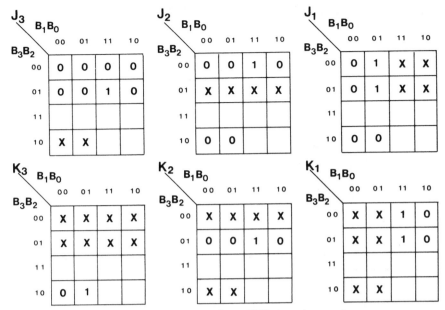

Fig. 3.6.2 K-maps of flip-flop inputs for a BCD decade counter

possible. However, the expression given above is just as satisfactory as it is the same as that for J_1. A circuit based on the above expressions is shown in Fig. 3.6.3.

3.6.3 Design of a BCD decade counter with consideration of unused states

A further example of the procedure which can be taken for the design of the state transition logic of sequential circuits will be given in this section. This example is concerned with the design of a BCD decade counter which has the same operating characteristics as the one described in the last section, but with the added specification that there should be a one step transition from any unused state to state 0000. The state transition diagram for this counter is shown in Fig. 3.6.4.

The flip-flop transitions and the corresponding inputs to the four J–K flip-flops used in the decade counter defined by Fig. 3.6.4 are shown in Table 3.6.4. Karnaugh maps of the J and K inputs are shown in Fig. 3.6.5.

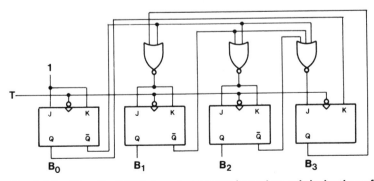

Fig. 3.6.3 Circuit of BCD decade counter based on minimisation of K-map of Fig. 3.6.2

Table 3.6.4   Flip-flop transitions and inputs for a BCD decade counter with a one step transition from any unused state to state 0000

STATE				REQUIRED FLIP-FLOP TRANSITIONS				REQUIRED FLIP-FLOPS INPUTS							
B_3	B_2	B_1	B_0	B_3	B_2	B_1	B_0	J_3	K_3	J_2	K_2	J_1	K_1	J_0	K_0
0	0	0	0	0→0	0→0	0→0	0→1	0	X	0	X	0	X	1	X
0	0	0	1	0→0	0→0	0→1	1→0	0	X	0	X	1	X	X	1
0	0	1	0	0→0	0→0	1→1	0→1	0	X	0	X	X	0	1	X
0	0	1	1	0→0	0→1	1→0	1→0	0	X	1	X	X	1	X	1
0	1	0	0	0→0	1→1	0→0	0→1	0	X	X	0	0	X	1	X
0	1	0	1	0→0	1→1	0→1	1→0	0	X	X	0	1	X	X	1
0	1	1	0	0→0	1→1	1→1	0→1	0	X	X	0	X	0	1	X
0	1	1	1	0→1	1→0	1→0	1→0	1	X	X	1	X	1	X	1
1	0	0	0	1→1	0→0	0→0	0→1	X	0	0	X	0	X	1	X
1	0	0	1	1→0	0→0	0→0	1→0	X	1	0	X	0	X	X	1
1	0	1	0	1→0	0→0	1→0	0→0	X	1	0	X	X	1	0	X
1	0	1	1	1→0	0→0	1→0	1→0	X	1	0	X	X	1	X	1
1	1	0	0	1→0	1→0	0→0	0→0	X	1	X	1	0	X	0	X
1	1	0	1	1→0	1→0	0→0	1→0	X	1	X	1	0	X	X	1
1	1	1	0	1→0	1→0	1→0	0→0	X	1	X	1	X	1	0	X
1	1	1	1	1→0	1→0	1→0	1→0	X	1	X	1	X	1	X	1

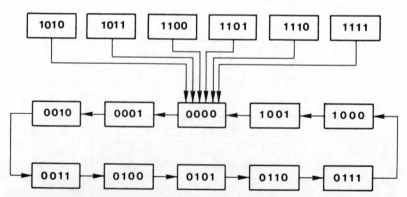

Fig. 3.6.4   State transition diagram of BCD decade counter with a one-step transition from any unused state to state 0000

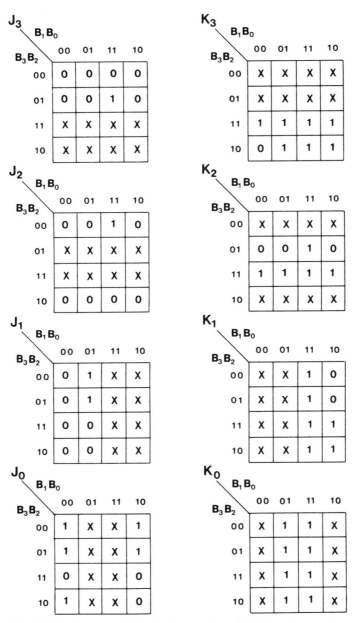

Fig. 3.6.5 K-maps of flip-flop inputs for a BCD decade counter with a one-step transition from any unused state to state 0000

The Karnaugh maps of Fig. 3.6.5 provide the following equations:

$$J_3 = B_2B_1B_0$$
$$K_3 = \overline{B_2B_1B_0}$$
$$J_2 = \overline{B_3}B_1B_0$$
$$K_2 = B_3 + B_1B_0$$
$$J_1 = \overline{B_3}B_0$$
$$K_1 = B_3 + B_1B_0$$
$$J_0 = \overline{B_3} + \overline{B_2}\overline{B_1}$$
$$K_0 = 1$$

It is to be noted that the expression for K_1 can be minimised. The form given above was chosen so that $K_2 = K_1$, reducing the gate count. A circuit implementing the above equations is shown in Fig. 3.6.6.

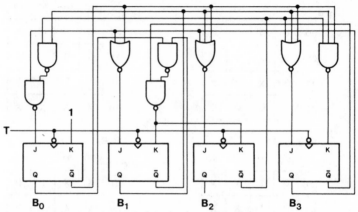

Fig. 3.6.6   Circuit of BCD decade counter with a one-step transition from any unused state to state 0000

3.6.4   Circuits containing clocked R–S flip-flops
The method described in Section 3.6.1 may be adapted to the design of the state transition logic of sequential circuits containing clocked R–S flip-flops by replacing Table 3.6.2 by Table 3.6.5.

Table 3.6.5   Inputs to a R–S flip-flop to provide the four possible flip-flop state transitions

FLIP-FLOP TRANSITION	FLIP-FLOP INPUTS	
	S	R
0 → 0	0	X
0 → 1	1	0
1 → 1	X	0
1 → 0	0	1

As some large-scale integrated circuits such as '*programmable logic sequencers*' (to be described in Chapter 6) contain clocked R–S flip-flops, the reader may be well advised to gain some experience with the design of sequential circuits using this type of flip-flop. It is suggested that the reader should consider alternative designs (using clocked R–S flip-flops instead of J–K flip-flops) for some of the circuits described in this chapter.

3.7 QUESTIONS

3.7.1 Shift-register: modes of operation
A four-bit shift-register is constructed from four edge-triggered D-type flip-flops and combinational circuits. The flip-flops have inputs D_0, D_1, D_2, D_3 and outputs A_0, A_1, A_2, A_3. The clock inputs are connected to the same shift-clock as shown in Fig. 3.7.1. The

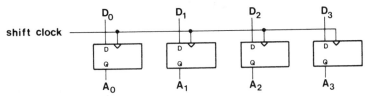

Fig. 3.7.1 Shift-register—modes of operation

register holds a 4-bit number with the left-most bit A_0 representing the sign bit. The register operates in four modes (three right shifts and one left shift) under the control of two control signals F_0, F_1 as shown in Table 3.7.1. Complete the table specifying the flip-flop inputs for each of the four modes of operation. From the table, obtain Boolean expressions for the flip-flop inputs.

Table 3.7.1 Shift-register: modes of operation

OPERATION	F_0	F_1	D_0	D_1	D_2	D_3
CYCLIC RIGHT SHIFT	0	0				
ARITHMETIC RIGHT SHIFT	0	1				
LOGICAL RIGHT SHIFT	1	0				
LOGICAL LEFT SHIFT	1	1				

3.7.2 Two shift-registers: modes of operation
Two shift-registers A and B have outputs A_0, A_1, A_2, A_3 and B_0, B_1, B_2, B_3. These registers can operate in one of eight modes specified by three control signals F_0, F_1 and F_2 according to Table 3.7.2.

It is to be noted that F_0 determines whether a logical shift or a cyclic shift is required; F_1 determines whether a left shift or a right shift is required and F_2 determines whether the two registers operate independently as two single length registers or together as a double length register. For example when $F_0 = 1$, $F_1 = 1$ and $F_2 = 1$, the contents of the A and B registers change *from* $A_0A_1A_2A_3$ in A and $B_0B_1B_2B_3$ in B *to* $B_3A_0A_1A_2$ in A and $A_3B_0B_1B_2$ in B.

Using edge-triggered D-type flip-flops and NAND-gates only, design the above shift-registers and associated logic. Represent your design by a set of Boolean equations *or* a logic diagram.

3.7.3 Counter circuit with three states
Two master-slave J–K flip-flops are to be used to produce the waveforms B_0 and B_1 shown

Table 3.7.2   Two shift-registers: modes of operation

F_0	F_1	F_2	MODE OF OPERATION
0	0	0	Logical left shift of both registers
0	0	1	Logical left shift of double register
0	1	0	Logical right shift of both registers
0	1	1	Logical right shift of double register
1	0	0	Cyclic left shift of both registers
1	0	1	Cyclic left shift of double register
1	1	0	Cyclic right shift of both registers
1	1	1	Cyclic right shift of double register

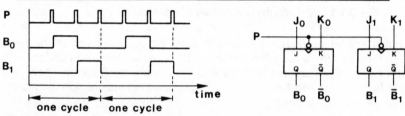

Fig. 3.7.2   Desired timing diagram and counter circuit

in Fig. 3.7.2 from the clock input P. It is suggested that a synchronous counter circuit should be used. Obtain Boolean expressions (or logic circuits) for the flip-flop inputs J_0, K_0, J_1 and K_1.

3.7.4   Counter circuit with six states

Three master-slave J–K flip-flops with connections to the same clock input as shown in Fig. 3.7.3 are to be used to produce the waveforms B_1, B_2, B_4 from the clock input P. Note that

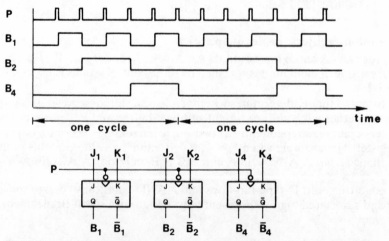

Fig. 3.7.3   Desired timing diagram and counter circuit using master-slave J–K flip-flops

only six of the possible eight states of the flip-flops are used. The flip-flops start in the state 000 (i.e. with $B_1 = 0$, $B_2 = 0$, $B_4 = 0$) and progress through states 100, 010, 110, 001, 101 (i.e. as in a binary up-counter) before returning again to state 000. Obtain Boolean expressions (or logic circuits) for the flip-flop inputs, J_1, K_1, J_2, K_2, J_4, K_4.

3.7.5 Circuits containing clocked R–S flip-flops

Using clocked R–S flip-flops, design:
  (i) a four-stage, synchronous, binary, up-down-counter,
  (ii) a synchronous BCD decade counter with a one step transition from any unused state to state 0000.

3.7.6 Clocked sequential circuit with four states

A clocked sequential circuit represented by the state transition diagram in Fig. 3.7.4 is to be designed using two master-slave J–K flip-flops. The nodes of the state transition

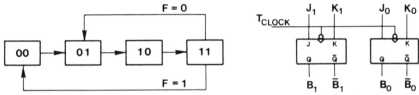

Fig. 3.7.4 State transition diagram and clocked sequential circuit with four states

diagram specify the states of the flip-flops B_1 and B_0. Note that an input control signal F is used to determine whether the transition from state 11 is to state 01 or to state 00. Obtain Boolean expressions for the flip-flop inputs.

3.7.7 Sequential circuit with two control inputs

A clocked sequential circuit represented by the state transition diagram in Fig. 3.7.5 is to be designed using two master-slave J–K flip-flops. The nodes of the state transition

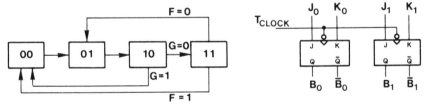

Fig. 3.7.5 State transition diagram and sequential circuit with two control inputs

diagram specify the states of the flip-flops B_0 and B_1. Note that an input control signal F is used to determine whether the transition from state 11 is to state 01 or to state 00, and an input control signal G is used to determine whether the transition from state 10 is to state 11 or to state 00. Obtain Boolean expressions for the flip-flop inputs.

3.7.8 Clocked sequential circuit with eight states

Fig. 3.7.6(a) is the state transition diagram of a clocked sequential circuit which has eight states 0–––7 and four external circuit inputs A, B, C, D. Fig. 3.7.6(b) shows the waveform of the clock signal T and the periods P during which the external circuit inputs may change state and settle to steady values. It is to be noted from Fig. 3.7.6(a) that when $A = 0$ the circuit is returned to state 0 by the next clock pulse. Other state transitions take place (on the next clock pulse) when the external circuit inputs are identical to the values specified.

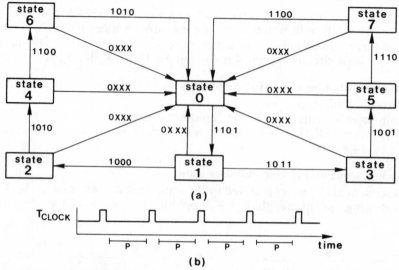

Fig. 3.7.6 Clocked sequential circuit with eight states—(a) state transition diagram, (b) waveform of clock signal

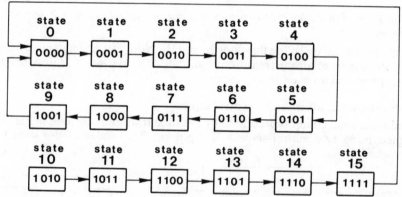

Fig. 3.7.7 State transition diagram with nodes defining states of flip-flops

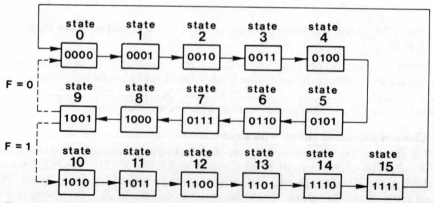

Fig. 3.7.8 State transition diagram of BCD decade counter/four-stage binary counter with nodes specifying flip-flop states

For example, a transition from state 0 to state 1 takes place when A = 1, B = 1, C = 0 and D = 1.

Design the sequential circuit described above. Draw a circuit diagram and provide complete documentation of your design.

3.7.9 Sequential circuit with sixteen states

(i) Design the sequential circuit represented by the state transition diagram shown in Fig. 3.7.7.

(ii) The state transition diagram of Fig. 3.7.8 represents a sequential circuit with a control input F. When F = 0, the circuit operates as a BCD decade counter. When F = 1, the circuit operates as a 4-stage binary counter. Design this circuit.

4 CIRCUITS FOR ARITHMETIC OPERATIONS

Circuits for the addition, subtraction, multiplication and division of fixed-point, binary operands

4.1 INTRODUCTION

The *central processing unit* of a computer contains circuits for performing arithmetic operations. Medium-to-large-scale computers would contain circuits for the four arithmetic operations of addition, subtraction, multiplication and division. In many smaller computers circuits for only addition and subtraction would be provided, and the more complex operations of multiplication and division would be *programmed* as sequences of additions, subtractions and shifts. These '*software*' implementations of multiplication and division would, of course, be much slower than corresponding '*hardware*' implementations using digital circuits designed especially for these operations.

Digital computers represent numbers by groups of binary digits. These groups are usually referred to as *computer 'words'*, and may vary in size from, say, 8 bits for a microprocessor to 64 bits for some large-scale computers. The accuracy of representing a number, of course, increases with the available number of bits.

For the representation of a number, the bits within a computer word are given some significance, e.g. sign or binary weighting. The manner in which this is done determines what is known as the '*format*' of the computer (number) word. The format of a *signed fixed-point binary number* would consist of one bit for the representation of sign and the remaining bits for the representation of binary weightings which determine the arithmetic value of the number. The *range* of numbers represented would depend on the *word-length*. An inherent problem of fixed-point number systems is that there is the possibility that an arithmetic operation on two numbers produces an 'out-of-range' result, i.e. a result which cannot be represented correctly by the number system. These so-called '*overflow*' conditions may be detected, however, by digital circuits.

In a '*floating-point*' number system, a number of bits (typically eight) are used to specify a multiplying constant (i.e. a scale factor) which is applied to the remaining (sign and binary weighting) bits of a number word to determine the arithmetic value of the number represented. This type of number system has the characteristic of a huge number range, and hence eliminates the overflow problem associated with fixed-point systems. Circuits for floating-point arithmetic operations are more complex than those fixed-point arithmetic operations.

The next section of this chapter will describe some formats of binary digits which can be used to represent numbers in digital circuits. The following sections will then describe various circuit arrangements for the four arithmetic operations of addition, subtraction, multiplication and division using 'fixed-point' binary numbers. Both serial and parallel presentation of numbers will be considered.

4.2 NUMBER REPRESENTATION

4.2.1 Fixed-point binary number representation

In the binary number system, bits of a number are given weightings of powers (positive, zero or negative) of two. In a fixed-point binary number system, the binary point is assumed to be fixed in relation to the bits of the number, and, in addition to the '*magnitude bits'* (with weightings of powers of two), a '*sign bit*' is used to specify whether the number is positive or negative. If the magnitude bits are used to specify the *absolute magnitude* of the number, and the sign bit is used to specify plus or minus with their normal significance, the number system is said to use a '*sign-magnitude*' representation of numbers. Examples of this method of representation are given in Fig. 4.2.1 which shows the weightings of the magnitude bits for a 16-bit fixed-point *fraction* and for a 16-bit fixed-point *integer*. It will be observed that, in the case of the 16-bit fixed-point fractions, the binary point is assumed to

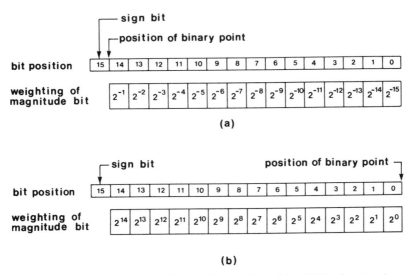

Fig. 4.2.1 Weightings of bit positions for—(a) 16-bit fixed-point fraction, and (b) 16-bit fixed-point integer

come *before the most-significant magnitude bit*, and hence the *range of numbers* (x) in this system is given by:

$$-(1-2^{-15}) \leqslant x \leqslant 1-2^{-15}$$

In the case of the 16-bit fixed-point integers, the binary point is assumed to come *after the least-significant magnitude bit*, and hence the *range of numbers* (x) in this system is given by:

$$-(2^{15}-1) \leqslant x \leqslant 2^{15}-1$$

The *parallel adder* utilising *full adders* has already been described as an example of a combinational circuit in Chapter 2. It is now instructive to consider what circuits are required for the arithmetic operations of addition and subtraction of two numbers A and B represented in sign-magnitude form. It will soon become apparent that the circuits must first sense the sign bits of A and B to determine whether the absolute values of A and B represented by the magnitude bits are to be added or subtracted (or further whether the absolute value of A should be subtracted from the absolute value of B or vice versa). Moreover, following a subtraction which can result in a negative difference, it may be necessary to form the absolute value of the difference and to adjust the sign bit of the result accordingly. An alternative approach to that outlined above which uses magnitude comparators is possible. However, both approaches require moderate amounts of hardware, and for the immediate purpose of designing an arithmetic unit which can add or subtract numbers in fixed-point binary form, there is no doubt that a great simplification can be achieved by an alternate method of representing numbers. The most widely used method (used in very early stored-program computers and in most digital computers today) is known as the *two's complement representation* of binary numbers.

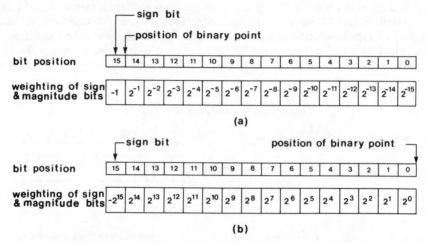

(a)

(b)

Fig. 4.2.2   Weightings of bit positions for—(a) two's complement 16-bit fixed-point fraction, and (b) two's complement 16-bit fixed-point integer

In the two's complement system the magnitude bits do *not* represent the absolute magnitude of the number but always specify positive contributions towards the arithmetic value of the number. This is achieved by assigning a negative weighting to the sign bit. Examples of two's complement numbers are given in Fig. 4.2.2. Note that for the case of the *two's complement 16-bit fraction*, the weighting of the sign bit is -1, and the *range of numbers* (x) is given by:

$$-1 \leqslant x \leqslant 1-2^{-15}$$

For the case of the *two's complement 16-bit integer*, the weighting of the sign bit is -2^{15}, and the *range of numbers* (x) is given by:

$$-2^{15} \leqslant x \leqslant 2^{15}-1$$

Using the two's complement system, addition and subtraction can proceed starting from the least-significant bits of the operands and treating in sequence the more significant bits

Table 4.2.1   Examples of two's complement addition and subtraction

ADDITION EXAMPLE	1	2	3	4
Augend	0.011	1.101	0.011	1.101
Addend	0.001	0.001	1.111	1.111
Sum	0.100	1.110	0.010	1.100

SUBTRACTION EXAMPLE	5	6	7	8
Minuend	0.011	1.101	0.011	1.101
Subtrahend	0.001	0.001	1.111	1.111
Difference	0.010	1.100	0.100	1.110

and finally the sign bit. This procedure is used irrespective of the signs of the operands, and the result obtained by ignoring the carry/borrow digits out of the sign bit position is the required answer (provided of course that the correct answer can be represented within the available number range). Note that the logic circuits for two's complement addition and subtraction treat the sign bit in the same way as magnitude bits (i.e. special treatment of the sign bit is not necessary). Verification of this procedure by examples treating all possible sign combinations should be carried out by the reader. Some examples using the operands 0.011 (three eighths), 1.101 (minus three eighths), 0.001 (one eighth) and 1.111 (minus one eighth) are given in Table 4.2.1.

One important characteristic of the two's complement number system is that *negation* (i.e. multiplying by -1 or 'forming the two's complement') of a number may be carried out by 'adding 1 in the least-significant place to the one's complement of the number'. The *one's complement* of a number is defined as the digit-by-digit complement of the number. As the one's complement of a number may be readily produced by EXCLUSIVE-OR gates, this characteristic of the two's complement system produces an effective method of carrying out subtraction (i.e. complementing and adding). Two examples of forming the two's complement of numbers are given in Table 4.2.2.

Table 4.2.2 Two examples of a method of producing the two's complement of a number

Number three eighths	0.011 0000 0000 0000
One's complement	1.100 1111 1111 1111
Least-significant bit	1
Two's complement	1.101 0000 0000 0000

Number minus three eighths	1.101 0000 0000 0000
One's complement	0.010 1111 1111 1111
Least-significant bit	1
Two's complement	0.011 0000 0000 0000

In the design of digital circuits for performing arithmetic operations on numbers, it is essential that the method of representing both input and output number(s) should be clearly defined. It is of course desirable that the representations of input and output numbers should be the same (as they are for two's complement fixed-point addition and subtraction). However, for some operations the number of significant bits of the output result may be more or less than the number of significant bits in each input number. For example, when an n-bit number consisting of a sign bit and $n-1$ magnitude bits is multiplied by another n-bit number (also consisting of a sign bit and $n-1$ magnitude bits), the resultant product consists of a sign bit and $2n-2$ magnitude bits (i.e. $2n-1$ bits altogether). When two word-length registers (i.e. n-stage registers) are used to hold the 'double-length' product, there is some flexibility concerning the positioning of the 'waste' bit. Two possibilities are shown in Fig. 4.2.3.

4.2.2 Floating-point binary number representation

Floating-point numbers are usually formed by the concatenation of three fields:

(i)   s : sign
(ii) e : exponent
(iii) f : fraction (or mantissa)

In a binary floating-point number system, the exponent is a *power of two* and specifies a

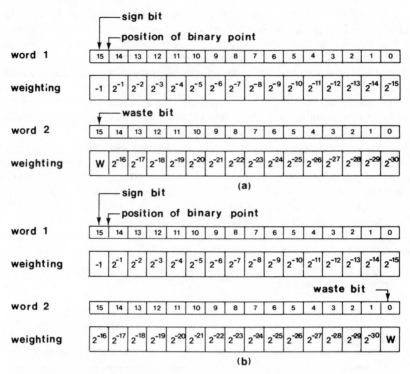

Fig. 4.2.3   Weightings of bit positions for double-length, two's complement 16-bit fixed-point fractions for—(a) waste bit in bit-15 of second word, and (b) waste bit in bit-0 of second word

scaling factor by which the fraction is to be multiplied to give the arithmetic value of the number.

The IEEE Standard on Floating-Point Arithmetic (IEEE Standard 754) defines floating-point formats which include a 32-bit basic single format and a 64-bit basic double format. Each of these formats has the three fields s, e and f as shown in Fig. 4.2.4.

The component fields of the 32-bit basic single format are a 1-bit sign s, an 8-bit biased exponent e and a 23-bit fraction f. The value of a number with this format is defined by Table 4.2.3.

Table 4.2.3   Value of number with the 32-bit basic single format of IEEE Standard 754

EXPONENT	FRACTION	VALUE	SIGNIFICANCE
$e = 255$	$f \neq 0$	NaN	'Not a number'
$e = 255$	$f = 0$	$(-1)^s \infty$	Signed infinity
$0 < e < 255$	–	$(-1)^s 2^{e-127} (1.f)$	Normalised number
$e = 0$	$f \neq 0$	$(-1)^s 2^{-126} (0.f)$	'Denormalised number'
$e = 0$	$f = 0$	$(-1)^s 0$	Signed zero

In the Table 4.2.3, the symbol NaN represents 'not a number', i.e. a symbolic entity encoded in a floating-point format. The symbol (1.f) represents a normalised binary

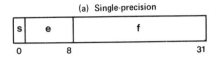

(a) Single-precision

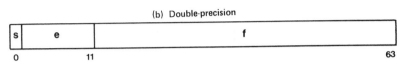

(b) Double-precision

Fig. 4.2.4 Format of floating-point numbers conforming to IEEE Standard 754—(a) single-precision, and (b) double-precision

number formed by an implicit 1 in the most significant place and the 23-bit fraction f. The number lies in the range:

$$1 \leqslant (1.f) < 2$$

The symbol $(0.f)$ represents a 'denormalised' binary number, i.e. an un-normalised number with a minimum exponent $(e = 0)$. Such a number is formed by an implicit 0 and the 23-bit fraction f. The number lies in the range:

$$0 < (0.f) < 1$$

An indication of the logical and arithmetic functions performed by units of a pipe-lined, floating-point adder/subtracter was given in Fig. 1.4.7 with its accompanying description in Section 1.4.3. Further description of the design of floating-point arithmetic circuits is beyond the scope of this book.

4.3 FIXED-POINT TWO'S COMPLEMENT BINARY ADDER/SUBTRACTER

4.3.1 Parallel adder/subtracter

The 'full adder' and its application in 'parallel adder' circuits for the addition of two binary numbers were described in Chapter 2. The approach taken with the development of the parallel adder can be extended to the development of a 'parallel adder/subtracter'. This is a combinational circuit with parallel inputs representing two numbers A and B, and with a control input D which specifies whether the circuit is to produce at its outputs the sum or difference of the two input numbers.

The parallel adder/subtracter utilises a circuit known as a 'full adder/subtracter'. This is a combinational circuit with four inputs A, B, C and D, and two outputs S and R. The input A represents one bit of the augend or minuend; B represents one bit of the addend or subtrahend; C represents the input carry or borrow bit and D is an input control signal which specifies whether addition or subtraction is to be performed. The output S represents one bit of the sum or difference, and R represents the output carry or borrow bit.

The truth table of the full adder/subtracter is shown in Table 4.3.1. This lists the values of the two outputs S and R for every combination of the four inputs A, B, C and D. That part of the table relating to addition has been presented earlier (in Chapter 2), and it is now necessary for the reader only to verify that the outputs for subtraction satisfy the rules of binary subtraction.

It is to be noted from Table 4.3.1 that the S output for addition is the same as the S output for subtraction (for the same values of A, B and C). Hence, the Boolean expression

Table 4.3.1   Truth table of adder/subtracter

	ADDITION								SUBTRACTION							
A (first number)	0	1	0	1	0	1	0	1	0	1	0	1	0	1	0	1
B (second number)	0	0	1	1	0	0	1	1	0	0	1	1	0	0	1	1
C (carry/borrow input)	0	0	0	0	1	1	1	1	0	0	0	0	1	1	1	1
D (control)	0	0	0	0	0	0	0	0	1	1	1	1	1	1	1	1
S (sum/difference)	0	1	1	0	1	0	0	1	0	1	1	0	1	0	0	1
R (carry/borrow)	0	0	0	1	0	1	1	1	0	0	1	0	1	0	1	1

for S is independent of D, and is the same as the expression for the 'sum output' of a 'full adder'. The eight canonical product terms for the output R which are specified by the truth table of Table 4.3.1 may be logically summed and the resultant sum-of-products expression simplified. This step is left to the reader. The minimised expressions for S and R are as follows:

$$S = A\overline{B}\overline{C} + \overline{A}B\overline{C} + \overline{A}\overline{B}C + ABC$$
$$R = \overline{D}AB + \overline{D}CA + BC + D\overline{A}B + D\overline{A}C$$

A circuit diagram of a full adder/subtracter which is based on the above equations is shown in Fig. 4.3.1.

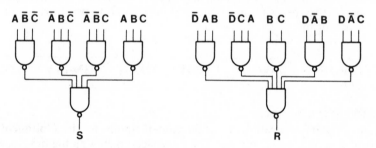

ABC̄   ĀBC̄   ĀB̄C   ABC   D̄AB   D̄CA   BC   DĀB   DĀC

S   R

Fig. 4.3.1   Circuit of a full adder/subtracter

A circuit of a 4-bit parallel adder/subtracter which utilises full adder/subtracters is shown in Fig. 4.3.2. This circuit may be described as a 'ripple parallel adder/subtracter' as the carry/borrow output of one full adder/subtracter stage is connected to the carry/borrow input of the next more significant stage. It is to be noted that when subtraction is being performed, the S outputs of Fig. 4.3.2 represent 'the number A minus the number B' as the truth table of Table 4.3.1 and the carry/borrow circuit of Fig. 4.3.1 is based on the fact that the A inputs represent the minuend and the B inputs represent the subtrahend.

An alternative (and more common) form of the parallel adder/subtracter is represented by the circuit shown in Fig. 4.3.3. This circuit carries out subtraction by adding the one's complement of the subtrahend plus one in the least-significant place to the minuend. Note that the circuit of Fig. 4.3.3, which is a 4-bit adder/subtracter, utilises EXCLUSIVE-OR gates and full adders. The four EXCLUSIVE-OR gates form a 4-bit 'true-complement gate' which produces at its outputs either the number B (in parallel) or the one's complement of this number. Note that when the control input D is zero, the signals B_3, B_2,

B_1, B_0 pass unchanged through the 'true-complement gate'. However, when D is equal to one, the signals $\overline{B}_3$, $\overline{B}_2$, $\overline{B}_1$, $\overline{B}_0$ appear at the outputs of the 'true-complement gate' and thence at the inputs of the full adders. Note particularly that the control input D is also connected to the carry input of the least-significant adder stage. This connection produces the one to be added in the least-significant bit position whenever subtraction is to be performed.

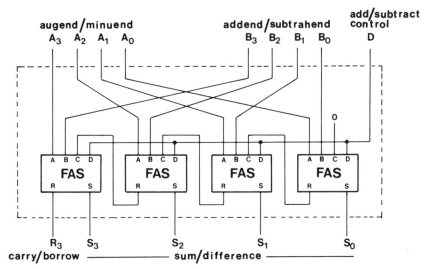

Fig. 4.3.2 Circuit of a four-bit, parallel adder/subtracter

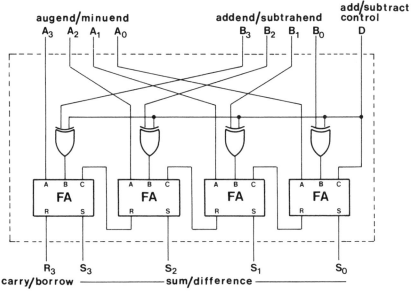

Fig. 4.3.3 Circuit of a parallel adder/subtracter using full adders and exclusive-OR gates

4.3.2 Overflow conditions

It is possible that the addition or subtraction of two 'in-range' numbers can produce a result which is outside the range of numbers which can be represented by a fixed-point number system. When this occurs in a fixed-point arithmetic unit, incorrect results are produced. It is, of course, essential that these overflow conditions be detected.

There are four overflow conditions in fixed-point two's complement addition and subtraction. These are:

(i) the generation of a carry bit into the sign bit position when two positive numbers are added,

(ii) the generation of no carry bit into the sign bit position when two negative numbers are added,

(iii) the generation of a borrow bit into the sign bit position when a positive number is subtracted from a negative number, and

(iv) the generation of no borrow bit into the sign bit position when a negative number is subtracted from a positive number.

These overflow conditions are defined by the truth table shown in Table 4.3.2 in which A_N is the sign bit of the augend or minuend; B_N is the sign bit of the addend or subtrahend; C_N is the carry/borrow bit into the sign bit position; D is the control signal specifying addition or subtraction; S_N is the resultant sign bit of the sum or difference and R_N is the resultant carry/borrow bit out of the sign bit position. (It is to be remembered that for 'in-range' two's complement addition and subtraction, R_N is ignored).

Table 4.3.2   Truth table of adder/subtracter with sign bit inputs and overflow conditions

	ADDITION								SUBTRACTION							
A_N (sign bit)	0	1	0	1	0	1	0	1	0	1	0	1	0	1	0	1
B_N (sign bit)	0	0	1	1	0	0	1	1	0	0	1	1	0	0	1	1
C_N (carry/borrow input)	0	0	0	0	1	1	1	1	0	0	0	0	1	1	1	1
D (control)	0	0	0	0	0	0	0	0	1	1	1	1	1	1	1	1
S_N (sum/difference sign)	0	1	1	0	1	0	0	1	0	1	1	0	1	0	0	1
R_N (carry/borrow)	0	0	0	1	0	1	1	1	0	0	1	0	1	0	1	1
V (overflow condition)	0	0	0	1	1	0	0	0	0	0	1	0	0	1	0	0

The four one's in the row of the truth table 4.3.2 which defines the overflow condition V specify four canonical product terms of the variables A_N, B_N, C_N and D. The logical sum of these terms provides the expression for V. This is as follows:

$$V = A_N B_N \overline{C_N}\overline{D} + \overline{A_N}\overline{B_N} C_N \overline{D} + \overline{A_N} B_N \overline{C_N} D + A_N \overline{B_N} C_N D$$

A circuit which produces V according to the above equation is shown in Fig. 4.3.4.

An alternative (and simpler) expression for the overflow condition V may be derived by closely examining the entries of the truth table of Table 4.3.2. In particular, the entries in the rows for C_N (carry/borrow input) and R_N (carry/borrow output) should be compared. The reader will observe that overflow occurs whenever R_N is different from C_N. Hence:

$$V = C_n \oplus R_N$$

This equation specifies that the overflow condition V may be detected using a single EXCLUSIVE-OR gate as shown in Fig. 4.3.4(b) (provided, of course, that the two signals C_N and R_N are available).

In some situations the signal C_N is not readily available. Consider for example the circuit of a parallel adder/subtracter given in Fig. 4.3.2 in which the two 4-bit operands A_3-–A_0

and B_3--B_0 are two's-complement numbers (with A_3 and B_3 being the sign bits). Expressions for the overflow condition V are:

$$V = A_3 B_3 \overline{C}_3 \overline{D} + \overline{A}_3 \overline{B}_3 C_3 \overline{D} + \overline{A}_3 B_3 \overline{C}_3 D + A_3 \overline{B}_3 C_3 D$$

$$V = R_3 \oplus C_3$$

Both of the above expressions are functions of C_3—the carry into the most-significant (sign bit) adder/subtracter stage. When the entire 4-bit adder/subtracter is implemented as a commercially available medium-scale integrated circuit, the carry signal C_3 is often an

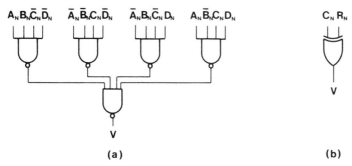

(a)　　　　　　　　　　　　　　　　　(b)

Fig. 4.3.4 Circuits for detection of arithmetic overflow

'internal' signal and is not available at an output pin of the circuit. An alternative expression which is independent of C_3 is therefore required. Such an expression is:

$$V = A_3 B_3 \overline{S}_3 \overline{D} + \overline{A}_3 \overline{B}_3 S_3 \overline{D} + \overline{A}_3 B_3 S_3 D + A_3 \overline{B}_3 \overline{S}_3 D$$

In the above expression S_3 is the sign of the result. The expression may be verified using the following equations for S_3 and $\overline{S}_3$:

$$S_3 = A_3 \overline{B}_3 \overline{C}_3 + \overline{A}_3 B_3 \overline{C}_3 + \overline{A}_3 \overline{B}_3 C_3 + A_3 B_3 C_3$$

$$\overline{S}_3 = \overline{A}_3 B_3 C_3 + A_3 \overline{B}_3 C_3 + A_3 B_3 \overline{C}_3 + \overline{A}_3 \overline{B}_3 \overline{C}_3$$

4.3.3 Condition flag generator

The overflow condition V described in Section 4.3.2 is an example of a number of arithmetic conditions detected by hardware (circuits) in digital computers. When applied to computers, these arithmetic conditions are often referred to as 'condition codes', 'condition flags' or 'flags'. Computer instructions are provided to test these conditions causing alternative sequences of instructions to be executed depending on their values. Eighteen conditions relating to fixed-point addition and subtraction operations are listed in Table 4.3.3. The Boolean expressions in this table refer to the 4-bit adder/subtracter shown in Fig. 4.3.5(a). In this figure the two operands are denoted by A_3--A_0 and B_3--B_0; the 4-bit result is denoted by S_3--S_0 and the carry (or borrow) output is denoted by R_3. Circuits for the generation of the condition flags of Table 4.3.3 are shown in Fig. 4.3.5(b). Extensions of Fig. 4.3.5 for the treatment of arithmetic operations in 8-bit microprocessors or 16-bit microprocessors or minicomputers may readily be made.

The Motorola 6800 microprocessor and the Digital Equipment Corporation PDP11 family of minicomputers have instructions for testing the first 14 conditions listed in Table 4.3.3. As far as the programmer's model of these computers is concerned, the four condition codes Z, N, C and V are clocked into four flip-flops following the completion of an operation such as addition or subtraction, and any of the 14 conditions may be detected

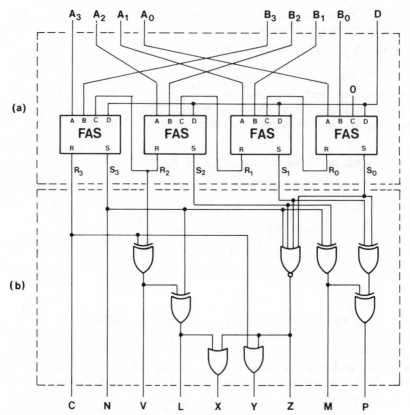

Fig. 4.3.5   Circuit of—(a) four-bit adder/subtracter, and (b) condition flag generator

by circuits driven by the outputs of these flip-flops. The significance of the condition codes Z, N, C and V are:

Z : zero
N : negative
C : carry/borrow
V : overflow

The last four conditions of Table 4.3.3 are defined in terms of the condition codes P and M. These have the following significance:

P : parity odd
M : normalised

The meaning of the term 'parity' was described in Section 2.6.3, and the term 'normalised' in the phrase 'normalised binary number' was used in Section 4.2.2. An instructive exercise now is for the reader to verify the Boolean expressions given in Table 4.3.3.

4.3.4   Serial adder/subtracter

Circuits of serial adder/subtracters are shown in Fig. 4.3.6(a) and (b). The circuit of Fig. 4.3.6(a) utilises a full adder/subtracter and a D-type flip-flop. The serial inputs A and B are connected to the A and B inputs of the full adder/subtracter, and the sum–difference output provides the serial output. The control input D specifies whether addition or subtraction is to be performed. The carry/borrow output of the full adder/subtracter is connected to the D-input of a D-type flip-flop. (The reader is asked not to confuse the 'control input D' with the D-input of the D-type flip-flop). This flip-flop delays the carry/

Table 4.3.3 Table of condition flags for the binary adder/subtracter of Fig. 4.3.5

FLAG	CONDITION	RESTRICTIONS
ZERO	$Z = \bar{S_3}\bar{S_2}\bar{S_1}\bar{S_0}$	
NOT EQUAL ZERO	$\bar{Z}$	
MINUS	$N = S_3$	
PLUS	$\bar{N}$	
CARRY/BORROW SET	$C = R_3$	
CARRY/BORROW CLEAR	$\bar{C}$	
LOWER OR SAME	$Y = C + Z$	SUBTRACTION OF POSITIVE OPERANDS
HIGHER	$\bar{Y}$	SUBTRACTION OF POSITIVE OPERANDS
OVERFLOW SET	$V = R_3 \oplus R_2$	TWO'S COMPLEMENT ADDITION/SUBTRACTION
OVERFLOW CLEAR	$\bar{V}$	TWO'S COMPLEMENT ADDITION/SUBTRACTION
LESS THAN ZERO	$L = N \oplus V$	TWO'S COMPLEMENT ADDITION/SUBTRACTION
GREATER THAN OR EQUAL ZERO	$\bar{L}$	TWO'S COMPLEMENT ADDITION/SUBTRACTION
LESS THAN OR EQUAL ZERO	$X = Z + L$	TWO'S COMPLEMENT ADDITION/SUBTRACTION
GREATER THAN ZERO	$\bar{X}$	TWO'S COMPLEMENT ADDITION/SUBTRACTION
PARITY ODD	$P = (S_3 \oplus S_2) \oplus (S_1 \oplus S_0)$	
PARITY EVEN	$\bar{P}$	
NORMALISED	$M = S_3 \oplus S_2$	TWO'S COMPLEMENT FRACTION
NOT NORMALISED	$\bar{M}$	TWO'S COMPLEMENT FRACTION

borrow output from the full adder/subtracter by one bit period, and feeds back the delayed carry/borrow bit to the carry/borrow input of the full adder/subtracter. Before the serial operation of the circuit commences, it is necessary to reset the D-type flip-flop initially (to zero). This may be achieved by using an 'initialisation pulse' T_I as indicated in Fig. 4.3.7.

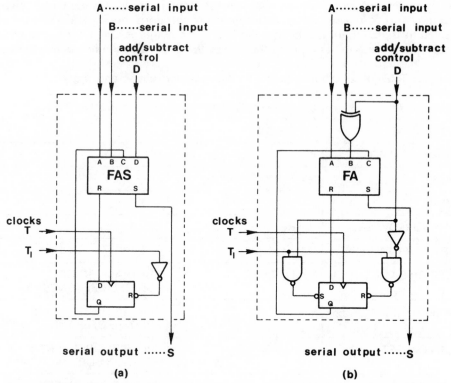

Fig. 4.3.6   Serial adder/subtracter—(a) using full adder/subtracter, and (b) using full adder and exclusive-OR gate

Note that the T_I pulse must occur before the first pulse of the clock input T which is used to synchronise the serial inputs A and B with the operation of the D-type flip-flop.

The alternative circuit of Fig. 4.3.6(b) utilises a full adder, an exclusive-OR gate and a D-type flip-flop. This circuit carries out subtraction by the method of 'complementing and adding'. This method (which has been described in earlier sections in connection with the parallel adder/subtracter) requires that the one's complement of the subtrahend plus one in the least-significant bit position should be added to the minuend when subtraction is to be performed. With serial inputs, the one's complement of the subtrahend B may be produced by a single exclusive-OR gate as shown in Fig. 4.3.6(b). The 'one in the least-significant bit position' may be provided by setting the carry/borrow flip-flop initially to one. This may be accomplished by the 'initialisation pulse' T_I of Fig. 4.3.6(b). Note that the 'active-LOW' S and R inputs of the D-type flip-flop (i.e. the carry/borrow flip-flop) used in Fig. 4.3.6(b) require signals which may be produced by two 2-input NAND-gates. These cause the flip-flop to be set initially to one when D is one and to be reset initially to zero when D is zero.

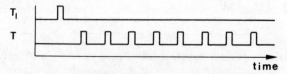

Fig. 4.3.7   Serial adder/subtracter timing waveforms

Serial adders and serial adder/subtracters require such a small amount of circuitry that in applications which require the addition or subtraction of more than two numbers (or perhaps many numbers) consideration should be given to their use provided, of course, that circuit performance requirements are such that sufficient time is available for serial operation and that the input numbers are in (or may be conveniently converted to) serial form. An example of an arithmetic unit for the serial addition of four numbers W, X, Y and Z is shown in Fig. 4.3.8. The circuit shown in Fig. 4.3.8 contains three serial adders, the first of which adds W and X; the second adds Y and Z, and the third adds the sums produced by the first and second. Note that the carry flip-flop of each serial adder must be reset initially to zero, and a clock pulse T must be used to synchronise all serial inputs with the operation of all flip-flops.

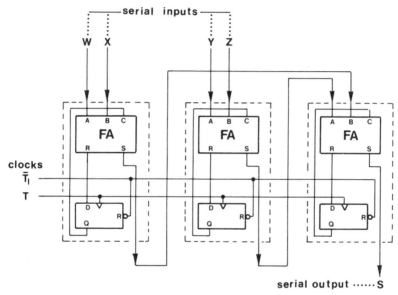

Fig. 4.3.8 Circuit for the serial addition of four numbers

It must be remembered that whenever one or more serial adders or adder/subtracters are used in a circuit, correct operation will be produced only if overflow conditions do not occur. Hence when circuits such as those of Fig. 4.3.6(a), Fig. 4.3.6(b) and Fig. 4.3.8 are used, *scaling* of the serial input numbers must be carried out so that overflow in *any* full adder (or full adder/subtracter) cannot occur. When there are two serial inputs, as in Fig. 4.3.6(a) or Fig. 4.3.6(b), overflow cannot occur if the absolute value of each input number when interpreted according to the format of Fig. 4.2.2(a) is less than one half. When there are four serial inputs, as in Fig. 4.3.8, overflow cannot occur if the absolute value of each input number is less than one quarter.

One characteristic of the two's complement number system which may have been deduced from the description provided in Section 4.2 is that the process of an 'arithmetic right shift' of a two's complement number requires the repeated duplication of the sign bit if this process is to produce a division by two for each bit position shifted. For example, the number minus three sixteenths may be represented by the eight bits 11101000, while one quarter of minus three sixteenths (i.e. minus three sixty-fourths) is represented by the eight bits 11111010 which is the first pattern of eight bits shifted two bit positions to the right with the sign bit repeated twice.

The above process of 'arithmetic right shift' may be applied to the scaling of two's complement numbers. However, instead of shifting the bit pattern to the right with a duplication of the sign bit, additional more significant bits which are a repeated duplication of the sign bit are attached so that there is no reduction in the accuracy of the input numbers. Hence for the example of the 8-bit input number 11101000 (representing minus three sixteenths), the 10-bit input number 1111101000 should be formed, and the addition or subtraction operation(s) should be carried out on 10-bit numbers.

4.4   CARRY LOOKAHEAD ADDER/SUBTRACTER

4.4.1   Carry lookahead principle

In a 'ripple carry parallel adder', the carry output of one full adder stage is connected to the carry input of the next more significant adder stage. In such an adder, it is possible that a carry signal will be generated in the least-significant stage and will ripple through all adder stages including the most-significant (sign bit) stage and thus affect all outputs. The time period which must be allowed from the instant all inputs are established to the time when the outputs of the adder may be sensed and perhaps clocked into flip-flops must be in excess of the 'worst-case' delay through the adder. This worst-case delay depends on the accumulated delays through the carry circuits of all full adders. When the number of adder stages is not large or when high operating speeds are not required, the ripple carry parallel adder is the most economical form of adder to use. However, when high speed is required, a carry lookahead adder can be used.

In a carry lookahead adder additional circuits are provided so that the carry outputs of a number of adder stages are produced with the same nominal delay and hence the sum outputs of a number of adder stages are also produced with the same nominal delay. The carry lookahead principle is that 'to minimise the delay through a parallel adder, the carry circuits of each full adder should not rely on the carry input to the full adder to determine the carry output and the sum output of that stage, but should *lookahead* over a number of adder stages to the carry input of a much less significant adder stage'. This approach of looking ahead over a number of adder stages, we shall call '*zero-level lookahead*'. The significance of this term and of the terms 'first-level lookahead' and 'second-level lookahead' etc., will become apparent later.

To demonstrate how the above principle of the carry lookahead adder may be implemented, we shall describe in this section the derivation of the circuit of a 4-bit zero-level carry lookahead adder. This adder has nine inputs of which four (A_3, A_2, A_1, A_0) represent a 4-bit number A; another four (B_3, B_2, B_1, B_0) represent a 4-bit number B and the ninth input C_0 is the carry input to the least-significant adder stage. The subscript 3 refers to the most-significant bit and the subscript 0 refers to the least-significant bit. The adder has five outputs C_4, S_3, S_2, S_1, S_0 of which S_3, S_2, S_1, S_0 represent the 4-bit sum, and C_4 represents the carry output of the most-significant adder stage.

We shall firstly define two functions of corresponding bits of the input numbers. These are the '*generate function*' G_n ($n = 3,2,1,0$) and the '*propagate function*' P_n ($n = 3,2,1,0$). These are defined as follows:

$$G_n = A_n B_n \qquad (n = 3,2,1,0) \tag{1}$$

$$P_n = A_n \oplus B_n \qquad (n = 3,2,1,0) \tag{2}$$

It will be observed that the 'generate function' G_n is simply the 'logical product' or the 'AND function' of the input signals A_n and B_n. The significance of the term 'generate' is that if $G_n = 1$ for the inputs to an adder stage, the adder stage will 'generate a carry' irrespective of what the input carry is. It will be observed also that the 'propagate function' P_n is simply the 'exclusive-OR function' of the input signals A_n and B_n. The significance of the term 'propagate' is that if $P_n = 1$ for the inputs to an adder stage, the adder stage will 'propagate the carry', i.e. the carry output of the adder stage will be equal to the carry input. The above statements concerning carry generation or propagation in full adders may be verified from the truth table of a full adder (see Table 2.7.2). This truth table provides the following canonical sum-of-products expression for the carry output R_n which may then be manipulated as shown:

$$R_n = \overline{A}_nB_nC_n+A_n\overline{B}_nC_n+A_nB_n\overline{C}_n+A_nB_nC_n \tag{3}$$

$$= (\overline{A}_nB_n+A_n\overline{B}_n)C_n+A_nB_n$$

$$\therefore \ R_n = G_n+P_nC_n \tag{4}$$

In a parallel adder, the carry output of one full adder stage is connected to the carry input of the next more significant stage. Hence,

$$R_n = C_{n+1} \tag{5}$$

The two equations (4) and (5) then produce the following equations for the 4-bit adder under consideration:

$$C_4 = G_3+P_3C_3 \tag{6}$$

$$C_3 = G_2+P_2C_2 \tag{7}$$

$$C_2 = G_1+P_1C_1 \tag{8}$$

$$C_1 = G_0+P_0C_0 \tag{9}$$

To implement the carry lookahead principle, the above equations may be manipulated as follows:

$$C_4 = G_3+P_3(G_2+P_2(G_1+P_1(G_0+P_0C_0))) \tag{10}$$

$$C_3 = G_2+P_2(G_1+P_1(G_0+P_0C_0)) \tag{11}$$

$$C_2 = G_1+P_1(G_0+P_0C_0) \tag{12}$$

$$C_1 = G_0+P_0C_0 \tag{13}$$

After the removal of all brackets by 'multiplying out', the above equations become:

$$C_4 = G_3+P_3G_2+P_3P_2G_1+P_3P_2P_1G_0+P_3P_2P_1P_0C_0 \tag{14}$$

$$C_3 = G_2+P_2G_1+P_2P_1G_0+P_2P_1P_0C_0 \tag{15}$$

$$C_2 = G_1+P_1G_0+P_1P_0C_0 \tag{16}$$

$$C_1 = G_0+P_0C_0 \tag{17}$$

An examination of the above equations shows that expressions for the output carry signals of the four full adders (C_4, C_3, C_2, C_1) have been derived in terms of the generate and propagate functions (G_n and P_n) and the carry input to the least-significant stage (C_0). Moreover all expressions are in the sum-of-products form and hence can be implemented by circuits with only two gate delays. Hence all four carry signals can be produced with the same nominal gate delays.

Once the carry signals have been established, it is necessary only to derive expressions for the sum signals in terms of the carry signals and other available signals in order to complete the design.

The truth table of the full adder produces the following expression for the sum output which may then be manipulated as shown:

$$S_n = A_n\overline{B}_n\overline{C}_n + \overline{A}_nB_n\overline{C}_n + \overline{A}_n\overline{B}_nC_n + A_nB_nC_n \qquad (18)$$

$$= (A_n\overline{B}_n + \overline{A}_nB_n)\overline{C}_n + (\overline{A}_n\overline{B}_n + A_nB_n)C_n$$

$$= P_n\overline{C}_n + \overline{P}_nC_n$$

$$\text{i.e., } S_n = P_n \oplus C_n \qquad (19)$$

Hence the sum output of a full adder stage may be formed by a single exclusive-OR gate from the propagate function for the stage and the carry input.

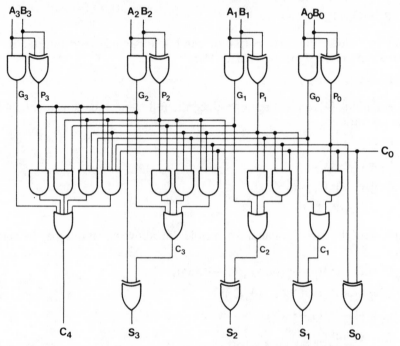

Fig. 4.4.1   Circuit of a four-bit, zero-level, carry lookahead adder

The complete 4-bit carry lookahead adder may now be implemented using equations 1, 2, 14, 15, 16, 17 and 19. The circuit defined by these equations is shown in Fig. 4.4.1.

4.4.2   First-level carry lookahead

An examination of the circuit of Fig. 4.4.1 shows that for a 4-bit zero-level carry lookahead adder, gates with five inputs are required, and five gates are required for the production of the most-significant carry signal. An attempt to apply the approach taken with a 4-bit adder directly to the design of a 16-bit adder (for example) soon reveals several limitations. The first limitation results from the 'fan-in' of the circuits used. The term 'fan-in' has been used with two meanings in the literature. One use of the term refers to the maximum allowable number of inputs to a gate which is determined by the electrical characteristics of the circuits used, and a second use refers to the load placed on the signal source by the input of a gate. It is the maximum allowable number of inputs to a gate which introduces the limitation to the zero-level carry lookahead adder. A second limitation is the large amount of circuitry required to produce each carry output signal when lookahead is applied over a large number of stages. A third limitation arises from practical consider-ations of circuit construction and packaging. These considerations limit the number of input and output signals which can be connected to a package.

The term *zero-level lookahead* has been used when carry circuits *lookahead over a number of individual adder stages* to the carry input of a much less significant adder stage. The term *first-level lookahead* will now be used to refer to *lookahead over a number of 'groups' of adder stages*.

The number of adder stages in a 'group' depends on methods of packaging and on other circuit constraints. It is now very common practice to provide four adder stages in an MSI/LSI integrated circuit package, and other circuits have been provided for the specific purpose of constructing carry lookahead adders of any number of stages.

To enable carry circuits to lookahead over a number of groups of adder stages, it is necessary for each group to produce what shall be called a *'first-level generate function'* and a *'first-level propagate function'*. We shall again use the symbols G and P for these functions, but we shall use a superscript I to indicate that it is a first-level function, and we shall use a subscript defining the range of adder stages in the group. Hence the group of four adder stages with inputs A_3, A_2, A_1, A_0 and B_3, B_2, B_1, B_0 will have a 'first-level generate function' and a 'first-level propagate function' designated G_{3-0}^I and P_{3-0}^I respectively.

The significance of the 'first-level generate function' G_{3-0}^I is that if $G_{3-0}^I = 1$, the group of four adder stages with inputs A_n, B_n ($n = 3$–0) will generate a carry irrespective of what the carry input to the least-significant adder stage is. The significance of the 'first-level propagate function' P_{3-0}^I is that if $P_{3-0}^I = 1$, the group of four adder stages with inputs A_n, B_n ($n = 3$–0) will propagate the carry input to the group, i.e. the carry output of the group will be the same as the carry input to the least-significant stage of the group. From the above description of the first-level generate and propagate functions, Boolean expressions for these functions may be derived. These are as follows:

$$G_{3-0}^I = G_3 + P_3 G_2 + P_3 P_2 G_1 + P_3 P_2 P_1 G_0 \tag{20}$$

$$P_{3-0}^I = P_3 P_2 P_1 P_0 \tag{21}$$

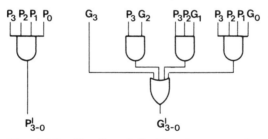

Fig. 4.4.2 Circuits of first-level, propagate and generate functions

Circuits corresponding to equations (20) and (21) are shown in Fig. 4.4.2. Integrated circuits designed specifically for the construction of carry lookahead adders usually contain circuits with equivalent function to those of Fig. 4.4.1 and Fig. 4.4.2 in the one package. A block diagram of such a package is shown in Fig. 4.4.3.

4.4.3 Design of a 16-bit carry lookahead adder

If a 16-bit carry lookahead adder is to be constructed, four packages with circuits represented by the block diagram of Fig. 4.4.3 are required. The first-level generate and propagate functions produced by the least-significant three of the four packages enable

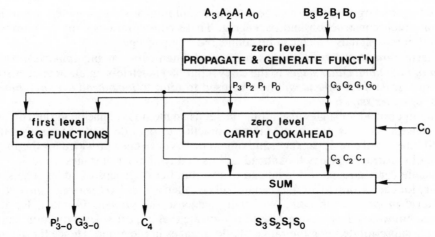

Fig. 4.4.3 Block diagram of four-bit, zero-level, carry lookahead adder with first-level, propagate and generate functions

carry lookahead to take place over groups (i.e. packages) of full adder stages. The relevant equations for a 16-bit carry lookahead adder are:

$$C_{12} = G^I_{11-8} + P^I_{11-8}G^I_{7-4} + P^I_{11-8}P^I_{7-4}G^I_{3-0} + P^I_{11-8}P^I_{7-4}P^I_{3-0}C_0 \tag{22}$$

$$C_8 = G^I_{7-4} + P^I_{7-4}G^I_{3-0} + P^I_{7-4}P^I_{3-0}C_0 \tag{23}$$

$$C_4 = G^I_{3-0} + P^I_{3-0}C_0 \tag{24}$$

Circuits corresponding to equations (22), (23) and (24) are shown in Fig. 4.4.4. This figure also contains circuits which produce what can be called a 'second-level generate function' and a 'second-level propagate function'. We shall again use the symbols G and P for these functions, but shall use a superscript II to indicate a second-level function and a subscript defining the range of adder stages represented by the function. The second-level functions enable carry lookahead to take place over *'groups of groups of adder stages'*. For 16 adder stages, the relevant equations are:

$$G^{II}_{15-0} = G^I_{15-12} + P^I_{15-12}G^I_{11-8} + P^I_{15-12}P^I_{11-8}G^I_{7-4} + P^I_{15-12}P^I_{11-8}P^I_{7-4}G^I_{3-0} \tag{25}$$

$$P^{II}_{15-0} = P^I_{15-12}P^I_{11-8}P^I_{7-4}P^I_{3-0} \tag{26}$$

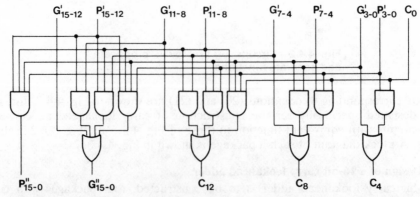

Fig. 4.4.4 Circuits for first-level, carry lookahead, and second-level, propagate and generate functions

Circuits corresponding to equations (25) and (26) are also shown in Fig. 4.4.4. Integrated circuit families usually provide a package containing circuits which are equivalent to all the circuits in Fig. 4.4.4, i.e. circuits corresponding to equations (22), (23), (24), (25) and (26). This enables carry lookahead adders of any number of stages to be readily constructed.

To illustrate the approach described above for the design of carry lookahead adders, the block diagram of a 16-bit carry lookahead circuit is shown in Fig. 4.4.5, and the associated Boolean equations are given below:

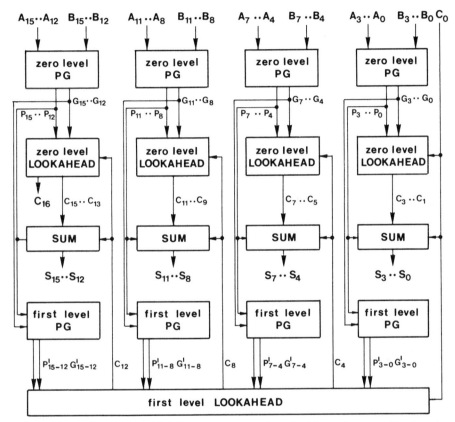

Fig. 4.4.5 Block diagram of 16-bit, carry lookahead adder using zero-level and first-level lookahead circuits

Zero-level generate and propagate functions:

$$G_n = A_n B_n \qquad (n = 15, \ldots, 0) \tag{27}$$

$$P_n = A_n \oplus B_n \qquad (n = 15, \ldots, 0) \tag{28}$$

First-level generate and propagate functions:

$$G^I_{15-12} = G_{15} + P_{15}G_{14} + P_{15}P_{14}G_{13} + P_{15}P_{14}P_{13}G_{12} \tag{29}$$

$$P^I_{15-12} = P_{15}P_{14}P_{13}P_{12} \tag{30}$$

$$G^I_{11-8} = G_{11} + P_{11}G_{10} + P_{11}P_{10}G_9 + P_{11}P_{10}P_9G_8 \tag{31}$$

$$P^I_{11-8} = P_{11}P_{10}P_9P_8 \tag{32}$$

$$G^I_{7-4} = G_7 + P_7 G_6 + P_7 P_6 G_5 + P_7 P_6 P_5 G_4 \tag{33}$$

$$P^I_{7-4} = P_7 P_6 P_5 P_4 \tag{34}$$

$$G^I_{3-0} = G_3 + P_3 G_2 + P_3 P_2 G_1 + P_3 P_2 P_1 G_0 \tag{20}$$

$$P^I_{3-0} = P_3 P_2 P_1 P_0 \tag{21}$$

First-level carry lookahead:

$$C_{12} = G^I_{11-8} + P^I_{11-8} G^I_{7-4} + P^I_{11-8} P^I_{7-4} G^I_{3-0} + P^I_{11-8} P^I_{7-4} P^I_{3-0} C_0 \tag{22}$$

$$C_8 = G^I_{7-4} + P^I_{7-4} G^I_{3-0} + P^I_{7-4} P^I_{3-0} C_0 \tag{23}$$

$$C_4 = G^I_{3-0} + P^I_{3-0} C_0 \tag{24}$$

Zero-level carry lookahead:

$$C_{16} = G_{15} + P_{15} G_{14} + P_{15} P_{14} G_{13} + P_{15} P_{14} P_{13} G_{12} + P_{15} P_{14} P_{13} P_{12} C_{12} \tag{35}$$

$$C_{15} = G_{14} + P_{14} G_{13} + P_{14} P_{13} G_{12} + P_{14} P_{13} P_{12} C_{12} \tag{36}$$

$$C_{14} = G_{13} + P_{13} G_{12} + P_{13} P_{12} C_{12} \tag{37}$$

$$C_{13} = G_{12} + P_{12} C_{12} \tag{38}$$

$$C_{11} = G_{10} + P_{10} G_9 + P_{10} P_9 G_8 + P_{10} P_9 P_8 C_8 \tag{39}$$

$$C_{10} = G_9 + P_9 G_8 + P_9 P_8 C_8 \tag{40}$$

$$C_9 = G_8 + P_8 C_8 \tag{41}$$

$$C_7 = G_6 + P_6 G_5 + P_6 P_5 G_4 + P_6 P_5 P_4 C_4 \tag{42}$$

$$C_6 = G_5 + P_5 G_4 + P_5 P_4 C_4 \tag{43}$$

$$C_5 = G_4 + P_4 C_4 \tag{44}$$

$$C_3 = G_2 + P_2 G_1 + P_2 P_1 G_0 + P_2 P_1 P_0 C_0 \tag{15}$$

$$C_2 = G_1 + P_1 G_0 + P_1 P_0 C_0 \tag{16}$$

$$C_1 = G_0 + P_0 C_0 \tag{17}$$

Sum output:

$$S_n = P_n \oplus C_n \qquad (n = 15, \ldots, 0) \tag{45}$$

Second-level generate and propagate functions:
(N.B.: these are not used for the 16-bit adder)

$$G^{II}_{15-0} = G^I_{15-12} + P^I_{15-12} G^I_{11-8} + P^I_{15-12} P^I_{11-8} G^I_{7-4} + P^I_{15-12} P^I_{11-8} P^I_{7-4} G^I_{3-0} \tag{25}$$

$$P^{II}_{15-0} = P^I_{15-12} P^I_{11-8} P^I_{7-4} P^I_{3-0} \tag{26}$$

4.4.4 Carry lookahead addition in the 'arithmetic-logic-unit/function-generator'—SN74181

The integrated circuit Type SN74181 is a 4-bit arithmetic-logic-unit which performs arithmetic or logical operations on two 4-bit numbers A_3–-A_0, B_3–-B_0 and an active-LOW carry-input signal $\overline{C}_n$. Four 'function-select inputs' S_3–-S_0 and a 'mode control input' M determine which function is performed. The outputs include four 'function outputs' F_3–-F_0 and an active-LOW carry output signal $\overline{C}_{n+4}$. Two output signals X and Y have the functions of the 'first-level propagate and generate functions' described in Section 4.4.2, and are used as inputs by a companion integrated circuit Type SN74182 ('carry lookahead generator') in high-speed adder/subtracter circuits. A 'comparator output' (A = B) is also provided so that the SN74181 may be used to compare the two input numbers.

The arithmetic and logical functions provided by the SN74181 are shown in the function table of Table 4.4.1. The functional logic diagram of the SN74181 is shown in Fig. 4.4.6. The objective of this section is to show how it may be verified that the functional logic diagram of Fig. 4.4.6 is consistent with the function table of Table 4.4.1 and the Boolean equations of a carry lookahead adder derived in earlier sections.

Table 4.4.1 Table showing the arithmetic and logical functions of the SN74181 for active-HIGH data

SELECTION				LOGIC FUNCTIONS	ARITHMETIC FUNCTIONS		
S_3	S_2	S_1	S_0	$M = H$	$M = L, \overline{C}_n = H$	$M = L, \overline{C}_n = L$
L	L	L	L	$F = \overline{A}$	$F = A$	$F = A$ PLUS 1
L	L	L	H	$F = \overline{A+B}$	$F = A+B$	$F = (A+B)$ PLUS 1
L	L	H	L	$F = \overline{A}B$	$F = A+\overline{B}$	$F = (A+\overline{B})$ PLUS 1
L	L	H	H	$F = 0$	$F =$ MINUS 1	$F =$ ZERO
L	H	L	L	$F = \overline{AB}$	$F = A$ PLUS $A\overline{B}$	$F = A$ PLUS $A\overline{B}$ PLUS 1
L	H	L	H	$F = \overline{B}$	$F = (A+B)$ PLUS $A\overline{B}$	$F = (A+B)$ PLUS $A\overline{B}$ PLUS 1
L	H	H	L	$F = A \oplus B$	$F = A$ MINUS B MINUS 1	$F = A$ MINUS B
L	H	H	H	$F = A\overline{B}$	$F = A\overline{B}$ MINUS 1	$F = A\overline{B}$
H	L	L	L	$F = \overline{A}+B$	$F = A$ PLUS AB	$F = A$ PLUS AB PLUS 1
H	L	L	H	$F = \overline{A \oplus B}$	$F = A$ PLUS B	$F = A$ PLUS B PLUS 1
H	L	H	L	$F = B$	$F = (A+\overline{B})$ PLUS AB	$F = (A+\overline{B})$ PLUS AB PLUS 1
H	L	H	H	$F = AB$	$F = AB$ MINUS 1	$F = AB$
H	H	L	L	$F = 1$	$F = A$ PLUS A	$F = A$ PLUS A PLUS 1
H	H	L	H	$F = A+\overline{B}$	$F = (A+B)$ PLUS A	$F = (A+B)$ PLUS A PLUS 1
H	H	H	L	$F = A+B$	$F = (A+\overline{B})$ PLUS A	$F = (A+\overline{B})$ PLUS A PLUS 1
H	H	H	H	$F = A$	$F = A$ MINUS 1	$F = A$

Signals with the designations D_3--D_0, E_3--E_0, $(D_3 \oplus E_3)$--$(D_0 \oplus E_0)$, Q_3--Q_0 are shown in Fig. 4.4.6. These signals are defined by the following equations:

$$D_n = \overline{A_n \overline{B}_n S_2 + A_n B_n S_3} \qquad (n = 3\text{--}0)$$
$$E_n = \overline{A_n + B_n S_0 + \overline{B}_n S_1} \qquad (n = 3\text{--}0)$$
$$Q_0 = M + C_n$$
$$Q_1 = M + E_0 + D_0 \overline{C}_n$$
$$Q_2 = M + E_1 + D_1 E_0 + D_1 D_0 \overline{C}_n$$
$$Q_3 = M + E_2 + D_2 E_1 + D_2 D_1 E_0 + D_2 D_1 D_0 \overline{C}_n$$

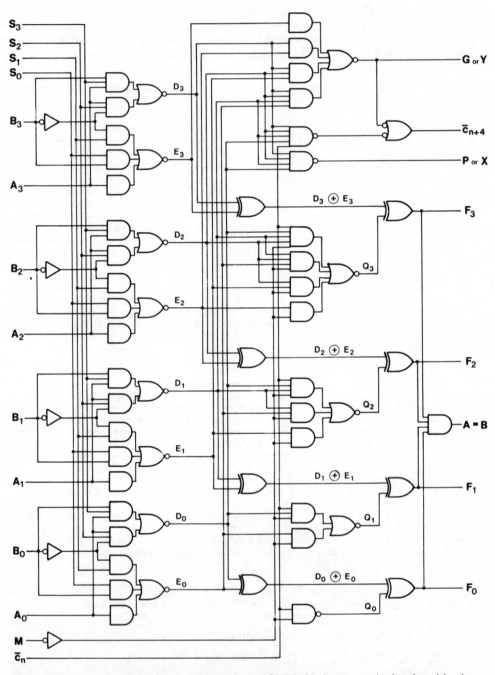

Fig. 4.4.6 Functional logic diagram of the SN74181 integrated circuit with the definition of intermediate signals used for circuit analysis

The output signals may now be defined in terms of these intermediate signals as follows:

$$F_n = Q_n \oplus (D_n \oplus E_n) \qquad (n = 3\text{--}0)$$
$$\overline{X} = D_3 D_2 D_1 D_0$$
$$\overline{Y} = E_3 + D_3 E_2 + D_3 D_2 E_1 + D_3 D_2 D_1 E_0$$
$$\overline{C}_{n+4} = E_3 + D_3 E_2 + D_3 D_2 E_1 + D_3 D_2 D_1 E_0 + D_3 D_2 D_1 D_0 \overline{C}_n$$
$$\{(A = B) \text{ comparator output}\} = F_3 F_2 F_1 F_0$$

Table 4.4.2 Table listing intermediate signals of the SN74181 when performing logical operations

S_3	S_2	S_1	S_0	D_n	E_n	$D_n \oplus E_n$
0	0	0	0	1	$\overline{A}_n$	$\overline{A}_n$
0	0	0	1	1	$\overline{A_n B_n}$	$\overline{A_n + B_n}$
0	0	1	0	1	$\overline{A}_n B_n$	$\overline{A_n B_n}$
0	0	1	1	1	0	0
0	1	0	0	$\overline{A_n + B_n}$	$\overline{A}_n$	$\overline{A_n B_n}$
0	1	0	1	$\overline{A_n + B_n}$	$\overline{A_n B_n}$	$\overline{B}_n$
0	1	1	0	$\overline{A_n + B_n}$	$\overline{A_n B_n}$	$A_n \oplus B_n$
0	1	1	1	$\overline{A_n + B_n}$	0	$A_n \overline{B}_n$
1	0	0	0	$\overline{A_n + B_n}$	$\overline{A}_n$	$\overline{A_n + B_n}$
1	0	0	1	$\overline{A_n + B_n}$	$\overline{A_n B_n}$	$A_n \oplus B_n$
1	0	1	0	$\overline{A_n + B_n}$	$\overline{A_n B_n}$	B_n
1	0	1	1	$\overline{A_n + B_n}$	0	$A_n B_n$
1	1	0	0	$\overline{A}_n$	$\overline{A}_n$	1
1	1	0	1	$\overline{A}_n$	$\overline{A_n B_n}$	$A_n + \overline{B}_n$
1	1	1	0	$\overline{A}_n$	$\overline{A}_n B_n$	$A_n + B_n$
1	1	1	1	$\overline{A}_n$	0	A_n

The SN74181 performs logical operations when $M = 1$, in which case the following equations hold:

$$Q_n = 1 \qquad (n = 3\text{--}0)$$
$$F_n = \overline{D_n \oplus E_n} \qquad (n = 3\text{--}0)$$

A table listing values of D_n, E_n and $\overline{D_n \oplus E_n}$ for the sixteen combinations of S_3, S_2, S_1 and S_0 is shown in Table 4.4.2. The last column of this table defines F_n, and is seen to be consistent with that given in Table 4.4.1.

The arithmetic function 'A plus B' is defined by the input condition $S_3 = 1, S_2 = 0, S_1 = 0, S_0 = 1$ and $M = 0$. Under these conditions, earlier equations reduce to:

$$D_n = \overline{A_n B_n} = \overline{G}_n \qquad\qquad (G_n = \text{Generate Function})$$

$$E_n = \overline{A_n + B_n} = \overline{R}_n \qquad\qquad (R_n = \text{Inclusive-OR Function})$$

$$D_n \oplus E_n = P_n \qquad\qquad (P_n = \text{Propagate Function})$$

$$Q_0 = C_n$$

$$\overline{Q}_1 = \overline{R}_0 + \overline{G}_0 \overline{C}_n$$

$$\overline{Q}_2 = \overline{R}_1 + \overline{G}_1 \overline{R}_0 + \overline{G}_1 \overline{G}_0 \overline{C}_n$$

$$\overline{Q}_3 = \overline{R}_2 + \overline{G}_2 \overline{R}_1 + \overline{G}_2 \overline{G}_1 \overline{R}_0 + \overline{G}_2 \overline{G}_1 \overline{G}_0 \overline{C}_n$$

$$\overline{C}_{n+4} = \overline{R}_3 + \overline{G}_3 \overline{R}_2 + \overline{G}_3 \overline{G}_2 \overline{R}_1 + \overline{G}_3 \overline{G}_2 \overline{G}_1 \overline{R}_0 + \overline{G}_3 \overline{G}_2 \overline{G}_1 \overline{G}_0 \overline{C}_n$$

$$X = \overline{G}_3 \overline{G}_2 \overline{G}_1 \overline{G}_0$$

$$\overline{Y} = \overline{R}_3 + \overline{G}_3 \overline{R}_2 + \overline{G}_3 \overline{G}_2 \overline{R}_1 + \overline{G}_3 \overline{G}_2 \overline{G}_1 \overline{R}_0$$

$$F_n = Q_n \oplus P_n \qquad (n = 3\text{--}0)$$

Equations (14)–(17) of Section 4.4.1 are equations for the carry signals of a parallel adder in terms of propagate and generate signals (Ps and Gs) and the input carry. The carry signals may also be expressed in terms of the inclusive-OR and generate signals (Rs and Gs). The derivation of these alternative expressions (given below) is suggested as an exercise for the reader.

$$\overline{C}_{n+1} = \overline{R}_0 + \overline{G}_0 \overline{C}_n$$

$$\overline{C}_{n+2} = \overline{R}_1 + \overline{G}_1 \overline{C}_{n+1}$$

$$\qquad = \overline{R}_1 + \overline{G}_1 \overline{R}_0 + \overline{G}_1 \overline{G}_0 \overline{C}_n$$

$$\overline{C}_{n+3} = \overline{R}_2 + \overline{G}_2 \overline{C}_{n+2}$$

$$\qquad = \overline{R}_2 + \overline{G}_2 \overline{R}_1 + \overline{G}_2 \overline{G}_1 \overline{R}_0 + \overline{G}_2 \overline{G}_1 \overline{G}_0 \overline{C}_n$$

$$\overline{C}_{n+4} = \overline{R}_3 + \overline{G}_3 \overline{C}_{n+3}$$

$$\qquad = \overline{R}_3 + \overline{G}_3 \overline{R}_2 + \overline{G}_3 \overline{G}_2 \overline{R}_1 + \overline{G}_3 \overline{G}_2 \overline{G}_1 \overline{R}_0 + \overline{G}_3 \overline{G}_2 \overline{G}_1 \overline{G}_0 \overline{C}_n$$

Hence the Q_1, Q_2 and Q_3 signals may be identified as carry signals, i.e.

$$Q_1 = C_{n+1}$$

$$Q_2 = C_{n+2}$$

$$Q_3 = C_{n+3}$$

Hence, the function outputs F_3--F_0 are given by:

$$F_0 = C_n \oplus P_0$$

$$F_1 = C_{n+1} \oplus P_1$$

$$F_2 = C_{n+2} \oplus P_2$$

$$F_3 = C_{n+3} \oplus P_3$$

These equations together with that for $\overline{C}_{n+4}$ clearly show that the function performed is 'A plus B'.

4.4.5 Analysis of SN74181 for subtraction

The control inputs of the SN74181 for subtraction are:

$$S_3S_2S_1S_0 = \text{LHHL}$$
$$M = \text{L}$$
$$\overline{C}_n = \text{L}$$

For these control inputs, intermediate signals are:

$$D_n = \overline{A}_n + B_n \qquad \text{(propagate or generate borrow)}$$
$$E_n = \overline{\overline{A}_n B_n} \qquad \text{(generate borrow)}$$
$$D_n \oplus E_n = A_n \oplus B_n$$
$$= \overline{P}_n$$
$$\overline{Q}_0 = \overline{C}_n$$
$$\overline{Q}_1 = E_0 + D_0 \overline{C}_n$$
$$\overline{Q}_2 = E_1 + D_1 E_0 + D_1 D_0 \overline{C}_n$$
$$\overline{Q}_3 = E_2 + D_2 E_1 + D_2 D_1 E_0 + D_2 D_1 D_0 \overline{C}_n$$

For subtraction the $\overline{C}_n$ input of the SN74181 represents an active-HIGH borrow signal. The D_n signals have the significance of 'propagate or generate borrow' conditions. The E_n signals have the significance of 'generate borrow' conditions. Using the symbols $\overline{C}_{n+1}$, $\overline{C}_{n+2}$ and $\overline{C}_{n+3}$ to represent the intermediate borrow signals, the 'borrow lookahead' equations may be written:

$$\overline{C}_{n+1} = E_0 + D_0 \overline{C}_n$$
$$\overline{C}_{n+2} = E_1 + D_1 E_0 + D_1 D_0 \overline{C}_n$$
$$\overline{C}_{n+3} = E_2 + D_2 E_1 + D_2 D_1 E_0 + D_2 D_1 D_0 \overline{C}_n$$

Hence the Q signals may be identified as the complements of the borrow signals:

$$Q_0 = \overline{\overline{C}_n}$$
$$Q_1 = \overline{\overline{C}_{n+1}}$$
$$Q_2 = \overline{\overline{C}_{n+2}}$$
$$Q_3 = \overline{\overline{C}_{n+3}}$$

The function outputs F_3--F_0 are given by:

$$F_0 = C_n \oplus \overline{P}_0 = \overline{C}_n \oplus P_0$$
$$F_1 = C_{n+1} \oplus \overline{P}_1 = \overline{C}_{n+1} \oplus P_1$$
$$F_2 = C_{n+2} \oplus \overline{P}_2 = \overline{C}_{n+2} \oplus P_2$$
$$F_3 = C_{n+3} \oplus \overline{P}_3 = \overline{C}_{n+3} \oplus P_3$$

The signals $\overline{C}_n$, $\overline{C}_{n+1}$, $\overline{C}_{n+2}$ and $\overline{C}_{n+3}$ are active-HIGH borrow signals. Hence F_0--F_3 are the output difference signals. The function performed by the SN74181 is 'A minus B'.

For subtraction, the first-level functions are given by:

$$X = \overline{D_3 D_2 D_1 D_0}$$
$$Y = \overline{E_3 + D_3 E_2 + D_3 D_2 E_1 + D_3 D_2 D_1 E_0}$$

where the Ds have the significance of 'propagate or generate borrow' conditions, and the Es have the significance of 'generate borrow' conditions.

The active-HIGH borrow output $\overline{C}_{n+4}$ is given by:

$$\overline{C}_{n+4} = \overline{Y} + \overline{X} \overline{C}_n$$

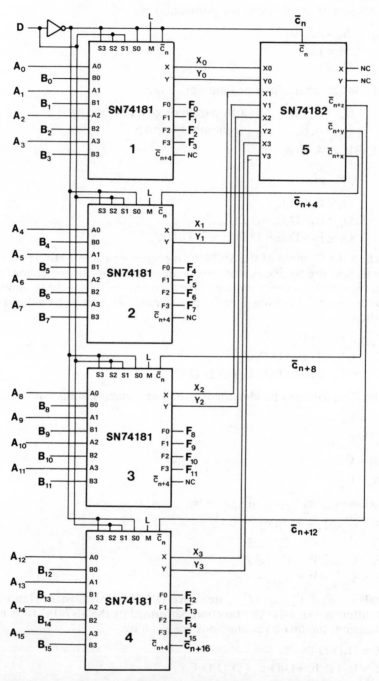

Fig. 4.4.7   Circuit of 16-bit, adder/subtracter using SN74181 and
SN74182 integrated circuits

4.4.6 Analysis of 16-bit adder/subtracter using SN74181 and SN74182 integrated circuits

The circuit of a 16-bit adder/subtracter containing four SN74181 integrated circuits and one SN74182 integrated circuit is shown in Fig. 4.4.7. The symbols used are:

$$D: \text{add/subtract control}$$
$$S_3S_2S_1S_0\overline{C}_nM: \text{control inputs of SN74181}$$
$$\overline{C}_n: \text{active-LOW carry input for addition or}$$
$$\text{active-HIGH borrow input for subtraction}$$
$$A_{15}\text{---}A_0: \text{first 16-bit input}$$
$$B_{15}\text{---}B_0: \text{second 16-bit input}$$
$$F_{15}\text{---}F_0: \text{16-bit result}$$
$$\overline{C}_{n+16}: \text{carry/borrow output}$$
$$\overline{C}_{n+x}: \overline{C}_{n+4} \text{ (carry/borrow input to second SN74181)}$$
$$\overline{C}_{n+y}: \overline{C}_{n+8} \text{ (carry/borrow input to third SN74181)}$$
$$\overline{C}_{n+z}: \overline{C}_{n+12} \text{ (carry/borrow input to fourth SN74181)}$$
$$X_0X_1X_2X_3: \text{first-level lookahead functions}$$
$$Y_0Y_1Y_2Y_3: \text{first-level lookahead functions}$$

For active-HIGH data, the functional block diagram of the SN74182 gives the following equations for $\overline{C}_{n+x}$, $\overline{C}_{n+y}$ and $\overline{C}_{n+z}$:

$$\overline{C}_{n+x} = \overline{Y_0X_0+Y_0C_n}$$
$$\overline{C}_{n+y} = \overline{Y_1X_1+Y_1Y_0X_0+Y_1Y_0C_n}$$
$$\overline{C}_{n+z} = \overline{Y_2X_2+Y_2Y_1X_1+Y_2Y_1Y_0X_0+Y_2Y_1Y_0C_n}$$

The application of De Morgan's theorems and other Boolean identities produces:

$$\overline{C}_{n+x} = \overline{Y}_0+\overline{X}_0\overline{C}_n$$
$$\overline{C}_{n+y} = \overline{Y}_1+\overline{X}_1\overline{Y}_0+\overline{X}_1\overline{X}_0\overline{C}_n$$
$$\overline{C}_{n+z} = \overline{Y}_2+\overline{X}_2\overline{Y}_1+\overline{X}_2\overline{X}_1\overline{Y}_0+\overline{X}_2\overline{X}_1\overline{X}_0\overline{C}_n$$

It is to be noted that the above expression for $\overline{C}_{n+x}$ is consistent with the expression for $\overline{C}_{n+4}$ derived in the analysis of the SN74181. Expressions for the $\overline{C}_{n+4}$ signals of the first, second and third SN74181 integrated circuits of Fig. 4.4.7 now may be written in the form:

$$\overline{C}_{n+4} = \overline{Y}_0+\overline{X}_0\overline{C}_n$$
$$\overline{C}_{n+8} = \overline{Y}_1+\overline{X}_1\overline{C}_{n+4}$$
$$\overline{C}_{n+12} = \overline{Y}_2+\overline{X}_2\overline{C}_{n+8}$$

Applying the carry lookahead principle to the above set of equations results in:

$$\overline{C}_{n+4} = \overline{Y}_0+\overline{X}_0\overline{C}_n$$
$$\overline{C}_{n+8} = \overline{Y}_1+\overline{X}_1\overline{Y}_0+\overline{X}_1\overline{X}_0\overline{C}_n$$
$$\overline{C}_{n+12} = \overline{Y}_2+\overline{X}_2\overline{Y}_1+\overline{X}_2\overline{X}_1\overline{Y}_0+\overline{X}_2\overline{X}_1\overline{X}_0\overline{C}_n$$

These agree with the equations which define the SN74182.

4.5 BINARY MULTIPLICATION

4.5.1 Multiplier types

Multiplication units which handle binary numbers in a fixed-point format are of four basic types. These are defined by the form, viz., serial or parallel, in which the multiplicand and multiplier are presented to the multiplication unit. The four basic types of multipliers are listed in Table 4.5.1.

Table 4.5.1 Types of multipliers

MULTIPLIER TYPE	MULTIPLICAND	MULTIPLIER
(i) parallel–parallel (ii) simultaneous (iii) iterative array (iv) combinational circuit	parallel	parallel
add-shift	parallel	serial
serial-multiplicand/ parallel-multiplier	serial	parallel
serial–serial	serial	serial

The multiplier which is presented with both the multiplicand and multiplier in parallel is a combinational circuit, and will produce at its outputs the product of the two input numbers after all circuits have settled to their steady-state values. This type of multiplier has been called a 'parallel–parallel multiplier' or a 'simultaneous multiplier'. It may be implemented as a two-dimensional 'iterative array' of identical 'cells' or as a combinational circuit constructed of commercially available integrated circuits. This type of multiplier is extremely fast, but requires large amounts of hardware.

The multiplier which treats the multiplicand in parallel and the multiplier serially has been described as an 'add-shift multiplier'. The use of the word 'add' in this term refers to the parallel addition of the multiplicand to the growing partial product, and the word 'shift' refers to steps in the procedure which cause both the growing partial product and the multiplier to be shifted by one bit position. It is this type of multiplier which is implemented in many (fixed-point) arithmetic units of digital computers.

The 'serial-multiplicand/parallel-multiplier' multiplier has quite a different structure to that required by the 'add-shift' procedure. In the former, multiples of the serial multiplicand are produced by one-bit-delay circuits; these are gated by the multiplier bits and then summed using serial adders. The application of this type of multiplier has been much less than that of the 'add-shift' design. However, it is quite possible that this type of multiplier could represent the most economical design in certain applications, especially those which require the multiplication of a serial number of a large number of bits (i.e. a high precision multiplicand) by another number of a much smaller number of bits (i.e. a low precision multiplier).

The 'serial–serial multiplier' requires a more complex timing unit than that required by other types of multipliers. However, only a single full adder is required, and in general much less hardware is required than for other types. It was this type of multiplier which was used in very early 'serial computers'. It is possible that, in certain applications which require a number of multiplications to be carried out in a specified time, the serial–serial multiplier would be the type of multiplier chosen, especially if it could be arranged for several multiplications to proceed simultaneously.

The multiplication of one multiplicand bit by one multiplier bit results in one sub-product bit which is then used (together with all other sub-product bits) to form the final product. The sub-product bit is produced according to the following 'multiplication table' (Table 4.5.2).

Table 4.5.2 Binary multiplication table

MULTIPLICAND BIT	MULTIPLIER BIT	SUB-PRODUCT BIT
0	0	0
0	1	0
1	0	0
1	1	1

It will be observed from the binary multiplication table of Table 4.5.2 that a sub-product bit may be produced from a multiplicand bit and a multiplier bit by an AND-gate. The addition of this bit to other sub-product bits requires the use of a full adder. For a multiplicand with n magnitude bits and a multiplier with n magnitude bits there are n^2 sub-product bits. For a parallel–parallel multiplier this will require n^2 full adders and n^2 AND-gates (or their equivalent). There are various methods of structuring the full adders and AND-gates of parallel–parallel multipliers. Some of these will be described in this chapter.

The amount of hardware required for the parallel–parallel multiplier may be reduced if either or both the multiplicand and the multiplier is treated serially. This reduction is achieved at the expense of speed of operation as more clock pulses are required for serial operation. The trade-off between hardware and speed is summarised by the following table (Table 4.5.3).

Table 4.5.3 Clock pulses, full adders and AND-gates required by the four basic types of multipliers

MULTIPLICAND	MULTIPLIER	CLOCK PULSES	FULL ADDERS	AND-GATES
parallel	parallel	0	n^2	n^2
parallel	serial	n	n	n
serial	parallel	$2n$	n	n
serial	serial	$n(n+1)$ or $2n^2$	1	1

The entries of Table 4.5.3 under the column heading 'clock pulses' deserve some comment. The entry 0 for the parallel–parallel multiplier is a consequence of the fact that this type of multiplier is a combinational circuit. However, one clock pulse may be required to clock the output of this combinational circuit into buffer flip-flops. The entry n for the 'add-shift multiplier' indicates that only a 'single length addition' is required while the entry $2n$ for the serial-multiplicand/parallel-multiplier indicates that a 'double length addition' is specified. The two entries for the serial–serial multiplier correspond to two different methods of implementation: the $n(n+1)$ entry indicates a single-length serial addition followed by a one bit shift, and the $2n^2$ entry indicates a double-length serial addition. As other hardware for timing and control is required, and various approaches to implementation using commercially available integrated circuits are possible, Table 4.5.3 should be used only as a guide to the relative amounts of hardware in the various types of multipliers. The following sections will provide more details of the design of the four basic types of multipliers.

4.5.2 Simultaneous multipliers

A simultaneous multiplier is a combinational circuit which has inputs which represent both the multiplicand and multiplier in parallel and which produces outputs which represent the 'double-length' product of the input numbers. This type of multiplier may be implemented as an *'iterative array'*. This is a two-dimensional array of a combinational circuit called a *basic cell* which has been so designed that there are only interconnections between each cell and neighbouring cells in the array. (This restriction on interconnections produces an array which lends itself to easy manufacture as a large-scale integrated circuit.) An iterative array designed for multiplication may be called a *'multiplier array'*.

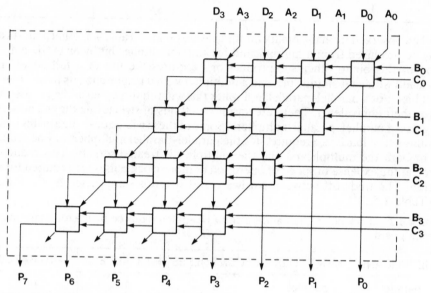

Fig. 4.5.1   Diagram of a 4 × 4 multiplier array

A diagram of a 4 × 4 multiplier array is shown in Fig. 4.5.1 and the basic cell used in this array is shown in Fig. 4.5.2. Note that the basic cell contains a single full adder and a single AND-gate. (The use of these two circuits was discussed briefly in the last section.) The basic cell has four inputs A, B, C, D and four outputs A', B', C', D', related by the equations:

$$A' = A$$
$$B' = B$$
$$C' = ABC + CD + ABD$$
$$D' = (D \oplus AB) \oplus C$$

Note that C' and D' are the carry output and the sum output (respectively) of the full adder which has inputs D, AB and C.

The multiplier array of Fig. 4.5.1 has the following inputs: (i) A_3, A_2, A_1, A_0 which represent the multiplicand A, (ii) B_3, B_2, B_1, B_0 which represent the multiplier B, (iii) C_3, C_2, C_1, C_0 which represent a number C and (iv) D_3, D_2, D_1, D_0 which represent a number D. The outputs of the multiplier array are P_7, P_6, --- P_0 which represent the 'product' P. This output number P is equal to 'A times B plus C plus D'. Of course, if only the product of the number A and the number B is required, then all the inputs representing the numbers C and D are set to zero.

It may be verified from Fig. 4.5.1 and Fig. 4.5.2 that all the 'sub-product bits' produced by the AND-gates of the cells in the multiplier array have been assigned the appropriate binary weightings, and the interconnections within the array are such that these 'sub-

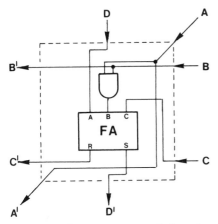

Fig. 4.5.2 Circuit of basic cell for multiplier array

product bits' are summed (by the full adders) with the correct recognition of these weightings. This is achieved firstly by the 'diagonal interconnections' of cells in Fig. 4.5.1 which effectively produce the (binary) multiples of the multiplicand which are added to the 'accumulated partial product' whenever the corresponding multiplier bit is equal to 'one', and secondly by using the sum and carry outputs of the full adders in 'top-to-bottom interconnections' and 'right-to-left interconnections' within the array (respectively). The right-most cell in the array produces the least-significant product bit (i.e. the bit with the lowest weighting), and the weighting of signals increases as they pass from right to left through 'columns of cells' in the array.

It is to be verified that the 'accumulated partial products' are represented by the outputs of cells in 'rows' of the array. In particular, these accumulated partial products are represented by the C' output of the most significant (i.e. left-most) cell in a row and the D' output of all cells in the row together with any product bits generated by cells in 'higher' rows in the array.

An examination of the 4×4 array shown in Fig. 4.5.1 will show that the '*propagation delay*' from input signals to output signals is $10T$ where T is the delay through a single cell. For an $n \times n$ multiplier array, the propagation delay will be $(3n-2)T$.

A reduction in the propagation delay of a multiplier array may be obtained by using a 'carry-save' technique. This technique will be described using the example of the 4×4 carry-save multiplier array shown in Fig. 4.5.3. This array uses the basic cell shown in Fig. 4.5.2, i.e. the same cell as that used in the array of Fig. 4.5.1. However, in the carry-save array, the carry output of a cell is connected to the carry input of a cell in the *next lower row* of the array (whereas in the array of Fig. 4.5.1 the carry output of a cell is connected to the carry input of a cell in the *same row* of the array). In the carry-save array the carry outputs of cells in a row of the array are not used to produce signals (at outputs of cells in the row) which represent the accumulated partial products, but they are '*saved*' and taken into account by cells in the next lower row of the array. With such an arrangement the outputs of cells in a row represent two numbers, the sum of which represents the accumulated partial product. These two numbers are (i) the number represented by the C' outputs of cells in a row and (ii) the number represented by the D' outputs of cells in a row.

As the last row in the array produces two numbers whose sum represents the more significant half of the product, these two numbers must be summed using a parallel adder before all the product bits can be formed. This parallel adder is represented by the full adders (FA) and half adders (HA) shown in Fig. 4.5.3. However, in the interests of high speed, a fast carry-lookahead adder could be used for this purpose.

Even if the ripple-carry parallel adder shown in Fig. 4.5.3 is used, and if it is assumed that the delay through a full adder or a half adder is approximately the same as the delay

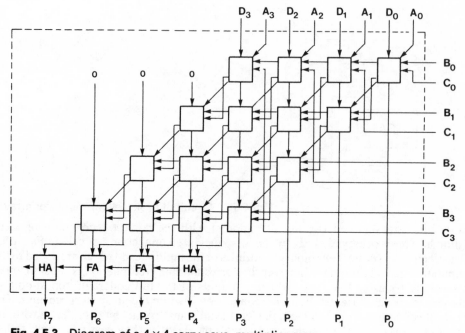

Fig. 4.5.3 Diagram of a 4 × 4 carry-save, multiplier array

(T) of the basic cell it may be shown that the propagation delay of an $n \times n$ carry-save multiplier array is equal to $2nT$. (This may be verified from Fig. 4.5.3.) This is a significant improvement over the $(3n-2)T$ delay of the array of Fig. 4.5.1.

Integrated circuits are now available for producing the 8-bit product of two 4-bit numbers. These integrated circuits may be used to construct simultaneous multipliers for multiplicands and multipliers of any specified 'bit length'. One obvious approach would be to divide the bits of both the multiplicand and the multiplier into groups of four bits, and to use a matrix of these integrated circuits. The 8-bit 'sub-products' produced by these integrated circuits would have to be given appropriate weightings, and the sub-products of the same weighting then summed to produce the final product. The weightings for a 16 × 16 multiplier are indicated by the diagram in Fig. 4.5.4 in which the sub-product of the lowest weighting is shown on the right, and the sub-product of the highest weighting is shown on the left. There are many methods of summing the sub-products. A description of these methods is beyond the scope of this book.

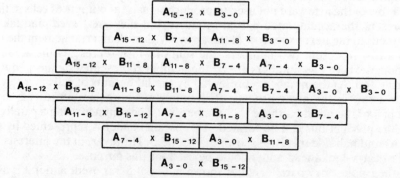

Fig. 4.5.4 Sub-products of a 16 × 16 multiplier using 4 × 4 multipliers

4.5.3 Add-shift multiplier

A circuit of an add-shift multiplication unit for 4-bit two's complement integers is shown in Fig. 4.5.5, and timing waveforms required by this unit are shown in Fig. 4.5.6. The circuit of Fig. 4.5.5 contains a register M (with outputs M_3, M_2, M_1 and M_0) which holds the multiplicand. This register remains unchanged throughout the multiplication procedure. The multiplier is initially held in a register Q (with outputs Q_3, Q_2, Q_1 and Q_0). A working register A (an accumulator with outputs A_3, A_2, A_1 and A_0) is initially cleared. The multiplication procedure to be described produces a double-length product in the A and Q registers, with the more significant half of the product in A and the less significant half in Q.

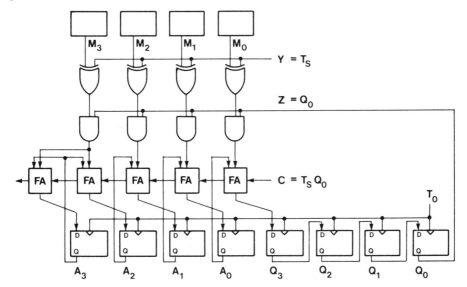

Fig. 4.5.5 Circuit of an 'add-shift multiplication' circuit for two's complement integers

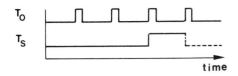

Fig. 4.5.6 Timing waveforms for an 'add-shift multiplication' unit for four-bit, two's complement numbers

The circuit of Fig. 4.5.5 contains a 5-bit parallel adder which is used to add the contents of register M through exclusive-OR gates and AND-gates. This 'gating' is such that the number formed is either (i) the multiplicand, (ii) the one's complement of the multiplicand or (iii) zero. The carry input to the least-significant adder stage is so arranged that one's complements of the multiplicand (whenever selected) are converted to two's complements. With these circuit connections, the parallel adder can produce at its outputs either (i) the contents of register A plus the contents of register M, (ii) the contents of register A minus the contents of register M, or (iii) the contents of register A unmodified.

It is to be noted that the two most-significant full adders in Fig. 4.5.5 have two common inputs. The additional adder is used for 'sign extension', and hence conditions of arithmetic overflow are avoided.

The five (sum) outputs of the parallel adder of Fig. 4.5.5 are connected to the inputs of the flip-flops A_3, A_2, A_1, A_0 and Q_3; and the inputs of flip-flops Q_2, Q_1 and Q_0 are such that the Q register may operate as a right shift-register. All flip-flops are clocked by the timing waveform T_0. This arrangement allows each of the operations 'add-shift', 'subtract-shift' or 'pass-shift' to be executed with a single clock pulse. The first two of these operations causes (i) the contents of register M to be added to or subtracted from the contents of register A, and then (ii) the result shifted right by one bit position and then stored in the combined A and Q registers. The operation pass-shift simply causes the contents of the combined A and Q registers to be shifted right by one bit position.

The add-shift multiplication procedure senses each bit of the multiplier in turn starting from the least-significant bit and progressing to the sign bit. With the circuit arrangement of Fig. 4.5.5, the multiplier bit to be used in each bit period is contained in the Q_0 flip-flop. Hence the procedure simply requires that for each magnitude bit of the multiplier, an add-shift operation is to be executed whenever $Q_0 = 1$, and a pass-shift operation is to be executed whenever $Q_0 = 0$. As the sign bit of a two's complement fraction has a weighting of -1, a subtract-shift operation is to be executed whenever this bit is equal to 1. A timing waveform T_s shown in Fig. 4.5.6 is used to differentiate between magnitude and sign bits. Hence the subtract-shift operation is defined by the condition $Q_0 T_s = 1$. The reader is now

Table 4.5.4   Examples of add-shift multiplication of two's complement integers

M_3	M_2	M_1	M_0
0	1	1	1

A_3	A_2	A_1	A_0	Q_3	Q_2	Q_1	Q_0
0	0	0	0	0	1	1	1
0	0	1	1	1	0	1	1
0	1	0	1	0	1	0	1
0	1	1	0	0	0	1	0
0	0	1	1	0	0	0	1

(a) Positive multiplicand, positive multiplier

M_3	M_2	M_1	M_0
1	0	0	1

A_3	A_2	A_1	A_0	Q_3	Q_2	Q_1	Q_0
0	0	0	0	0	1	1	1
1	1	0	0	1	0	1	1
1	0	1	0	1	1	0	1
1	0	0	1	1	1	1	0
1	1	0	0	1	1	1	1

(b) Negative multiplicand, positive multiplier

M_3	M_2	M_1	M_0
0	1	1	1

A_3	A_2	A_1	A_0	Q_3	Q_2	Q_1	Q_0
0	0	0	0	1	0	0	1
0	0	1	1	1	1	0	0
0	0	0	1	1	1	1	0
0	0	0	0	1	1	1	1
1	1	0	0	1	1	1	1

(a) Positive multiplicand, negative multiplier

M_3	M_2	M_1	M_0
1	0	0	1

A_3	A_2	A_1	A_0	Q_3	Q_2	Q_1	Q_0
0	0	0	0	1	0	0	1
1	1	0	0	1	1	0	0
1	1	1	0	0	1	1	0
1	1	1	1	0	0	1	1
0	0	1	1	0	0	0	1

(b) Negative multiplicand, negative multiplier

asked to verify that the circuit of Fig. 4.5.5 does in fact implement the add-shift multiplication procedure as described above.

Examples of add-shift multiplication of two's complement integers are given in Table 4.5.4. An example of each of the possible combinations of signs for the multiplicand and multiplier is given. In each example given in Table 4.5.4 the value of the multiplicand is shown under the headings M_3, M_2, M_1 and M_0; and the value of the multiplier is shown in the first row under the headings Q_3, Q_2, Q_1 and Q_0. The zeros in the first row under the headings A_3, A_2, A_1 and A_0 show that the accumulator (A register) is initially cleared. The following four rows under the 'A' and 'Q' headings give the contents of the A and Q register following each of the four clock pulses of the timing waveform T_0 (of Fig. 4.5.6).

A further extension of the circuit of Fig. 4.5.5 is required to handle two's complement fractions. From an earlier description of formats of double-length binary fractions (given in Section 4.2) the reader will recall that one convenient format requires that (i) word-1 (or the first register) should hold the more significant half of the number (including the sign bit) with the binary point assumed between the first and second (most-significant) bits of the word, and (ii) word-2 (or the second register) should hold the less significant half of the number with the first bit being the waste bit. In the case of a 4 × 4 multiplication unit both the multiplicand and multiplier are represented by a sign bit and three magnitude bits, and the resultant product is represented by a sign bit and six magnitude bits. In the circuit of Fig. 4.5.7, the resultant product is held in the flip-flops A_3, A_2, A_1, A_0, Q_2, Q_1 and Q_0, with flip-flop Q_3 representing the waste bit set to zero.

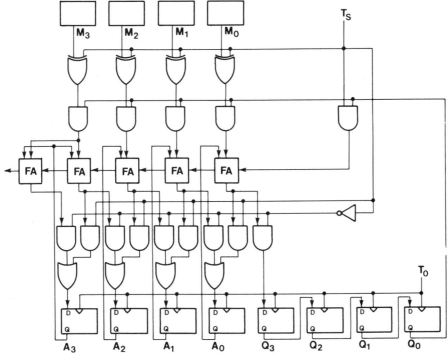

Fig. 4.5.7 Circuit of an 'add-shift multiplication' unit for two's complement fractions

The reader will observe that the only additional gates in the circuit of Fig. 4.5.7 which do not appear in the circuit of Fig. 4.5.5 are those which form the data selector. This logical unit is used to position correctly the more significant half of the product. It is to be noted that the 'select signal' of this data selector is T_s, and hence the circuit of Fig. 4.5.7 will produce exactly the same intermediate results as the circuit of Fig. 4.5.5 for the first three clock pulses of T_0. However, for the fourth and last clock pulse the output of the parallel adder without any shifting of bits is set directly into the A register. One gate of the data selector also causes this clock pulse to set zero into Q_3. It is now suggested that the reader should modify the last line in the tables of Table 4.5.4, to provide examples of add-shift multiplication of two's complement fractions as defined by the circuit of Fig. 4.5.7.

4.5.4 Multiplication unit with serial multiplicand and serial multiplier

A circuit of a 'serial–serial' multiplication unit is given in Fig. 4.5.8 and timing signals required by this circuit are shown in Fig. 4.5.9. The circuit of Fig. 4.5.8 is a development of the circuit of Fig. 4.5.5 (i.e. an add-shift multiplication unit for two's complement integers). Note that the parallel adder of Fig. 4.5.5 has been replaced by a serial adder in Fig. 4.5.8. The three registers (M, A and Q) take the form of shift registers in Fig. 4.5.8, but have the same functions as those in Fig. 4.5.5, viz. the M-register is used to hold the multiplicand, the Q-register initially holds the multiplier and the combined A–Q registers finally hold the double-length product.

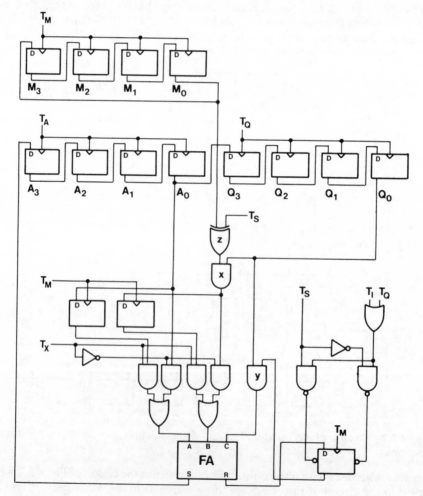

Fig. 4.5.8 Circuit of a 'serial–serial' multiplication unit

An examination of the timing waveforms of Fig. 4.5.9 will show that each of the basic operations (i.e. add-shift, subtract-shift and pass-shift) is executed using five clock pulses. The first four clock pulses are applied to the M-register, the fifth is applied to the Q-register, and all five are applied to the A-register. It will be observed that the flip-flop interconnections of the Q-register in Fig. 4.5.8 are the same as those in Fig. 4.5.5. Indeed the function of the T_Q clock of Fig. 4.5.9 is the same as that of the T_0 clock of Fig. 4.5.6, i.e. to shift the register to the right so that the multiplier bits are presented in turn at the output of the Q_0 flip-flop and so that one product bit is shifted into Q_3.

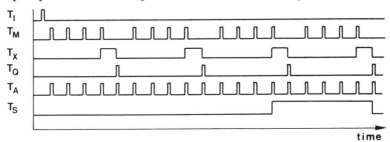

Fig. 4.5.9   Timing waveforms for 'serial–serial' multiplication unit

The full adder of Fig. 4.5.8 has serial inputs with a word-length of five bits, and has the function of the five full adders of Fig. 4.5.5. The first input of the full adder takes the form of the four-bit serial output (A_0) of the A-register with sign bit extension; the second input is the four-bit serial output (M_0) of the M-register (gated by T_s and Q_0) with sign bit extension, and the third input is the output of the carry-borrow flip-flop (gated by Q_0).

The serial sign bit extension of each of the serial outputs of the A and M (shift) registers is achieved by a D-type flip-flop which effectively delays the serial signal by one bit period. A 'data or sign extension select signal' T_X (see Fig. 4.5.9) is then used to select *either* the shift-register output (for the first four bit periods) *or* the shift-register output delayed by one bit period (for the fifth bit period).

The multiplier bit Q_0 gates the serial multiplicand signal M_0 via the AND-gate labelled x in Fig. 4.5.8. The multiplier bit Q_0 is also used to gate the carry/borrow input to the full adder via the AND-gate labelled y. Hence, when $Q_0 = 0$, the contents of the A-register pass unchanged through the serial adder.

Whenever $Q_0 = 1$ when $T_s = 0$ (see the timing waveforms of Fig. 4.5.9 for the significance of T_s), the contents of the M-register are added to the contents of the A-register. This is achieved by the gates labelled x, y and z, and the circuits concerned with the resetting and setting of the carry/borrow flip-flop. These circuits also cause the contents of the M-register to be subtracted from the contents of the A-register whenever $Q_0 = 1$ and $T_s = 1$ as required by the add-shift multiplication procedure for two's complement fractions.

Following a serial 4-bit addition or subtraction the contents of the combined A- and Q-registers are shifted right by one binary place at the times defined by the pulses of the T_Q clock (see Fig. 4.5.9). When this occurs the serial input into stage A_3 of the A-register is the resultant sum of the full adder when the sign extension bits are applied.

From the description provided above, and from the information contained in Fig. 4.5.8 and Fig. 4.5.9, the reader is advised to verify by example that the circuit of Fig. 4.5.8 can produce the product of two 4-bit two's complement integers.

4.5.5   Multiplication unit with serial multiplicand and parallel multiplier

A circuit diagram of a multiplication unit with serial multiplicand and parallel multiplier inputs is shown in Fig. 4.5.10. This diagram assumes (i) an 8-bit multiplicand signal consisting of four bits which define a 4-bit positive integer followed by four (more significant) zeros, (ii) a 4-bit multiplier register with outputs Q_3, Q_2, Q_1 and Q_0 which define a second 4-bit positive integer and (iii) a serial (product) output representing an 8-bit positive integer.

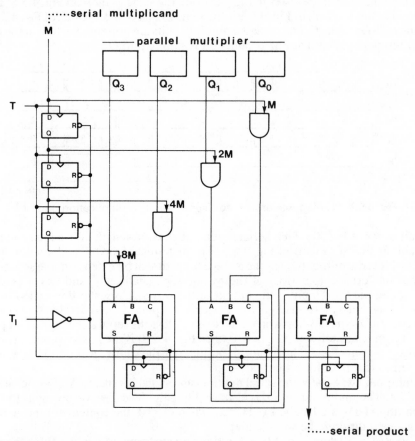

Fig. 4.5.10 Circuit diagram of a multiplication unit with serial multiplicand, parallel multiplier and serial product

The circuit of Fig. 4.5.10 utilises the fact that a D-type flip-flop may be used to delay a serial signal by one bit period and hence to produce at its output a signal representing two times the number represented by the input signal. Hence, a chain of D-type flip-flops can produce 'binary multiples' of the input signal. In Fig. 4.5.10 three D-type flip-flops are used to produce signals representing 2M, 4M and 8M where M is the multiplicand. The signals M, 2M, 4M and 8M are gated by the multiplier bits of corresponding weighting, i.e. by the signals Q_0, Q_1, Q_2 and Q_3. The outputs of the four AND-gates of Fig. 4.5.10 then represent the four partial products. These may be summed using three serial adders as shown. The carry flip-flops of these adders are initially reset by the 'initialisation' clock pulse T_I. This clock is also used to reset all the D-type flip-flops. The main clock T would consist of eight pulses. This clock, which must be in synchronism with the serial input, is used to control the carry flip-flops of the full adders. The output of the final serial adder in the tree-structured circuit arrangement represents the serial product.

4.6 BINARY DIVISION

4.6.1 Restoring and non-restoring binary division algorithms

A block diagram of an arithmetic unit suitable for the implementation of binary division is shown in Fig. 4.6.1. This arithmetic unit, which is similar to those used in early parallel computers, contains three registers (M, A and Q) and a parallel adder/subtracter. The M-register holds the divisor and remains unchanged throughout the division procedure. A double-length register formed by the A and Q registers initially holds the double length dividend. The outputs of the A-register and the M-register are connected to the inputs of the parallel adder/subtracter, the outputs of which are connected to the inputs of the A-register. The signs of the divisor and the dividend initially determine the add/subtract control. The signs of the divisor and the 'remainder' formed at the outputs of the adder/ subtracter then determine the quotient digit which is entered into the serial input of the Q (shift) register. This is carried out at the time when the entire contents of the A- and Q-registers are shifted one bit position to the left. In the following steps of the procedure, the signs of the divisor and the remainder determine both the add/subtract control and the quotient digit. The quotient digits are therefore formed one digit at a time starting from the most-significant (sign) digit and progressing to the least-significant magnitude digit.

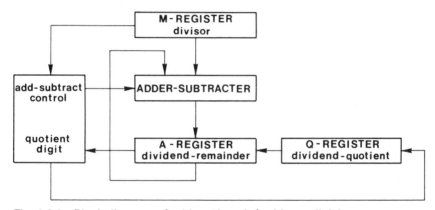

Fig. 4.6.1 Block diagram of arithmetic unit for binary division

Two binary division algorithms may be applied using the circuit arrangement of Fig. 4.6.1. These are the 'restoring binary division algorithm' and the 'non-restoring binary division algorithm'. Both algorithms (as described in this section) assume two's complement fractions for input and output numbers. Hence, if the quotient is to be correctly represented by a binary fraction which has an absolute value less than unity, then the absolute value of the divisor must be greater than the absolute value of the dividend. If this is not the case, then an 'overflow condition' occurs. As minus one can be represented in a two's complement number system for binary fractions, and plus one cannot be represented, the special cases when the divisor and dividend have the same absolute value but different signs should produce the correct results when the algorithm is applied; however, when divisor and dividend have the same absolute value and same sign, an 'overflow condition' occurs.

The restoring binary division algorithm is analogous to the 'long division' procedure taught at school. A simple example of the application of this algorithm is shown in Fig. 4.6.2. In this figure, the 7-bit dividend is 0.100 xyz. The digits of the less significant half are represented by the symbols x, y and z so that they may be identified in steps of the procedure, but will be assumed to be zero in any arithmetic operations which involve them. The 4-bit divisor is represented by S.110, where the symbol S has been used for the divisor so that it may be identified (with other divisor bits) in steps of the procedure. The value of S will be assumed to be zero in any arithmetic operation which involves it. Hence, the simple example given in Fig. 4.6.2 deals with a positive divisor (of magnitude three quarters) and a positive dividend (of magnitude one half).

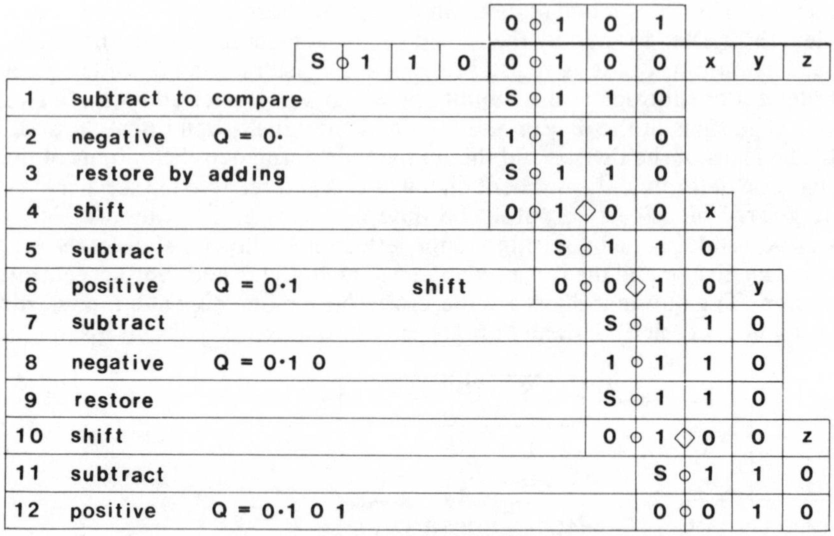

						0 ○ 1	0	1			
		S ○ 1	1	0	0 ○ 1	0	0	x	y	z	
1	subtract to compare		S ○ 1	1	0						
2	negative	Q = 0·	1 ○ 1	1	0						
3	restore by adding		S ○ 1	1	0						
4	shift		0 ○ 1 ◇ 0	0	x						
5	subtract			S ○ 1	1	0					
6	positive	Q = 0·1 shift		0 ○ 0 ◇ 1	0	y					
7	subtract				S ○ 1	1	0				
8	negative	Q = 0·1 0			1 ○ 1	1	0				
9	restore				S ○ 1	1	0				
10	shift				0 ○ 1 ◇ 0	0	z				
11	subtract					S ○ 1	1	0			
12	positive	Q = 0·1 0 1				0 ○ 0	1	0			

Fig. 4.6.2   Example of restoring, binary division

In line 1 of Fig. 4.6.2 the binary points of divisor and dividend are aligned and a subtraction is executed. This is done to compare the magnitude of divisor and dividend. Line 2 shows that the result is negative, and hence indicates that the division process may proceed as the quotient can be represented correctly. The first quotient digit (the sign digit) is formed at this point, and hence the quotient may be written in the form 0.---.

If the division process is implemented using the circuit arrangement represented by Fig. 4.6.1, and if it is assumed that the result of the 'first subtraction' is actually clocked into the A-register, then at the stage of the division process represented by line 2 of Fig. 4.6.2, the original dividend bits (0.100) held in the A-register would be overwritten by the result (1.110). To '*restore*' the original dividend bits, the divisor must be added to the result held in the A-register (as indicated by line 3 of Fig. 4.6.2), and the new result clocked into the A-register (as indicated by line 4).

The operation of 'bringing down the next dividend digit' used in 'long division' is shown in line 4 of Fig. 4.6.2 by the introduction of the digit x. Using the circuit arrangement of Fig. 4.6.1, this operation is achieved by a one bit shift to the left of the A- and Q-registers. A shift of the binary point from the position marked by the circle in line 4 of Fig. 4.6.2 to the position marked by the diamond results. This shift aligns binary points of shifted dividend and divisor as shown in line 5, at which stage a subtraction is executed producing the result shown in line 6. The validity of this last subtraction must be verified as the shift of the binary point in line 4 produces an operand (1.00x) which is negative using the normal interpretation of two's complement binary fractions. What appears to be an overflow condition does in fact produce the correct result in line 6. This results from the magnitude relationship which exists, viz. that the divisor is greater (in absolute magnitude) than the dividend, and hence two times the dividend minus the divisor (the operation represented by step 4, 5 and 6 of Fig. 4.6.2) will always be less than unity (in absolute magnitude). Further analysis and verification will be left to the reader.

The positive result produced in line 6 of Fig. 4.6.2 specifies a quotient digit of one, and hence at this stage the quotient takes the form 0.1––. Line 6 also shows a shift of the result followed by a further subtraction in line 7. The procedure described above is repeated until all required quotient digits have been formed.

In summary the restoring binary division algorithm when applied to positive two's complement fractions is seen to consist of a sequence of subtractions and additions of the 'dividend/remainder' and the divisor. Whenever the remainder (produced by a subtraction) is negative a quotient digit of zero is recorded, and an addition is performed to 'restore' the dividend/remainder which is then shifted one place to the left. Whenever the remainder is positive, a quotient digit of one is recorded and the newly formed remainder is shifted one place to the left.

When the dividend and divisor can take any combinations of signs, modifications to the process described above are required. These modifications are concerned with the conditions required for the additions, subtractions and shifts, and the method of forming quotient digits. These modifications will not be described. However, the required techniques would be similar to those used for the superior 'non-restoring binary division algorithm' which will now be described.

An example of the application of the non-restoring binary division algorithm to positive two's complement fractions is shown in Fig. 4.6.3. The example deals with the same dividend (i.e. 0.100 xyz) and the same divisor (i.e. S.110) as those used in Fig. 4.6.2. The significance of the symbols x, y, z, S and the layout of the diagram are also the same as those of Fig. 4.6.2.

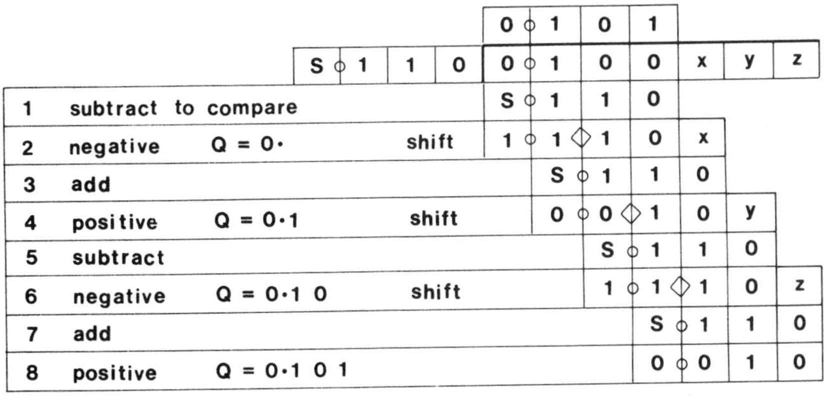

#	operation	Q	shift									
							0 φ 1	0	1			
				S φ 1	1	0	0 φ 1	0	0	x	y	z
1	subtract to compare						S φ 1	1	0			
2	negative	Q = 0·	shift				1 φ 1 ◇ 1	0	x			
3	add						S φ 1	1	0			
4	positive	Q = 0·1	shift				0 φ 0 ◇ 1	0	y			
5	subtract						S φ 1	1	0			
6	negative	Q = 0·1 0	shift				1 φ 1 ◇ 1	0	z			
7	add						S φ 1	1	0			
8	positive	Q = 0·1 0 1					0 φ 0	1	0			

Fig. 4.6.3 Example of non-restoring, binary division

Line 1 of Fig. 4.6.3 shows that the binary points of the divisor and dividend are aligned (as before) and a subtraction is performed. The negative result shown in line 2 indicates that the divisor is greater (in magnitude) than the dividend, and hence the process can continue. The first quotient digit is formed, and the result (i.e. remainder) is shifted by one binary place 'bringing down' the next digit x. This is followed by an addition in line 3 which produces the remainder in line 4. Note that this line is identical to line 6 of Fig. 4.6.2.

This relationship may be proved using the reasoning which follows. If the dividend and divisor are represented by the symbols d and D respectively, the remainder defined by line 2 of both Fig. 4.6.2 and Fig. 4.6.3 may be represented by $d-D$. From this intermediate result (and D), it is required to form $2d-D$. The non-restoring division algorithm achieves this by shifting d–D, i.e. by forming $2(d$–$D)$ and then by adding this doubled remainder to D. Hence the non-restoring division algorithm utilises the simple algebraic identity:

$$2(d$–$D)+D = 2d$–$D$$

The method used by the restoring division algorithm is to be compared. This produces $2d$–D from d–D and D by (i) adding D to d–D (i.e. restoring d), (ii) shifting d to produce $2d$, and (iii) subtracting D from $2d$. This requires one extra addition/subtraction operation to those required for the non-restoring algorithm, and hence is less efficient.

From an inspection of Fig. 4.6.3 it may be seen that the non-restoring division process consists of a sequence of subtract-shift or add-shift operations. For the case of the division process with a positive dividend and positive divisor (such as the example given in Fig. 4.6.3), the process begins with a subtraction. If the remainder produced by an arithmetic operation is negative, a zero quotient digit is recorded, and the next arithmetic operation carried out is addition. Again if the remainder produced by an arithmetic operation is positive, a quotient digit of one is recorded, and the next arithmetic operation carried out is subtraction. Subtract-shift or add-shift operations are repeated until all required quotient digits have been formed.

When dividend and divisor can take either sign, the non-restoring division process requires that the add/subtract control and the quotient digit should be defined as follows:

1. a subtraction is executed if the signs of the divisor and dividend/remainder are the same, and an addition is executed if these signs are different;
2. the quotient digit is equal to one if the signs of the divisor and remainder are the same, and the quotient digit is equal to zero if these signs are different.

Two implementations of the non-restoring binary division process (one combinational and the other sequential) are given in following sections. Worked examples of the sequential implementation will also be given.

4.6.2   Iterative array for non-restoring binary division

A circuit of an iterative array for non-restoring binary division of two's complement fractions is shown in Fig. 4.6.4, and the circuit of the basic cell used in this array is shown in Fig. 4.6.5.

The basic cell of Fig. 4.6.5 is seen to consist of a full adder and an exclusive-OR gate. The cell has inputs M, A, B, C and outputs M′, A′, B′, C′ related by the equations:

$$M' = M$$
$$A' = (A \oplus C) \oplus (M \oplus B)$$
$$B' = B$$
$$C' = AC + (A+C)\,(M \oplus B)$$

Alternatively the A′ and C′ outputs may be considered simply as the sum and carry outputs of the full adder with inputs A, C and $M \oplus B$. The B input may also be considered as a control signal which determines whether the M signal or its complement is to be applied to the full adder.

The iterative array of Fig. 4.6.4 contains 4×4 basic cells and five exclusive-NOR circuits. The 4-bit divisor is represented by the signals M_3, M_2, M_1 and M_0; and the 7-bit dividend is represented by the signals A_3, A_2, A_1, A_0, A_{-1}, A_{-2} and A_{-3}. The array produces a 4-bit quotient represented by the signals Q_3, Q_2, Q_1 and Q_0, and a 3-bit 'remainder' represented by the signals R_2, R_1 and R_0.

The elements of the array of Fig. 4.6.4 have been numbered, and certain signals have been identified with symbols to assist with the description which follows. The exclusive-NOR gate 1 produces the control signal B_1 which is equal to one or zero depending on whether the signs of the dividend and divisor are the same or different respectively. When

$B_1 = 0$, the divisor signals M_3, M_2, M_1 and M_0 pass unchanged to the full adders of cells 5, 4, 3 and 2. The divisor is therefore added to the dividend signals A_3, A_2, A_1 and A_0, forming the remainder E_3, E_2, E_1 and E_0. When $B_1 = 1$, the one's complement of the divisor passes to the full adders of cells 5, 4, 3 and 2. However, the B_1 signal which passes unchanged through 5, 4, 3 and 2 is also connected to the C input of cell 2. This signal introduces a carry input into the least-significant adder stage and hence changes the one's complement of the

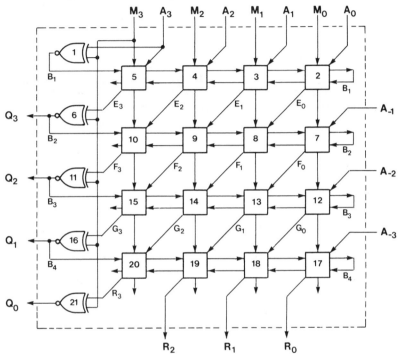

Fig. 4.6.4 Circuit of an iterative array for non-restoring, two's complement division of binary fractions

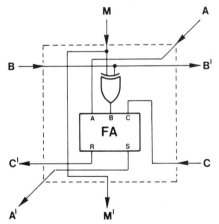

Fig. 4.6.5 Circuit of basic cell used in iterative array for non-restoring, two's complement division of binary fractions

divisor into two's complement. The sign of the remainder produced by cells 5, 4, 3 and 2 is the signal E_3. This is used in the exclusive-NOR gate 6 to produce the sign bit of the quotient Q_3 which is equal to the add/subtract control signal B_2. This control signal determines whether the divisor is added to or subtracted from the shifted remainder represented by the signals E_2, E_1, E_0 and A_{-1}. The remainder produced by this operation is represented by the signals F_3, F_2, F_1 and F_0 of which F_3 is the sign digit which then determines the next quotient digit Q_2 and the next add/subtract control signal B_3. This process continues until all quotient digits are produced.

The iterative array of Fig. 4.6.4 is, of course, a combinational circuit. However, it will be observed that the worst case propagation delay through the array is the sum of the propagation delays of *every* element in the array. The sequence in which the signals in the array settle is specified by the element numbers 1, 2, --- 21. Verification by the reader is advised.

4.6.3 Sequential circuit for non-restoring binary division

A diagram of a sequential circuit for non-restoring binary division is shown in Fig. 4.6.6, and the timing waveforms required by this circuit are shown in Fig. 4.6.7. This circuit assumes (i) a 4-bit divisor held throughout the division process in M_3, M_2, M_1 and M_0, and (ii) a 7-bit dividend initially set in A_3, A_2, A_1, A_0, Q_3, Q_2 and Q_1. The circuit produces a 4-bit quotient in Q_3, Q_2, Q_1 and Q_0 and a 3-bit 'remainder' in A_3, A_2 and A_1.

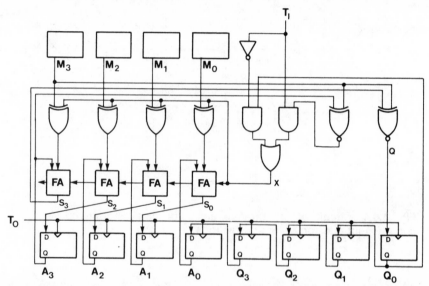

Fig. 4.6.6 Sequential circuit for non-restoring division of two's complement fractions

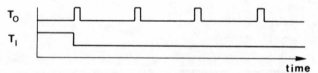

Fig. 4.6.7 Timing waveforms for sequential circuit for non-restoring division of two's complement fractions

For the first clock pulse the add/subtract control is the exclusive-NOR of the signs of the divisor and dividend (M_3 and A_3 respectively). For subsequent clock pulses the most recent quotient digit (Q_0) is used as the add/subtract control. The timing signal T_1 shown in Fig. 4.6.7 selects between these two functions.

In view of the detailed descriptions given in earlier sections, it will be left to the reader to confirm that the circuit of Fig. 4.6.6 does, in fact, carry out the non-restoring binary division process. Examples are, however, provided in Table 4.6.1. The first line in each of the four tables of Table 4.6.1 gives the initial states of the flip-flops A_3, A_2, A_1, A_0, Q_3, Q_2, Q_1, Q_0. The four subsequent lines in each table give the states of the flip-flops following each of the four pulses of the clock T_0, shown in Fig. 4.6.7.

Table 4.6.1 Examples of non-restoring binary division of two's complement fractions

M_3	M_2	M_1	M_0
0	1	1	0

A_3	A_2	A_1	A_0	Q_3	Q_2	Q_1	Q_0
0	1	0	0	x	y	z	∅
1	1	0	x	y	z	∅	0
0	1	0	y	z	∅	0	1
1	1	0	z	∅	0	1	0
0	1	0	∅	0	1	0	1

(a) Positive divisor, positive dividend

M_3	M_2	M_1	M_0
1	0	1	0

A_3	A_2	A_1	A_0	Q_3	Q_2	Q_1	Q_0
0	1	0	0	x	y	z	∅
1	1	0	x	y	z	∅	1
0	1	0	y	z	∅	1	0
1	1	0	z	∅	1	0	1
0	1	0	∅	1	0	1	0

(b) Negative divisor, positive dividend

M_3	M_2	M_1	M_0
0	1	1	0

A_3	A_2	A_1	A_0	Q_3	Q_2	Q_1	Q_0
1	1	0	0	x	y	z	∅
0	1	0	x	y	z	∅	1
1	1	0	y	z	∅	1	0
0	1	0	z	∅	1	0	1
1	1	0	∅	1	0	1	0

(c) Positive divisor, negative dividend

M_3	M_2	M_1	M_0
1	0	1	0

A_3	A_2	A_1	A_0	Q_3	Q_2	Q_1	Q_0
1	1	0	0	x	y	z	∅
0	1	0	x	y	z	∅	0
1	1	0	y	z	∅	0	1
0	1	0	z	∅	0	1	0
1	1	0	∅	0	1	0	1

(d) Negative divisor, negative dividend

4.7 QUESTIONS

The thirteen questions provided in Section 4.7.1 to 4.7.13 (inclusive) are relatively straightforward questions designed to strengthen the reader's understanding of the material covered in Chapter 4. The three questions provided in Section 4.7.14 to 4.7.16 (inclusive) may require some instructor assistance.

4.7.1 Overflow with fixed-point addition/subtraction

Table 4.7.1 shows input operands (in hexadecimal) of a 16-bit adder/subtracter. The table also has columns for the output result and an overflow flag. Complete the table.

Table 4.7.1

AUGEND/ MINUEND	ADDEND/ SUBTRAHEND	OPERATION	OUTPUT	OVERFLOW FLAG
0000	0001	subtraction	FFFF	0
4000	4001	addition		
4000	4001	subtraction		
8000	A001	addition		
8000	A001	subtraction		
0FFF	FFFF	addition		
0FFF	FFFF	subtraction		

4.7.2 Condition flag generator of parallel adder/subtracter

 (i) Verify the Boolean expressions given in Table 4.3.3 for the condition flags of the 4-bit adder/subtracter in Fig. 4.3.5.
 (ii) Consider a 16-bit adder/subtracter with operand inputs A_{15}--A_0 and B_{15}--B_0. Design circuits for the detection of the conditions listed in Table 4.3.3.

4.7.3 Overflow detector for serial adder/subtracter

Consider the serial adder/subtracter of Fig. 4.3.6(b) and the associated timing waveforms of Fig. 4.3.7. The clock T is shown containing eight pulses and hence would be suitable for 8-bit operands. Design a circuit to detect arithmetic overflow. Specify whatever timing waveforms may be required.

4.7.4 Carry lookahead adder using SN74181 and SN74182 integrated circuits

Using SN74181 and SN74182 integrated circuits design a 32-bit carry lookahead adder.

4.7.5 Overflow detection in adder/subtracter using SN74181 integrated circuit

A SN74181 integrated circuit is used as a 4-bit, two's complement adder/subtracter in which the inputs A_3 and B_3 are the sign bits of the two 4-bit operands. The integrated circuit is used to generate other functions of the operands as well as addition and subtraction. Design a circuit which will detect the condition of arithmetic overflow in an addition or subtraction operation.

4.7.6 Adder/subtracter with scaled output

The operand inputs A_3--A_0, B_3--B_0 of a circuit containing a SN74181 integrated circuit represent two 4-bit two's complement numbers A and B. The circuit produces a truncated 4-bit result representing either $\frac{1}{2}(A+B)$ or $\frac{1}{2}(A-B)$ corresponding to the values 0 or 1 (respectively) of a control signal D. Design the circuit.

4.7.7 Add-shift multiplication of two's complement fractions

Consider Fig. 4.5.7—a circuit of an add-shift multiplication unit for two's complement fractions. The associated timing waveforms are defined by Fig. 4.5.6. Consider values of M_3--M_0 and initial states of the flip-flops A_3--A_0, Q_3--Q_0 defined by Tables 4.7.2(a), (b), (c) and (d). In each of these tables there are four blank rows, each of which is to be used to define the states of A_3--A_0, Q_3--Q_0 following each of the pulses (in time sequence) of the clock T_0. Complete the tables.

4.7.8 Carry-save multiplier array

Consider Fig. 4.5.3—a diagram of a 4 × 4 carry-save multiplier array. This array utilises the basic cell shown in Fig. 4.5.2. For the case when $A_3A_2A_1A_0 = 1111$, $B_3B_2B_1B_0 = 1111$,

Table 4.7.2

(a)

M₃	M₂	M₁	M₀
0	1	1	0

A₃	A₂	A₁	A₀	Q₃	Q₂	Q₁	Q₀
0	1	0	1	0	1	1	1

(b)

M₃	M₂	M₁	M₀
1	0	1	0

A₃	A₂	A₁	A₀	Q₃	Q₂	Q₁	Q₀
0	1	0	1	0	1	1	1

(c)

M₃	M₂	M₁	M₀
0	1	1	0

A₃	A₂	A₁	A₀	Q₃	Q₂	Q₁	Q₀
0	1	0	1	1	0	0	1

(d)

M₃	M₂	M₁	M₀
1	0	1	0

A₃	A₂	A₁	A₀	Q₃	Q₂	Q₁	Q₀
0	1	0	1	1	0	0	1

$C_3C_2C_1C_0 = 1111$ and $D_3D_2D_1D_0 = 1111$, mark on a diagram of the array all the intermediate signals (such as the C' and D' outputs of every cell) and the array's outputs P_7--P_0. Verify that the outputs have been produced correctly from the known inputs.

4.7.9 Non-restoring binary division

The four tables of Table 4.6.1 provide examples of non-restoring binary division of two's complement fractions. The tables list values of signals M_3--M_0, A_3--A_0, Q_3--Q_0 defined by the sequential circuit of Fig. 4.6.6 and the associated timing waveforms of Fig. 4.6.7. Reproduce the tables for the following values of M_3--M_0 and initial states of A_3--A_0:

(a) M_3--$M_0 = 0111$, A_3--$A_0 = 0110$
(b) M_3--$M_0 = 1001$, A_3--$A_0 = 1010$
(c) M_3--$M_0 = 0111$, A_3--$A_0 = 0111$
(d) M_3--$M_0 = 0111$, A_3--$A_0 = 1001$

Are the correct results produced for conditions (c) or (d)?

4.7.10 Iterative array for non-restoring binary division

Consider Fig. 4.6.4—a circuit of an iterative array for non-restoring division of binary fractions. The inputs of this array are the 4-bit divisor (M_0--M_0) and the 7-bit dividend

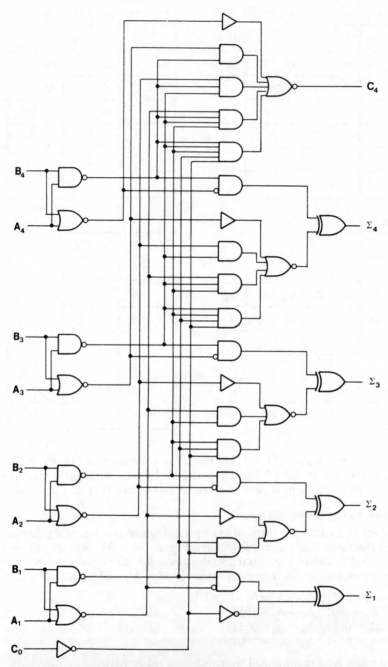

Fig. 4.7.1 Functional logic diagram of four-bit, binary full adder with fast carry (SN74LS283)

$(A_3\text{--}A_0, A_{-1}, A_{-2}, A_{-3})$. Write down all intermediate signals, viz: $B_1\text{--}B_4$, $E_3\text{--}E_0$, $F_3\text{--}F_0$, $G_3\text{--}G_0$, R_3 and the array's outputs, viz: $Q_3\text{--}Q_0$, $R_2\text{--}R_0$ for the input conditions:

$$M_3M_2M_1M_0 = 0110$$

$$A_3A_2A_1A_0A_{-1}A_{-2}A_{-3} = 0100000$$

It is to be noted that the above corresponds to the conditions of Table 4.6.1(a), and hence most of the required intermediate signals and outputs may be obtained from appropriate entries of this table.

4.7.11 Conversion from sign-magnitude to two's complement representation

A 16-bit fixed-point fraction with sign-magnitude representation as in Fig. 4.2.1(a) is held in a register with outputs $A_{15}\text{--}A_0$. Signals $B_{15}\text{--}B_0$ define the fraction with two's complement representation as in Fig. 4.2.2(a). Design circuits which produce $B_{15}\text{--}B_0$ from $A_{15}\text{--}A_0$.

4.7.12 Binary full adder with fast carry—SN74LS283

The integrated circuit type SN74LS283 is described as a '4-bit binary full adder with fast carry'. This integrated circuit performs the addition of two 4-bit binary numbers $A_1\text{--}A_4$, $B_1\text{--}B_4$ and an input carry signal C_0. The outputs are the four sum outputs $\Sigma_1\text{--}\Sigma_4$ and the carry output C_4 from the most-significant bit position. Carry-lookahead circuits are provided across all four bits. Input and output signals are represented in their true form. The functional logic diagram of this integrated circuit is shown in Fig. 4.7.1. Verify that this functional logic diagram is consistent with the Boolean equations of the carry-lookahead adder given in Section 4.4.

4.7.13 Design of add-shift multiplier

A circuit containing four MSI integrated circuits with interconnections required for the construction of an add-shift multiplier is shown in Fig. 4.7.2. The circuit contains a switch register M with outputs $M_3\text{--}M_0$ and two shift-registers A and Q with outputs $A_3\text{--}A_0$, $Q_3\text{--}Q_0$. The switch register M may be used to load A and Q initially, and is then used to hold the multiplicand during the multiplication procedure. The multiplier is initially held in Q, and the multiplication procedure produces a double length product in A and Q. Two's complement integers will be assumed for both the multiplicand and multiplier.

The multiplication unit is controlled by two toggle switches R_1 and R_0. Each of the operations listed in Table 4.7.3 is initiated by pressing a pushbutton.

Table 4.7.3 Controls for add-shift multiplier

R_1	R_0	FUNCTION
0	0	Multiply Q by M producing a double length product in A and Q
1	0	Load M into A
0	1	Load M into Q
1	1	Load M into A and Q

The three types of integrated circuits used in the multiplier are:
(i) SN74181 Arithmetic logic unit/function generator
(ii) SN74157 Quadruple 2-line-to-1-line data selector/multiplexer
(iii) SN7495A 4-bit parallel-access shift register

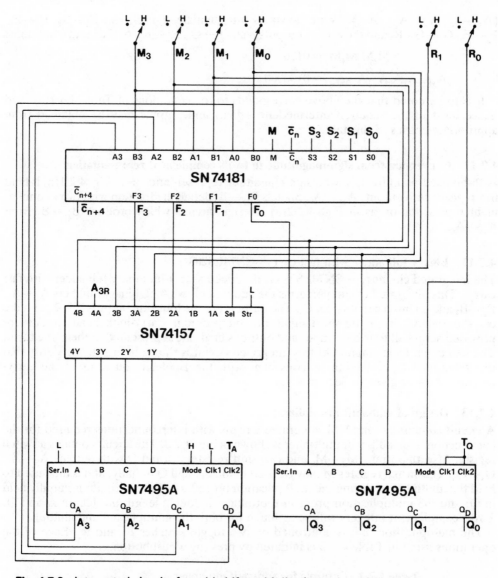

Fig. 4.7.2 Integrated circuits for add-shift multiplier (question of Section 4.7.13)

The significance of the symbols in Fig. 4.7.2 is:

$M, \overline{C}_n, S_3, S_2, S_1, S_0$: control inputs of SN74181

A_{3R} : serial input to A_3 on right shift

T_A : clock for A

T_Q : clock for Q

Assuming that each 'load' operation can be carried out by pressing the pushbutton once, and that the 'multiply' operation can be carried out by pressing the pushbutton four times, design and construct circuits for producing the above signals.

4.7.14   Sign-magnitude adder/subtracter

Two 16-bit fixed-point fractions A and B with sign-magnitude representation as in Fig. 4.2.1(a) are held in two registers with outputs A_{15}–A_0 and B_{15}–B_0. Signals S_{15}–S_0 define the sum 'A plus B' or the difference 'A minus B' (also in sign-magnitude representation) depending on whether a control signal D equals 0 or 1 respectively. Design circuits which produce S_{15}–S_0 from D, A_{15}–A_0 and B_{15}–B_0.

4.7.15   Simultaneous multiplier

Consider the design of a simultaneous multiplier which has as inputs two 4-bit, two's complement operands A_3, A_2, A_1, A_0 and B_3, B_2, B_1, B_0.

4.7.16   Overflow on division

Consider the circuit of the iterative array for non-restoring, two's-complement division of binary fractions given in Fig. 4.6.4. Design a circuit for the detection of overflow (i.e. the condition when the output of the array is incorrect).

5 TIMING AND CONTROL CIRCUITS

Introductory examples of synchronous and asynchronous timing of digital circuits

5.1 INTRODUCTION

5.1.1 Basic concepts of timing and control

Timing and control circuits are required for the interconnection of digital subsystems. These subsystems may take the form of any of the combinational, sequential or arithmetic circuits described in earlier chapters. When subsystems are interconnected, the requirements of proper 'synchronisation' become very important as a digital system can operate correctly only if its component subsystems perform their time-interrelated functions correctly at all times.

Timing signals are, of course, necessary for the reliable operation of sequential circuits (as described in Chapter 3) as these circuits are designed to produce a sequence of outputs (in time) from a given sequence of inputs and known initial conditions. These timing signals take the form of 'clocks' consisting of either a continuous sequence or a fixed number of repetitively produced clock pulses (with a clock pulse defined as a low-to-high transition followed soon after by a high-to-low transition or vice versa). Clocks are used for the synchronisation of flip-flops, and may be derived from various sources such as an astable multivibrator, a monostable multivibrator loop, a recorded clock track on a magnetic drum or disc and so on. Other timing waveforms may be derived using a variety of techniques, some of which are described in following sections.

Combinational circuits such as those described in Chapters 2 and 4 have input-to-output relationships which may be completely defined by a set of Boolean equations. However, these relationships hold only after the inputs to the combinational circuit have been established and after switching transients in the circuit have decayed to zero. Although the combinational circuits themselves may not have clocks or other timing waveforms as inputs, timing considerations are required, as it must be known when the outputs of the combinational circuits have settled and have meaningful values. When this is the case the outputs may be sensed by, for example, clocking them into flip-flops.

The adjectives *'synchronous'* and *'asynchronous'* have been used to describe methods of timing digital systems. The term *'synchronous timing'* may be defined as a method of timing and control of digital systems where a specified duration of time is allowed for the reliable execution of every operation carried out by every subsystem or individual circuit. The term 'operation' in this definition refers to a digital process such as (i) the production of the sum of two 16-bit, two's complement operands, (ii) the arithmetic right shifting of the contents of a shift-register, (iii) the incrementing of a binary up-counter, or (iv) the generation of a signal defined by a complex Boolean expression and so on. An operation may be as simple as the setting of a flip-flop with subsequent sensing, or as complex as the generation of the quotient of two 64-bit, floating-point numbers. The term 'reliable execution' in the definition implies that the time allowed for each operation must be based on 'worst-case' conditions, viz.: maximum propagation delay for each component circuit, and input signals (including operands) which produce the maximum delay.

An example of a digital system with synchronous timing is a system in which all flip-flops are controlled by timing waveforms derived from a single astable multivibrator. Examples of techniques of generating useful timing and control are given in Section 5.2. This includes the technique of defining signals representing time 'phases' during which various synchronous operations are executed. However, the sequence of entering and leaving phases is dependent not only on the main system clock, but also on system generated signals as well. This approach to system timing in which the end of one phase can initiate the beginning of another is similar in principle to the approach taken with asynchronous timing.

Asynchronous timing in a digital system is characterised by the production of a 'start pulse' to begin each operation and an 'end pulse' to signal the end of one operation and the start of another. The time taken by each operation can be variable (as compared with the fixed time taken by each operation in a system with synchronous timing), and can be designed to be of a duration which is just sufficient for the reliable execution of the operation. In principle, then, a system with asynchronous timing can operate faster than one with synchronous timing, the improvement in speed being dependent on the difference between the *mean time* and the *worst-case time* to perform each operation. The variable time taken by each operation can be either (or both) *component-dependent* or *operand-dependent*. Digital systems with completely asynchronous timing down at the component gate level are extremely uncommon. However, 'asynchronous parallel adders' have been built, and there are techniques of designing multipliers (such as a multiplier recoding scheme which may be applied to add-shift multipliers) which result in execution times depending on the input operands.

A circuit component which is extremely useful for the design of asynchronous timing circuits is the monostable multivibrator. Circuits using this component are described in Section 5.3.

A *control signal* is a signal which specifies the mode of operation of a multi-function circuit. For example, the 'add/subtract control' input of a binary adder-subtracter specifies whether addition or subtraction is to be performed, and the 'select control' input of a '2-line-to-1-line' data-selector specifies which of the two data inputs is to be selected and channelled to the output. Control signals in a digital system will be, in general, functions of internal states and external inputs. As such, they may be specified by sets of Boolean equations, and implemented by combinational circuits. However, in some systems a systematic approach to the generation of all or most of the required signals can result in a system with more organised structure and with better flexibility. For this application circuit elements such as 'decoders', 'encoders', 'programmable read-only-memory', 'programmable-logic-arrays', 'micro-programmed control unit', etc. can be used to advantage.

It has been stated already that timing and control circuits are required for the interconnection of digital subsystems. As these subsystems may have attributes such as 'synchronous timing', 'asynchronous timing', 'parallel', 'serial', 'binary', 'binary-coded-decimal', 'electro-mechanical', etc., a number of 'interfacing' problems are suggested. These include:

(i) the interconnection of two synchronous subsystems,
(ii) the interconnection of two asynchronous subsystems,
(iii) the interconnection of a synchronous subsystem with an asynchronous subsystem,
(iv) parallel to serial conversion and vice versa,
(v) code conversion,
(vi) interfacing with non-digital signals, and so on.

Not all of these problems are discussed in this chapter. However, some examples are given and in the next section we begin by describing an elementary problem of interconnecting two synchronous subsystems (a shift-register and a binary counter). This is done to introduce some of the problems of timing and control.

5.1.2   Elementary example of timing and control

Fig. 5.1.1 gives details of two proposed arrangements for counting the number of ONEs produced by the serial output of a shift-register. Fig. 5.1.1(a) shows a circuit containing five master-slave J–K flip-flops, of which three are interconnected to form a 3-stage shift-register and the other two to form a 2-stage, synchronous, binary up-counter. The waveform of the clock input to the shift-register is shown in Fig. 5.1.1(c). It is assumed that the shift-register may be loaded initially with a 3-bit number, and that the binary counter may be cleared initially (using PRESET and CLEAR inputs which are not shown). The basis of the circuit arrangement is that the serial output (A_2) of the shift-register is used to

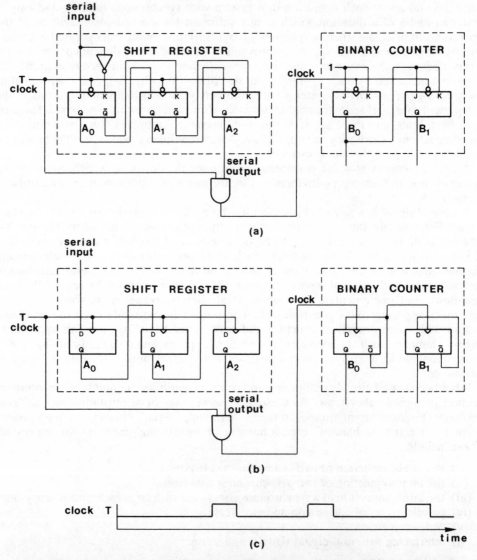

Fig. 5.1.1 Proposed arrangements for counting the number of ONEs produced by the serial output of a shift-register—(a) shift-register and binary counter containing master-slave J–K flip-flops, (b) shift-register and binary counter containing positive-edge-triggered D-type flip-flops, and (c) clock waveform

gate the clock (T) using an AND-gate, and the gated clock (from the output of the AND-gate) is used to increment the binary counter. After three clock pulses, the binary counter outputs (B_0 and B_1) should represent the number of ONEs (0, 1, 2 or 3) initially held in the 3-bit shift-register.

Fig. 5.1.1(b) shows a circuit containing five positive-edge-triggered D-type flip-flops. The circuit arrangement is similar to that of Fig. 5.1.1(a) and is based on the same design approach and assumptions described above. Again, Fig. 5.1.1(c) shows the waveform of the clock applied to the shift-register.

By referring to Chapter 3, the reader may verify that the circuits for the shift-registers and binary counters given in Fig. 5.1.1(a) and Fig. 5.1.1(b) are correct. In addition, the AND-gate performs the correct function of 'signal gating'. In spite of this, the circuit of Fig. 5.1.1(b) will never work correctly, and the circuit of Fig. 5.1.1(a) may be improved!! The timing details of Fig. 5.1.2 show why this is so.

Fig. 5.1.2(a) gives the timing details of the circuit containing D-type flip-flops (Fig. 5.1.1(b)). This figure shows that the first bit of the serial output is available at the shift-register output (A_2) up until the rising edge of the first clock pulse. This output therefore cannot gate the clock pulse correctly as it appears at a different time!! The same problem exists with the second and third bit outputs, and the circuit will never work as required.

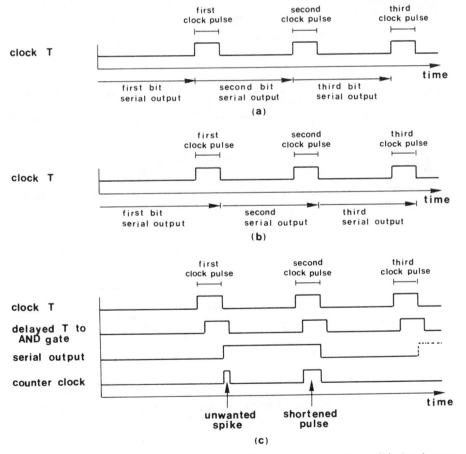

Fig. 5.1.2 Timing details—(a) circuit containing D-type flip-flops, (b) circuit containing J–K flip-flops, and (c) timing waveforms illustrating the possibility of incorrect operation of the circuit containing J–K flip-flops due to signal delays

Fig. 5.1.2(b) gives the timing details of the circuit containing J–K flip-flops (Fig. 5.1.1(a)). This figure shows that the first bit of the serial output is available at the shift-register output (A_2) up until the falling edge of the first clock pulse. Hence, this output can gate the clock pulse as designed. The same time relationship between serial output and corresponding clock pulse holds for the second and third bit outputs, and hence the circuit of Fig. 5.1.1(a) will probably operate as designed. However, there is one possible source of trouble! This arises because the end of the gating signal (the shift-register output A_2) occurs theoretically at precisely the same time as the falling edge of the clock. Trouble arises if the clock signal T is delayed before it reaches the input of the AND-gate as shown in Fig. 5.1.2(c). (In a complex system, this is always a possibility as a clock signal may be produced by several driver gates to solve 'fan-out' problems, and there may be a difference in the propagation delay of these gates.) Fig. 5.1.2(c) shows that if the T signal to the AND-gate is delayed, this gate can produce an unwanted spike and can shorten the duration of an input pulse. The unwanted spike could increment the binary counter producing an incorrect result. It is also possible that the binary counter is *not* incremented by a shortened pulse.

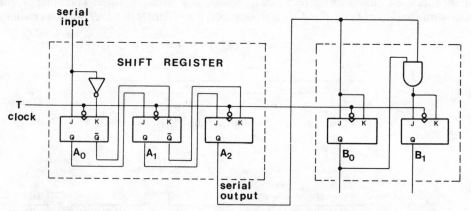

Fig. 5.1.3   Circuit for counting the number of ONEs produced by the serial output of a shift-register

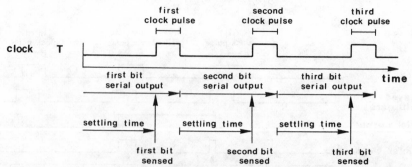

Fig. 5.1.4   Timing details of circuit for counting the number of ONEs produced by the serial output of a shift-register

A reliable circuit for counting the number of ONEs produced by the serial output of a shift-register is shown in Fig. 5.1.3. This circuit utilises master-slave J–K flip-flops whose clock inputs are all driven from the clock signal T. The serial output A_2 is used essentially as an 'enable' input to a 2-stage binary counter. The timing details are shown in Fig. 5.1.4. It is to be noted that the serial outputs appear up until the falling edge of the clock pulse. They are 'sensed' at the rising edge of the clock pulse and the master flip-flops of the B_0 and B_1 flip-flops are set accordingly at this time. Fig. 5.1.4 shows that the allowed settling time of the combinational circuits used in the circuit (i.e. the AND-gate) is the time between the falling edge of one clock pulse and the rising edge of the next. Although absolute times are not specified in Fig. 5.1.4 a one gate delay will almost certainly cause no trouble and the circuit of Fig. 5.1.3 should provide both correct and reliable operation.

5.2   SYNCHRONOUS TIMING

5.2.1   Clocked sequential circuits

An example of a system with synchronous timing is a 'clocked sequential circuit' represented by the circuit in the dotted outline in Fig. 5.2.1. In this circuit the clock input of every flip-flop is driven from the clock signal T which causes the inputs to the flip-flops to be sensed at equally spaced intervals in time. The clock signal T is also used in 'conditioning and synchronisation circuits' which convert circuit inputs into signals which have the same electrical characteristics (voltage levels, etc.) as (and which change in synchronism with) the signals of the clocked sequential circuit. Fig. 5.2.1 shows that the flip-flop inputs and the final circuit outputs are produced by combinational circuits with inputs coming from flip-flop outputs and the outputs of the conditioning and synchronisation circuits.

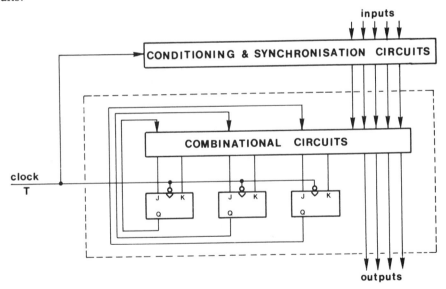

Fig. 5.2.1   Circuit with synchronous timing (shown in dotted outline)

Fig 5.2.2 shows the available settling time of the combinational circuits of Fig. 5.2.1. It is assumed that the only type of flip-flop used is the master-slave J–K flip-flop, and that for such a flip-flop, the outputs of the slave flip-flop appear at the falling edge of the clock T, and the J–K inputs are sensed and set into the master flip-flop on the rising edge of the clock. Hence, the available settling time is the time between the falling and rising edges of the clock as illustrated in Fig. 5.2.2.

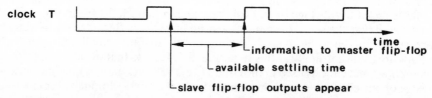

Fig. 5.2.2 Available settling time of combinational circuits of a circuit with synchronous timing containing master-slave J–K flip-flops

Fig. 5.2.3 shows the available settling time of the combinational circuits of a clocked sequential circuit which utilises positive-edge-triggered D-type flip-flops. With this type of flip-flop, the positive edge of the clock causes both the sensing of the data input and the subsequent settling of the flip-flop. Hence, the available settling time is the time between consecutive positive edges of the clock (i.e. the full clock period).

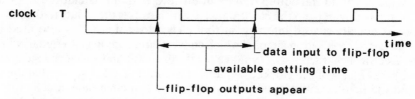

Fig. 5.2.3 Available settling time of combinational circuits of a circuit with synchronous timing containing positive-edge-triggered D-type flip-flops

It is to be stressed that when designing clocked sequential circuits, it is highly desirable that flip-flops of only one type are used. This recommendation should be extended to all digital systems whenever practicable, as the satisfaction of all timing requirements in systems containing two or more different types of flip-flops is significantly more difficult, and any oversight on the designer's part can lead to unreliable operation.

Some techniques for the design of clocked sequential circuits were described in Chapter 3. Further extensions and examples are given in following sections.

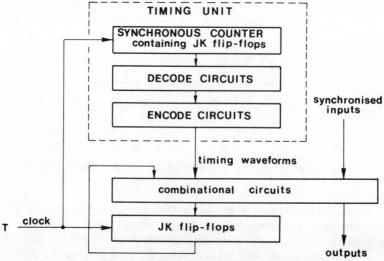

Fig. 5.2.4 Block diagram of a timing unit for the generation of timing waveforms used by a circuit with synchronous timing

5.2.2   Generation of timing waveforms

5.2.2.1   *Counter-decode-encode circuit*

One very useful and simple approach to the generation of timing waveforms for a circuit with synchronous timing is represented by the block diagram of Fig. 5.2.4. This approach utilises a circuit configuration which is described as a 'counter-decode-encode circuit'. The counter is a synchronous counter driven by the clock signal T. It contains flip-flops of the same type as that used elsewhere in the circuit (e.g. master-slave J–K flip-flops drawn in the diagram), and the entire circuit (including the timing circuits) may be considered as a clocked sequential circuit. The decode circuits provide complete decoding of the counter outputs, and the encode circuits (which are functionally equivalent to a set of OR-gates) combine the decoded outputs to produce the required timing waveforms.

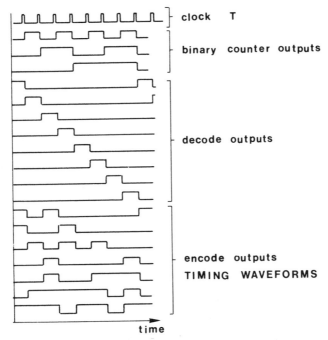

Fig. 5.2.5   Examples of timing waveforms

Examples of timing waveforms which may be produced by a simple counter-decode-encode circuit are shown in Fig. 5.2.5. This circuit contains a 3-stage synchronous binary counter whose outputs are decoded by a 3-line-to-8-line decoder. Any of the decoder outputs may be combined as inputs to a set of OR-gates to produce a number of timing waveforms. The waveforms shown in Fig. 5.2.5 are given only as examples of what can be achieved. However, they should clearly demonstrate the flexibility of the approach.

5.2.2.2   *Waveforms for an elementary educational computer*

Fig. 5.2.6 is the block diagram of an elementary educational computer used at the University of Sydney in the 1960s. The computer utilised a simple 'single-address' architecture based on an 8-bit word. The registers of the computer consisted of a 4-bit program counter (C), a 4-bit memory address register (P), an 8-bit accumulator (A) and an instruction register (R) composed of two 4-bit registers (R_O and R_A). All registers were implemented as shift-registers, and all data-transfers and arithmetic operations were carried out serially. The memory consisted of a pin-board and a shift-register, and was organised to provide a serial output V from fifteen locations with 'read-only' capability and one location with 'read-write' capability.

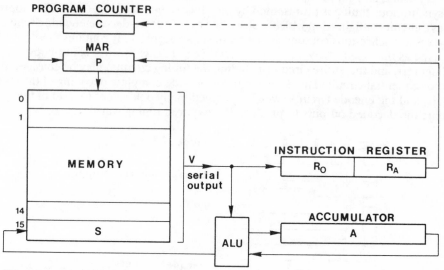

Fig. 5.2.6 Block diagram of an elementary, educational computer

The physical form of the computer was a cabinet containing clearly engraved sub-assemblies which could be interconnected using patch leads. These sub-assemblies consisted of (i) timing unit, (ii) memory with memory address register, (iii) program counter, (iv) instruction register, (v) accumulator, and (vi) four logic panels containing NOR-gates and flip-flops.

Experiments using the computer were concerned with (i) computer design, (ii) implementation of a design, and (iii) very elementary machine language programming techniques.

Some of the timing signals provided by the timing unit are shown in Fig. 5.2.7. Two 'interleaved clocks' (T_0 and T_2) were provided. The T_2 clock was used to increment a 5-stage binary counter with outputs B_1, B_2, B_4, B_8 and B_{16}. The outputs of the most-significant three stages of this counter are shown in Fig. 5.2.7. Because the T_0 and T_2 clocks

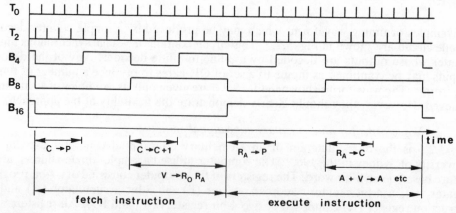

Fig. 5.2.7 Timing waveforms of elementary, educational computer

are interleaved, the binary counter signals clearly 'span' the T_0 pulses, and hence the problem discussed in Section 5.1.2 is avoided. The binary counter signals or Boolean functions of these signals therefore may be used to gate T_0 pulses to produce suitable clock pulses for the shift-registers of the computer.

The period of time defined by the waveforms of Fig. 5.2.7 is the period required for the execution of an instruction stored in memory. Some of the operations carried out during this '*instruction cycle*' of the computer are indicated on the diagram. The 'instruction cycle' consists of two basic 'phases', viz.: the '*fetch instruction phase*' during which the instruction to be executed is 'fetched' from memory and loaded into the instruction register, and the '*execute instruction phase*' during which the instruction in the instruction register is decoded and the appropriate operations are executed. Fig. 5.2.7 shows that during the 'fetch instruction phase' there is a data-transfer from the program counter C to the memory address register P (represented by $C \rightarrow P$), and this is followed by a transfer from memory to the instruction register (represented by $V \rightarrow R_0 R_A$). During this latter data-transfer the program counter is incremented (represented by $C \rightarrow C+1$) in readiness for the next instruction cycle. During the 'execute instruction phase', there is a data-transfer from that part (R_A) of the instruction register defining an operand address to the memory data register P (represented by $R_A \rightarrow P$), and this is followed by the execution of the instruction defined by the contents of R_0. Two examples of this operation required for instruction execution are given. The first requires the addition of the operand from memory to the contents of the accumulator (represented by $A+V \rightarrow A$), and the second requires the over-writing of the 'incremented program counter' (represented by $R_A \rightarrow C$).

It will be observed from Fig. 5.2.7 that the timing waveforms B_4, B_8 and B_{16} may be used to define the operations carried out during the instruction cycle of the computer. For example, the data-transfer $C \rightarrow P$ may be performed by applying the four T_0 clock pulses defined by the condition $\overline{B}_4 B_8 B_{16} = 1$ to both the C and P shift-registers. Further, it may be observed that the memory address register P is required to operate as a shift-register only for the conditions $\overline{B}_4 B_8 \overline{B}_{16} = 1$ and $\overline{B}_4 \overline{B}_8 B_{16} = 1$. Hence, the 'shift clock' for P (P_{SHIFT}) may be defined by the Boolean equation:

$$P_{SHIFT} = \overline{B}_4 \overline{B}_8 T_0$$

The timing waveforms may also be used to 'gate' data signals. For example, it will be observed that the serial input to P (P_{IN}) should be equal to the serial output of C (C_{OUT}) when $\overline{B}_4 \overline{B}_8 \overline{B}_{16} = 1$, and it should be equal to the serial output of R_A (R_{AOUT}) when $\overline{B}_4 \overline{B}_8 B_{16} = 1$. As the Boolean expression for P_{SHIFT} already contains the term $\overline{B}_4 \overline{B}_8$, the following equation may be used for the definition of P_{IN}:

$$P_{IN} = C_{OUT} \overline{B}_{16} + R_{AOUT} B_{16}$$

Boolean equations for the shift clocks and the serial inputs of the other shift-registers may be derived in a manner similar to that used above, and the logical design of an elementary computer may be represented by a set of such equations.

The use of repetitive timing waveforms such as those of Fig. 5.2.7 provides an extremely simple, yet versatile, method for the timing and control of a digital system. It is simple because the timing waveforms are easy to produce, and after the timing unit has been designed, much of the remaining parts of the digital system design may be accomplished using Boolean Algebra and other techniques for handling combinational circuits. The method is also very versatile as long sequences of operations may be controlled, and the execution of any operation may be made dependent on system conditions. The method, however, does suffer from some inefficiencies, and other methods can produce higher speeds of operation. For example, the timing waveforms of Fig. 5.2.7 show that the four T_0 pulses defined by $\overline{B}_4 \overline{B}_8 B_{16} = 1$ are *always* provided in the instruction cycle so that the contents of R_A are transferred to the memory address register P (represented by $R_A \rightarrow P$ in

Fig. 5.2.7). This is done so that the operand with the address specified by the instruction is presented at the serial output (V) of the memory during the eight clock periods defined by $B_8 B_{16} = 1$ during which the instruction is executed. For example, for the ADD instruction, the operation $A + V \rightarrow A$ is performed. However, the instruction set of the computer includes a number of instructions which do *not* require an operand from memory. For example, an 'unconditional transfer of control' instruction requires an operation $R_A \rightarrow C$, and the memory output V is not used at all. Hence, the operation $R_A \rightarrow P$ would not have been necessary for this type of instruction. Inefficiencies like this are not important for an educational computer. However, for high performance digital systems, designers often attempt to minimise the number of time periods during which no effective operation is performed. If this is the design objective, then a timing unit producing repetitive timing waveforms is unsuitable.

5.2.2.3   *Waveforms for an early serial computer*

Some timing waveforms of an early serial computer are shown in Fig. 5.2.8. This computer used a 32-bit word, and the 32-bit periods defined by the waveforms $D_0 \text{---} D_5$, $S_0 \text{---} S_5$ had to be produced repetitively from the clock T which was derived from a permanently recorded clock track on a magnetic drum. The $S_0 \text{---} S_5$ waveforms represented 'segments' within a word period, and the $D_0 \text{---} D_5$ waveforms represented 'digits' within a segment. With this arrangement, any bit within a word period could be specified by the logical product of a 'segment' waveform and a 'digit' waveform. An examination of Fig. 5.2.8 will show that each of the six segments contains four, five or six digits.

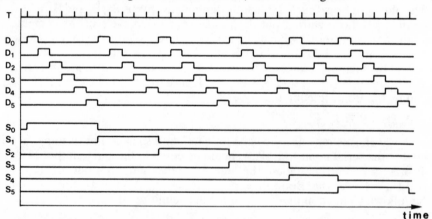

Fig. 5.2.8   Some timing waveforms of an early serial computer

A circuit for generating the waveforms of Fig. 5.2.8 may be designed using the 'counter-decode-encode' arrangement described in Section 5.2.2.1. However, an alternative design may be obtained by first considering the state transition diagram shown in Fig. 5.2.9. This diagram represents a circuit which may be described as a '*coupled-counter circuit*'. Clearly two counters, viz.: a D-counter with states $D_0 \text{---} D_5$ and an S-counter with states $S_0 \text{---} S_5$, are involved, and the state transitions are dependent on the states of both counters.

It will be observed from either Fig. 5.2.8 or Fig. 5.2.9 that the D-counter is either 'incremented' or 'reset' by the clock pulse T, and that whenever the D-counter is reset, the S-counter is incremented. A signal R may be defined as either (i) the condition for resetting the D-counter, or (ii) the condition for not incrementing the D-counter, or (iii) the condition for incrementing the S-counter. Fig. 5.2.9 shows that a Boolean equation for R is:

$$R = S_4 D_3 + (S_1 + S_3) D_4 + D_5$$

A block diagram of a coupled-counter circuit defined by Fig. 5.2.9 is shown in Fig. 5.2.10. It will be observed that each of the counters is implemented by a counter circuit containing three master-slave J–K flip-flops, and that the flip-flop outputs are decoded to

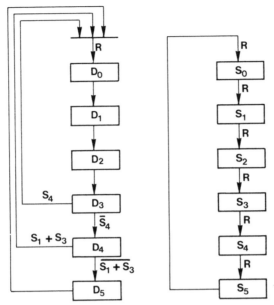

Fig. 5.2.9 State transition diagram of 'coupled-counter' circuit for generation of timing waveforms

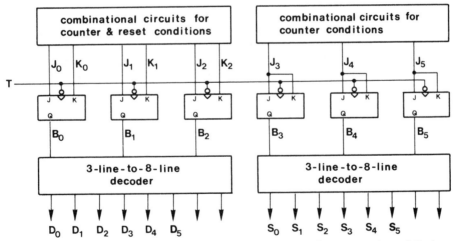

Fig. 5.2.10 Block diagram of 'coupled-counter' circuit for generation of timing waveforms

produce the segment and digit waveforms. It is assumed that the six flip-flops B_0---B_5 are initially reset. The flip-flop inputs are now defined by Table 5.2.1. Note that when $R = 0$, the values for J_0, K_0, J_1, K_1, J_2 and K_2 define a synchronous, binary up-counter for the flip-flops B_0, B_1 and B_2; and that when $R = 1$, these flip-flop inputs cause the B_0, B_1 and B_2 flip-flops to be reset. Again, when $R = 0$, the zero values for J_3 ($= K_3$), J_4 ($= K_4$) and J_5 ($= K_5$)

inhibit the changing of the B_3, B_4 and B_5 flip-flops; and when $R = 1$, these flip-flop inputs define a synchronous, binary up-counter for the B_3, B_4 and B_5 flip-flops.

Table 5.2.1 Table defining flip-flop inputs for coupled-counter circuit

R	J_0	K_0	J_1	K_1	J_2	K_2	J_3	J_4	J_5
0	1	1	B_0	B_0	B_0B_1	B_0B_1	0	0	0
1	0	1	0	1	0	1	1	B_3	B_3B_4

From Table 5.2.1 the following Boolean equations may be derived:

$$J_0 = \overline{R}$$
$$K_0 = 1$$
$$J_1 = \overline{R}B_0$$
$$K_1 = R + B_0$$
$$J_2 = \overline{R}B_0B_1$$
$$K_2 = R + B_0B_1$$
$$J_3 = K_3 = R$$
$$J_4 = K_4 = RB_3$$
$$J_5 = K_5 = RB_3B_4$$

These equations, together with the equation defining R, clearly define the combinational circuits of Fig. 5.2.10. This completes the design of the circuit for generating the timing waveforms of Fig. 5.2.8.

5.2.2.4 *Sector number sequence for a magnetic drum*
When magnetic drums were used as main memories in early serial computers, one technique which was used to improve the computer's performance was to position word-length 'sectors' of each track of the drum in such a way that sectors with consecutive addresses did *not* occupy consecutive physical positions on the track but were spaced with a number of sectors in between. As computer instructions are obeyed in the sequence defined by the instruction's address for a large part of the running time of a program, this spacing of sectors with consecutive addresses provided time for the execution of an instruction and minimised the time required to gain access to the next stored instruction.

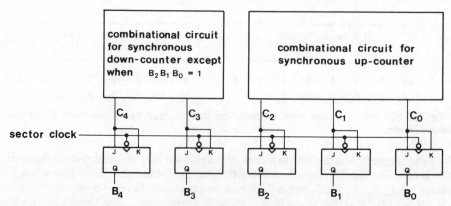

Fig. 5.2.11 Block diagram of circuit for generation of sector number sequence

Table 5.2.2 Sector number sequence of a magnetic drum

SECTOR NUMBER SEQUENCE						SEQUENCE CONTINUED					
DECIMAL	BINARY					DECIMAL	BINARY				
	B_4	B_3	B_2	B_1	B_0		B_4	B_3	B_2	B_1	B_0
0	0	0	0	0	0	16	1	0	0	0	0
25	1	1	0	0	1	9	0	1	0	0	1
18	1	0	0	1	0	2	0	0	0	1	0
11	0	1	0	1	1	27	1	1	0	1	1
4	0	0	1	0	0	20	1	0	1	0	0
29	1	1	1	0	1	13	0	1	1	0	1
22	1	0	1	1	0	6	0	0	1	1	0
15	0	1	1	1	1	31	1	1	1	1	1
8	0	1	0	0	0	24	1	1	0	0	0
1	0	0	0	0	1	17	1	0	0	0	1
26	1	1	0	1	0	10	0	1	0	1	0
19	1	0	0	1	1	3	0	0	0	1	1
12	0	1	1	0	0	28	1	1	1	0	0
5	0	0	1	0	1	21	1	0	1	0	1
30	1	1	1	1	0	14	0	1	1	1	0
23	1	0	1	1	1	7	0	0	1	1	1
16	1	0	0	0	0	0	0	0	0	0	0

An example of a sector number sequence is shown in Table 5.2.2. This sequence applies to a magnetic drum in which each track is divided into 32 sectors. An examination of the sequence in decimal shows that a sector number is obtained from the preceding number by subtraction of 7 (modulo-32).

A close examination of the binary sequence (B_4, B_3, B_2, B_1 and B_0 of Table 5.2.2) will confirm that the block diagram of Fig. 5.2.11 will provide a convenient method for the generation of the sector number sequence. Note the method suggested by Fig. 5.2.11 is that used for clocked sequential circuits as the clock input of all flip-flops are driven from the same clock signal which, in this case, is a 'sector clock', i.e. a clock signal providing 32 equally spaced clock pulses for each drum revolution.

Fig. 5.2.11 shows that the B_2, B_1 and B_0 flip-flops are connected as a synchronous up-counter, and that the B_4 and B_3 flip-flops operate as a synchronous down-counter except for the condition $B_2B_1B_0 = 1$. This circuit arrangement implements a subtraction of 7 as a subtraction of 8 combined with an addition of 1. However, the subtraction of 8 (i.e. the decrementing of the B_4, B_3 counter) is inhibited when the B_2, B_1, B_0 counter changes from 111 to 000 as an effective subtraction of 8 is performed in this case by the B_2, B_1, B_0 counter which performs the operation of 'addition of 1 (modulo-8)'.

From the preceding discussion, the inputs C_0---C_4 of the flip-flops B_0---B_4 of Fig. 5.2.11 may be defined as follows:

$$C_0 = 1$$
$$C_1 = B_0$$
$$C_2 = B_1 B_0$$
$$C_3 = \overline{B_2 B_1 B_0}$$
$$C_4 = \overline{B_2 B_1 B_0} \, \overline{B_3}$$

These equations and Fig. 5.2.11 define the circuit for generating the sector number sequence defined by Table 5.2.2.

5.2.3   Timing phases

5.2.3.1   *Concept and implementation of timing phases*

It was stated in Section 5.2.2.2 that one of the inefficiencies of the timing arrangement which used cyclic timing waveforms was that in some time periods no effective operation was performed and that this arrangement did not lend itself to a maximisation of operating speed. This source of timing inefficiency is removed by using the concept of 'timing phases'. A timing phase may be defined broadly as a time duration in which an effective operation is performed. When this concept is used in the design of a digital system, the timing of systems operations will consist of a *sequence of timing phases*, and, in general, there will be no time duration in which no effective operation is performed.

The concept of timing phases requires the use of a 'phase clock' which is used to clock 'phase flip-flops' defining different timing phases, and, in addition, consideration must be given to mechanisms which cause, for example, one phase to follow another, one phase to be entered only on specified system conditions, one phase to be inserted between another two on certain conditions and so on. Within a timing phase, other timing waveforms may be required, and it is possible that different timing phases will require different timing waveforms. Hence, timing phases may be of different time duration. An example of waveforms of a phase clock and internal timing waveforms is given in Fig. 5.2.12. In this diagram, a timing phase is the time between consecutive pulses of the phase clock.

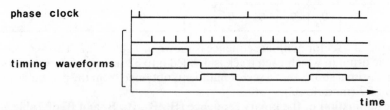

Fig. 5.2.12   Examples of phase clock and timing waveforms

An example is given in the next section (Section 5.2.3.2) of the phase logic of a digital computer. In this example, the computer contains a ferrite-core memory, and the phase clock may be identified as a signal which initiates a 'memory cycle'. In addition, the internal timing waveforms may be identified as the waveforms required for reading from and writing into the core memory together with other waveforms required for the execution of various phase operations. Flip-flops are, of course, used for the definition of phases. However, the configuration of flip-flops with their associated input logic can take several forms. Two of these are represented by Fig. 5.2.13 and Fig. 5.2.14.

Fig. 5.2.13 represents phase control circuits where N flip-flops are used to represent 2^N phases. This method minimises the number of flip-flops but requires additional decode

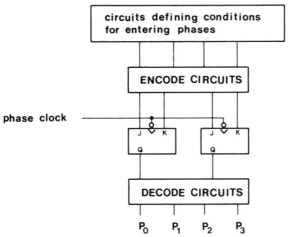

Fig. 5.2.13 Block diagram of 'phase control' circuits using N flip-flops to represent 2^N phases (in this diagram $N = 2$)

circuits to produce signals representing the various phases. In Fig. 5.2.13 two flip-flops are shown. These define the four phases P_0, P_1, P_2 and P_3. When using this approach, it is necessary to derive signals defining the *conditions for entering the different phases*. These signals must then be encoded to produce the required flip-flop inputs.

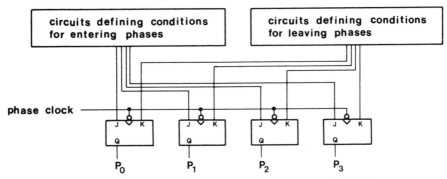

Fig. 5.2.14 Block diagram of 'phase control' circuits using N flip-flops to represent N phases (in this diagram $N = 4$)

Fig. 5.2.14 represents phase control circuits where N flip-flops are used to represent N phases. Using this approach it is necessary to derive signals defining both the *conditions for entering the different phases* and the *conditions for leaving the different phases*. This approach utilises more flip-flops than that required by the approach represented by Fig. 5.2.13. However, the encode and decode circuits of Fig. 5.2.13 are not required, and it will be shown in the next section that the phase control circuits may be derived very readily from the phase (state) transition diagram of the system with minimal design effort.

5.2.3.2 *Phase logic of a digital computer*

Fig. 5.2.15 provides the phase (state) transition diagram which defines the phase logic of a digital computer. This computer contains a ferrite-core memory, and the nine phases represented in Fig. 5.2.15 by the symbol P with various subscripts define memory cycles in which defined operations are performed. Although the significance of these subscripts and the details of the operations performed in each phase are of little concern in the present context of designing the phase logic, the names of the nine phases are listed below to provide a little insight into the design of a 'second-generation' computer. The nine phases are:

P_{FI} : Fetch instruction

P_{PO} : Programmed operator

P_{ID} : Indirect addressing

P_{IX} : Index instruction

P_{EX} : Execute instruction (one instruction subroutine)

P_{E0} : Execution cycle 0

P_{E1} : Execution cycle 1

P_{E2} : Execution cycle 2

P_{E3} : Execution cycle 3

It is assumed that in Fig. 5.2.15 the initial state of the computer is represented by P_{FI}, and that during any memory cycle of phases P_{FI}, P_{ID} and P_{EX}, data is read from memory to determine the signals represented by the symbol C (i.e. condition) with various subscripts. Again, although the significance of the subscripts is of little concern in the present context, the C signals are defined below for completeness:

C_{IA} : Instruction assembled

C_{PO} : Programmed operator

C_{ID} : Indirect addressing

C_{IX} : Index instruction

C_{EX} : Execute instruction

C_{NMC} : Instruction does not require a memory cycle for execution

C_H : Hierarchy instruction (a class of instruction which requires more than one memory cycle for execution)

C_{30} : Instruction 30 which requires four memory cycles for execution

The conditions C_{PO}, C_{ID}, C_{IX} and C_{EX} are mutually exclusive and C_{IA} is defined by:

$$\overline{C}_{IA} = C_{PO} + C_{ID} + C_{IX} + C_{EX}$$

Fig. 5.2.16 shows the time relationship of the phase clock T_p and the times at which the outputs of the memory in phases P_{FI}, P_{ID} and P_{EX} are latched and used as inputs to the phase logic.

Fig. 5.2.17 gives an example of a phase sequence. In this figure, the symbol I represents an instruction cycle, i.e. the time taken to fetch and execute a stored instruction.

Fig. 5.2.18 provides the circuit diagram of the phase logic defined by Fig. 5.2.15 and the above description. Note first the similarity in overall structure of the circuit diagram of Fig. 5.2.18 and the state transition diagram of Fig. 5.2.15. The circuit of Fig. 5.2.18 utilises master-slave J–K flip-flops with clock inputs of all flip-flops driven by the phase clock T_p. There are nine flip-flops representing nine phases and hence signals for entering and leaving the phases are required. The signals for entering each phase may be derived from the state transition diagram of Fig. 5.2.15. For example, the AND-gates 6 and 11 determine the transition from P_{E0} to either P_{FI} or P_{E1} depending on whether $C_H = 0$ or 1 respectively.

An examination of Fig. 5.2.18 will show that two methods are used for resetting flip-flops, i.e. for leaving phases. The first is used for phases which occur for only one phase period at a time. These phases are P_{PO}, P_{IX}, P_{E0}, P_{E1}, P_{E2} and P_{E3}. For these flip-flops the Q

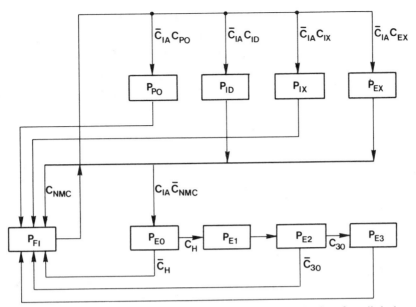

Fig. 5.2.15 State transition diagram of the phase logic of a digital computer

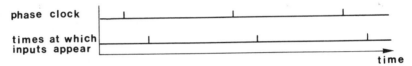

Fig. 5.2.16 Timing of phase clock and inputs for the phase logic of a digital computer

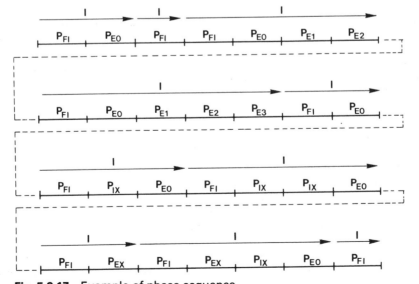

Fig. 5.2.17 Example of phase sequence

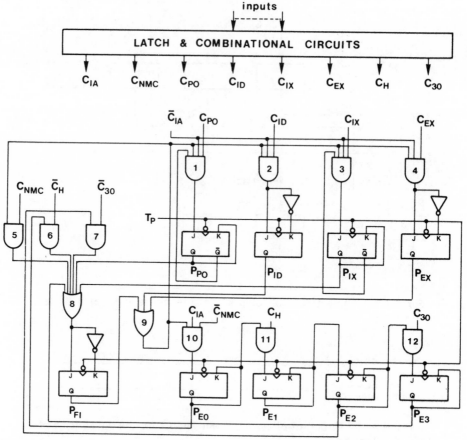

Fig. 5.2.18   Circuit diagram of the phase logic of a digital computer

output is connected to the K input, and hence on the next phase clock, the flip-flop is reset. The second is used for phases which can last for two or more consecutive phase periods. These phases are P_{FI}, P_{ID} and P_{EX}. For each of these flip-flops, the inverter causes the flip-flop to be reset if the signal causing the entry to the phase goes to zero. Further examination of Fig. 5.2.18 will verify that all state transitions defined by Fig. 5.2.15 have been implemented.

5.3   ASYNCHRONOUS TIMING

5.3.1   Application of monostable multivibrators

In a system with asynchronous timing, each 'operation' is initiated by a 'start pulse', and an 'end pulse' is produced to terminate one operation and to initiate another. The time allowed for each operation may be adjusted to that which is just sufficient for reliable operation. A circuit component which is extremely useful for the design of a system with these characteristics is the 'monostable multivibrator'.

A monostable multivibrator is a circuit with two states of which only one state is stable. The circuit may be triggered into the other state by an input pulse, and it will remain in this (unstable) state for a time duration which is determined by circuit components (normally a resistor-capacitor arrangement). There are monostable multivibrator circuits which will trigger on either a positive edge (i.e. a LOW to HIGH transition of the trigger input) or a negative edge (i.e. a HIGH to LOW transition). Some circuits also provide an 'enable' input so that the triggering of the circuit may be made dependent on a system condition. The 'pulse width' of the monostable multivibrator, i.e. the time duration in the unstable state after triggering may be made dependent on the setting of a potentiometer and hence may be 'continuously adjustable' over a range determined by other circuit components.

A monostable multivibrator circuit may provide either 'non-retriggerable operation' or 'retriggerable operation'. With a non-retriggerable monostable multivibrator, reliable and predictable circuit operation will not be produced if the spacing between two consecutive trigger input pulses is less than a value specified by a circuit parameter known as a 'duty cycle'. The allowable duty cycle of a non-retriggerable monostable multivibrator is simply a percentage figure relating the pulse width to the minimum spacing of trigger pulses for correct circuit operation. A typical range of duty cycles of non-retriggerable monostable multivibrators is 50–80%. With a retriggerable monostable multivibrator, the circuit's timing operation may be restarted even while this operation is in progress, i.e. while the circuit is in its unstable state. A monostable multivibrator may also be 'resettable' which means that an additional 'reset' input can be used to force the circuit into its stable state at any time.

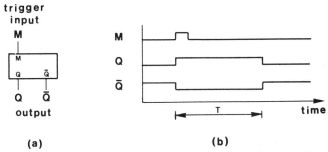

Fig. 5.3.1 Monostable multivibrator—(a) symbol, and (b) input–output timing waveforms

In this chapter, it will be assumed that all monostable multivibrators used in circuit examples trigger on positive edges of their trigger inputs and are restricted to non-retriggerable operation. The symbol used for a monostable multivibrator is shown in Fig. 5.3.1(a) in which M represents the trigger input, and Q and $\overline{Q}$ represent complementary outputs. Input-output timing waveforms are shown in Fig. 5.3.1(b).

A 'chain of monostable multivibrators' in which the $\overline{Q}$ output of one monostable multivibrator is connected to the M input of the next monostable multivibrator in the chain can produce a sequence of timing waveforms. An example is given in Fig. 5.3.2 in which the symbol T represents an input pulse which produces the timing waveforms Q_0, Q_1, Q_2 and Q_3. The pulse periods T_0, T_1, T_2 and T_3 are adjustable by varying the settings of potentiometers used in the monostable multivibrator circuits.

A useful building block for the design of an asynchronous timing unit is represented by Fig. 5.3.3. Fig. 5.3.3(a) gives a circuit containing two monostable multivibrators and an AND-gate. The symbol T represents a 'start pulse' which initiates an operation under the control of a 'control start signal' C. The output of the first monostable multivibrator Q_0 is a signal which can be used to 'control the operation', and the output of the second monostable multivibrator Q_1 can be used as the 'end pulse' signifying the end of the operation (and the start of another). Relevant timing waveforms are shown in

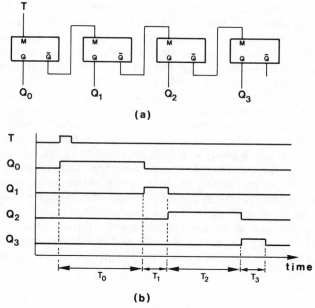

Fig. 5.3.2 Chain of monostable multivibrators—
(a) circuit, and (b) timing waveforms

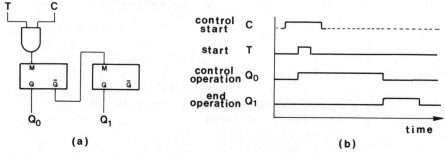

Fig. 5.3.3 Asynchronous timing using two monostable multivibrators—
(a) circuit, and (b) timing waveforms

Fig. 5.3.3(b). The building block of Fig. 5.3.3(a) and related concepts of asynchronous timing are used in two examples described in the following sections (Sections 5.3.2 and 5.3.3).

5.3.2 Timing circuit for ferrite-core memory

A simplified timing circuit for a digital computer containing a ferrite-core memory is shown in Fig. 5.3.4. Examples of timing waveforms are given in Fig. 5.3.5.

A ferrite-core memory contains a large number of toroids (cores) of (magnetic) ferrite material arranged in either a two-dimensional or a three-dimensional array. Each core represents a binary digit with the two directions of magnetisation (clockwise and anticlockwise) representing binary 0 and 1. Each core is threaded with a number of wires required for reading information from the cores and writing information into the cores. Reading is accomplished by passing current pulses through selected wires and by sensing the voltages induced in 'sense wires'. This latter operation is accomplished by 'strobing' the outputs of sense amplifiers (used to amplify these induced voltages) into the flip-flops of a 'memory

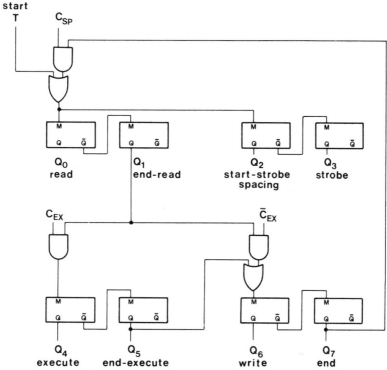

Fig. 5.3.4 Simplified timing circuit for digital computer containing ferrite-core memory

data register'. Reading is 'destructive' as all read cores are set into the 0 state. To 'regenerate' (or 'restore') the information lost by the reading process back into the memory, further current pulses are passed through selected wires as part of a writing process which writes the contents of the memory data register into selected cores of the memory.

Writing data into a ferrite-core memory is accomplished by setting the data into the memory data register and by initiating a 'read-write cycle' in which the strobing of the sense amplifier outputs is inhibited. The reading process 'clears' (i.e. sets to zero) the selected cores and the following writing process stores the contents of the memory data register into these cores.

A ferrite-core memory may be designed to operate with a *'read-execute-write cycle'* (also called a 'split memory cycle'). With such a cycle, data may be read from selected cores into the memory data register; the contents of this register may then be used with other data in an arithmetic or logic operation to produce a result which is then loaded into the memory data register, over-writing the earlier contents, and finally the new contents of this register are written into the selected cores. In a read-execute-write cycle, time must be allowed for the reliable execution of the arithmetic/logic operation between the reading and writing parts of the cycle. However, this time is not required for a normal read-write cycle for reading from or writing into the memory as described above.

In a digital computer containing a ferrite-core memory the signal which determines when the memory cycle is to be a read-execute-write cycle may be determined by the data read from the memory. In Fig. 5.3.4 and Fig. 5.3.5. this signal is denoted C_{EX}. It will be assumed that this signal becomes available at the rising edge of the strobe pulse (Q_3).

The simplified timing circuit for a digital computer containing a ferrite-core memory shown in Fig. 5.3.4 can be structured using four of the 'building blocks' (represented by Fig. 5.3.3) and described in the previous section (Section 5.3.1). The significance of the outputs of the eight monostable multivibrators (of Fig. 5.3.4) is as follows:

Q_0: READ (i.e. the waveforms of the current pulse for reading)

Q_1: END-READ (i.e. the end of the read waveform)

Q_2: START-STROBE-SPACING (i.e. the time duration between the start of the memory cycle and the strobe pulse)

Q_3: STROBE (i.e. the pulse for sensing the amplified induced voltages from the sense wires)

Q_4: EXECUTE (i.e. the time allowed for the execute part of a read-execute-write memory cycle)

Q_5: END-EXECUTE (i.e. the end of the execute waveform)

Q_6: WRITE (i.e. the waveform of the current pulse for writing)

Q_7: END (i.e. the end of the memory cycle)

An examination of Fig. 5.3.4 will show that the 'start pulse' (T) triggers both the Q_0 and Q_2 monostable multivibrators. The pulse width of Q_2 is less than that of Q_0 (being typically 30–50% that of Q_0). Hence, Q_3 will be produced before Q_1. On the rising edge of Q_3, it is assumed that data is read from the core memory and the signal C_{EX} is defined at approximately this time. This signal is used to gate the Q_1 pulse. If $C_{EX} = 1$, Q_1 will trigger Q_4 and not Q_6. In this case, Q_5 follows Q_4 and is used to trigger Q_6 at the end of which Q_7 is produced to signify the end of the cycle. Alternatively if $C_{EX} = 0$, Q_1 will trigger Q_6 and not Q_4, and at the end of Q_6, Q_7 is again produced to signify the end of the cycle.

Fig. 5.3.4 shows that the end pulse Q_7 is fed back (via an AND-OR-gate) to the trigger input of Q_0. This circuit interconnection produces a continuous sequence of memory

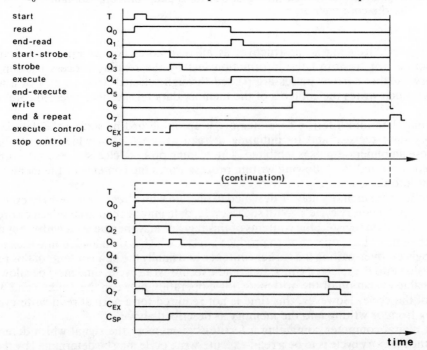

Fig. 5.3.5 Examples of timing waveforms for digital computer containing ferrite-core memory

cycles, some of which may be of the 'read-execute-write' type with the remainder of the 'read-write' type as explained above. Memory cycles may be terminated by gating the end pulse Q_7 with a 'stop signal' C_{SP}, and may be initiated again by a pulse applied to the 'start signal' T of the timing circuit.

Examples of timing waveforms are given in Fig. 5.3.5. These should now be analysed by the reader to confirm his/her understanding of the timing circuit of Fig. 5.3.4.

5.3.3 Timing circuit for a multiplier recoding technique

T ιe *'add-shift'* mechanism for binary multiplication was described in Chapter 4. It is recalled that this mechanism requires the sensing of the multiplier bits one bit at a time to control the execution of a sequence of 'add-shift' or 'pass-shift' operations. In an add-shift operation, the multiplicand is added to the 'accumulated partial product' and the result shifted one bit position to the right. In a pass-shift operation, the accumulated partial product is just shifted one bit position to the right.

Circuit configurations for implementing an add-shift multiplier were described in Chapter 4. Part of one of these configurations with some slight modifications is reproduced in Fig. 5.3.6. In this figure, the multiplicand is held in a register represented by the flip-flops M_3, M_2, M_1 and M_0, and the accumulated partial product is held in another register represented by the flip-flops A_3, A_2, A_1 and A_0. The arithmetic-logic-unit is used to add the contents of the two registers. For such an operation the data path from the output of flip-flop A_3 to the input of flip-flop A_2 is indicated by the symbol p1 in Fig. 5.3.6 and similar data paths apply to other flip-flops. The arithmetic-logic-unit may be 'by-passed' by providing the AND-OR-gates of Fig. 5.3.6, and by introducing an alternative data path

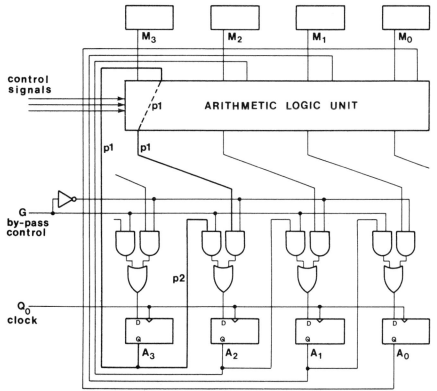

Fig. 5.3.6 Circuit arrangement to by-pass the arithmetic-logic-unit for shift operations

indicated by the symbol p2. This alternative data path may be used for shift operations, and, as it passes through a much smaller number of gates in cascade, a much smaller 'settling time' could be used for these operations.

This section describes a '*multiplier-recoding*' technique which maximises the number of pass-shift operations in an 'add-shift multiplication' procedure. Using this technique together with the circuit configuration represented by Fig. 5.3.6, the mean time taken by the multiplication procedure may be substantially reduced.

The term 'multiplier-recoding' is used here to describe the process of translating (i.e. recoding) the sequence of 0s and 1s defined by the serial representation of the multiplier (in the order of increasing bit significance) into an equivalent sequence of 0s, +1s and −1s. Hence a binary representation with allowable values 0 and 1 is recoded into a 'ternary' representation with three allowable values of 0, +1 and −1. In the present context, these three values (0, +1 and −1) define the three operations 'pass', 'add' and 'subtract' respectively, and it is therefore assumed that the arithmetic-logic-unit and associated circuitry utilised by the multiplier can perform any of the three operations 'pass-shift', 'add-shift' and 'subtract-shift'.

An example of a recoded multiplier is shown in Table 5.3.1. In this table the digits are set out using the normal convention of increasing digit significance running from right to left. For the example of Table 5.3.1 the binary coded multiplier contains the nine 1s and hence nine 'add-shift operations' are involved; however, the ternary coded multiplier contains only three +1s or −1s, and hence only three 'add-shift' or 'subtract-shift' operations are involved.

Table 5.3.1 Example of multiplier recoding

MULTIPLIER (BINARY)	0	0	1	1	1	1	1	0	1	1	1	1	0
RECODED MULTIPLIER	0	+1	0	0	0	0	0	−1	0	0	0	−1	0

The recoding of binary sequences may be achieved by introducing the concept of a 'string of ones' (which shall be referred to simply as a '*string*'). Two or more consecutive ones in a binary sequence will constitute a string by definition. In addition, an 'isolated zero' will be defined as a zero which is flanked by ones which form part of a string, and finally an 'isolated one' will be defined as a one which is not a member of a string and which is flanked by zeros. The example of Table 5.3.1 shows a single string with an isolated zero.

The procedure of recoding an n-bit binary multiplier may be accomplished by examining two multiplier bits P_{i+1} and P_i in the ith step of the procedure (for $i = 1---n$) and by producing control signals which determine whether the 'present operation to be performed' is to be a pass-shift, add-shift or subtract-shift operation. A flip-flop must be used to record which of the two operations add-shift or subtract-shift was last performed. This flip-flop must be set initially to the state which specifies that the last operation performed was add-shift. To satisfy the previously given definitions of 'string', 'isolated zero' and 'isolated one', the 'present operation to be performed' must be determined according to Table 5.3.2.

Points of detail such as how to specify P_{i+1} for $i = n$ and what modifications are required to handle two's complement multipliers will not be discussed here. For the present purpose, we shall assume that the circuit configuration of Fig. 5.3.6 is used, and that the clock signal Q_0 applied to the D-type flip-flops A_3, A_2, A_1 and A_0 of Fig. 5.3.6 will be applied to the D-type flip-flop specifying the last operation performed but also the D-type flip-flops of the multiplier register which provides the signals P_{i+1} and P_i. Hence, it is assumed that the control signal G to by-pass the arithmetic-logic-unit (see Fig. 5.3.6) may

Table 5.3.2 Multiplier recoding technique

MULTIPLIER $P_{i+1}P_i$		LAST ARITHMETIC OPERATION	INTERPRETATION	PRESENT OPERATION
1	1	add-shift	initiate string	subtract-shift
0	0	subtract-shift	terminate string	add-shift
1	0	subtract-shift	isolated zero	subtract-shift
0	1	add-shift	isolated one	add-shift
All other conditions			ones within strings or zeros outside strings	pass-shift

be formed (according to the requirements of the above table) soon after the rising edge of the clock signal Q_0. This control signal (G) determines which of the data paths (viz.: p1 or p2 of Fig. 5.3.6) is to be selected. However, it must also determine *when* the next Q_0 pulse is to occur. If G = 0, data path p1 is selected and the time duration before the next Q_0 pulse must be sufficient for the reliable execution of an add/subtract-shift operation. This time duration will be denoted by T_A. Alternatively if G = 1, data path p2 is selected and the time duration before the next Q_0 pulse may be shorter than T_A, being just sufficient for the reliable execution of a shift operation. This time duration will be denoted by T_s.

Part of the timing circuit for generating the clock signal Q_0 is shown in Fig. 5.3.7. This circuit assumes that the first (least-significant) pair of multiplier digits is sensed before the start signal T is produced to trigger the Q_0 monostable multivibrator for the first time. Soon after the front edge of this first Q_0 pulse, a new pair of multiplier digits is formed (as the Q_0 clock is also used to shift the multiplier register) and the new value of the control signal G is established. Hence this signal can be used to gate the Q_1 pulse which is triggered on the falling edge of Q_0. If G = 1, the rising edge of Q_1 triggers Q_2 and not Q_4; and if G = 0, the rising edge of Q_1 triggers Q_4 and not Q_2. The pulse width of Q_2 is adjusted so that the sum of the pulse widths of Q_0 and Q_2 is equal to T_s which is the allowed settling time for

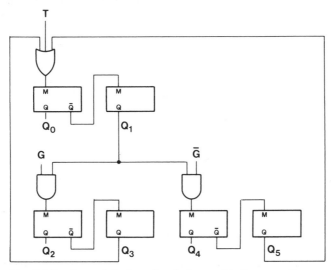

Fig. 5.3.7 Part of timing circuit for multiplier recoding

a shift operation. Similarly, the pulse width of Q_4 is adjusted so that the sum of the pulse widths of Q_0 and Q_4 is equal to T_A which is the allowed settling time for an add/subtract-shift operation.

When $G = 1$, the falling edge of Q_2 triggers Q_3, and Q_3 in turn triggers Q_0 which, in this case, performs a shift operation. Alternatively, when $G = 0$, the falling edge of Q_4 triggers Q_5, and Q_5 in turn triggers Q_0 which, in this case, performs an add/subtract-shift operation.

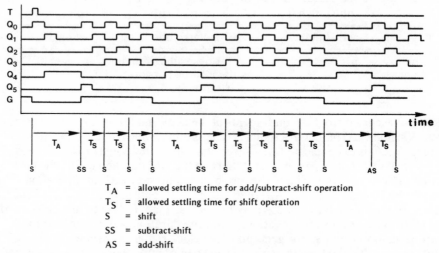

T_A = allowed settling time for add/subtract-shift operation
T_S = allowed settling time for shift operation
S = shift
SS = subtract-shift
AS = add-shift

Fig. 5.3.8   Example of timing waveforms for multiplier recoding

The reader is now advised to analyse the waveforms of Fig. 5.3.8 which should be found to be consistent with the description given above. These waveforms have also been drawn to correspond to the example of the recoded multiplier given in Table 5.3.1.

It is to be noted that that part of the timing circuit which counts the number of Q_0 pulses and which terminates the multiplication procedure has been omitted from Fig. 5.3.7. It is also possible that the circuit of Fig. 5.3.7 may be simplified by a reduction of the number of monostable multivibrators. However, this should be of little concern for the present purpose, as the intention has been to utilise the building block of Fig. 5.3.3(a), and to provide a very interesting application of monostable multivibrators.

5.3.4   Some timing diagram conventions

Timing diagrams presented earlier in this chapter have assumed ideal circuit characteristics, viz.:

 (i) extremely small rise and fall times, and
 (ii) extremely small delays between signal transitions (e.g. when the transition of one
      signal causes the transition of another).

An illustration of a more realistic representation of timing waveforms is given in Fig. 5.3.9. This figure uses sloped lines to represent the rising and falling edges of each waveform, thus indicating that rise and fall times are finite and not always negligibly small. In addition the waveforms corresponding to circuits in cascade are shown with definite delays.

The curved arrows in Fig. 5.3.9 indicate the relationships between some edges of the timing waveforms. For example the two arrows which start from the front edge of the T waveform indicate that it is the LOW-to-HIGH transition of T which causes the Q_0 and Q_2 monostable multivibrators to be triggered. The arrow which starts from the falling edge of

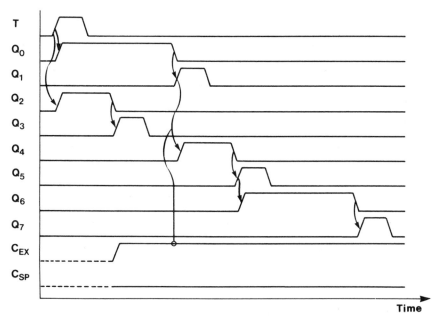

Fig. 5.3.9 Diagram illustrating some timing diagram conventions (This diagram corresponds to the top section of Fig. 5.3.5)

Q_0 indicates that it is the $\overline{Q}_0$ signal which triggers the Q_1 monostable multivibrator. Finally it is to be noted that the arrow starting from the rising edge of the Q_1 waveform is linked with a line starting from a small circle which defines the high level of the C_{EX} waveform. This indicates that the condition $C_{EX} = 1$ *enables* the triggering of the Q_4 monostable multivibrator by the rising edge of the Q_1 waveform.

The conventions used in the timing diagram of Fig. 5.3.9 provide a better understanding of the inter-relationship between the various waveforms.

5.4 DESIGN EXAMPLE

5.4.1 Specifications
A simple timing unit under the control of a pushbutton and a switch X is to be designed. Whenever the pushbutton is depressed signals F_0, F_1 and F_2 are to be produced. These signals, which are dependent on the setting of the switch X, are defined by Fig. 5.4.1 in which F_{00}, F_{10} and F_{20} are the required signals when $X = 0$, and F_{01}, F_{11} and F_{21} are the signals when $X = 1$.

It is to be noted from Fig. 5.4.1 that the edges of the signals F_0, F_1 and F_2 are defined by the rising edge of a clock signal T_C. The signal T_I also shown in Fig. 5.4.1. has the function of a 'clear' signal. It may be considered that this signal (T_I) is derived from an 'initial set' pushbutton or from a 'power-on' circuit (i.e. a circuit which produces an active signal only when the power is initially turned on).

5.4.2 Design of timing unit
The approach to the design of the timing unit taken in this section is the approach described in earlier chapters for clocked synchronous circuits. In this approach all flip-flops are of the same type, and are clocked by the system clock T_C. Outputs of the circuit

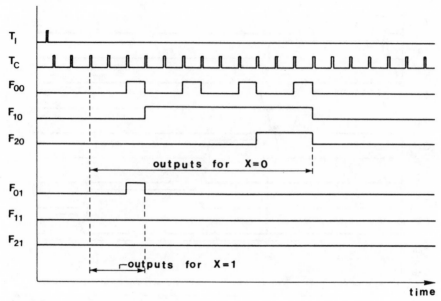

Fig. 5.4.1   Timing unit waveforms

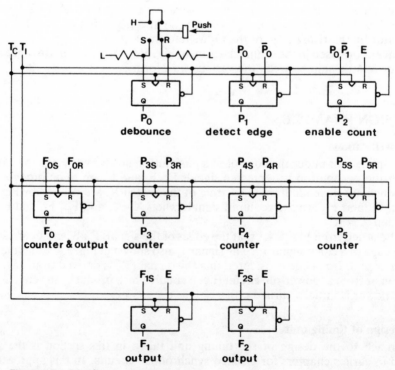

Fig. 5.4.2   Flip-flops of timing unit

are the flip-flop outputs themselves (whenever possible), or Boolean functions of the flip-flop outputs and input signals. The signal T_1 is initially used to reset all flip-flops.

From the specifications of the circuit given in Section 5.4.1, it is possible to identify several sections of the design which appear to have general application. These sections are:

  (i) the 'debouncing' of a pushbutton,
 (ii) the detection of the front edge of a waveform,
(iii) the generation of a 'pulse' which is low for 'l' clock periods and high for 'h' clock periods ($l = 2$, $h = 1$ for Fig. 5.4.1),
 (iv) the counting of pulses, and
  (v) start-stop control for the generation of pulses.

One solution of the present problem is based on the nine positive-edge-triggered R–S flip-flops shown in Fig. 5.4.2. The functions of the flip-flops are as follows:

P_0 : debounce pushbutton
P_1 : detect edge
P_2 : enable/disable counter
F_0 : counter and output
P_3 : counter
P_4 : counter
P_5 : counter
F_1 : output
F_2 : output

The circuit details for the P_0 flip-flop in Fig. 5.4.2 show how a flip-flop (or two cross-coupled NAND-gates) may be used to debounce a pushbutton or switch. After the S contact (see Fig. 5.4.2) 'makes' with the moving arm of the pushbutton for the first time, and goes 'high' for a time which is sufficient for the P_0 flip-flop to be set (to one), subsequent making and breaking of the S contact will not alter the state of the P_0 flip-flop. Again on the release of the pushbutton, after the R contact makes with the moving arm for the first time and goes 'high' for a time which is sufficient to reset the flip-flop, subsequent making and breaking of the R contact will not alter the state of the flip-flop. Hence the depression and release of the pushbutton results in a single low-to-high transition and a single high-to-low transition of P_0 as shown in Fig. 5.4.3.

The S and R inputs of the P_1 flip-flop are P_0 and $\overline{P}_0$ respectively. Hence the P_1 waveform is the same as that of P_0 but delayed by one clock period (as shown in Fig. 5.4.3). The condition $P_0\overline{P}_1$ may now be used to detect the low-to-high transition of P_0 (delayed by one clock period).

The counter enable/disable flip-flop, P_2 operates as a 'start-stop' flip-flop. It is set by the condition $P_0\overline{P}_1$ (with the significance explained above) and it is reset by the 'end' condition E. This condition may be derived from the timing waveforms of Fig. 5.4.3, and is defined by:

$$E = XF_0 + \overline{X}F_0P_4P_5$$

The four flip-flops F_0, P_3, P_4 and P_5 are used as a four-stage counter to define the 12 clock periods labelled 'outputs for $X = 0$' in Fig. 5.4.1. The design of such a counter follows methods described in earlier chapters. However the counter does have an 'enable' input P_2. Hence P_2 should be 'ANDed' with signals which set and reset the counter flip-flops. In addition the 'end' condition E requires all flip-flops to be reset. Hence $\overline{E}$ should be 'ANDed' with signals which set counter flip-flops, and E should be 'ORed' with signals which reset these flip-flops.

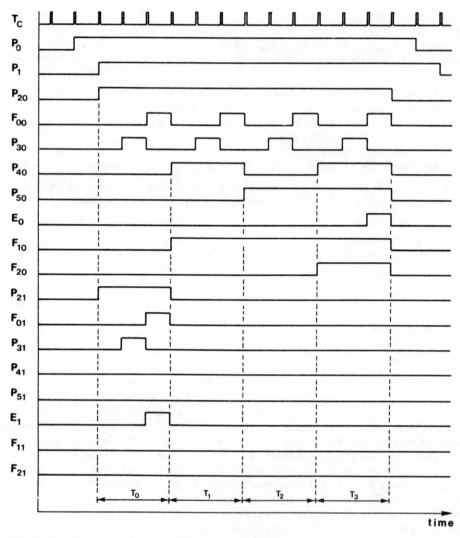

Fig. 5.4.3   Internal and external timing waveforms

Signals which set and reset the counter flip-flops are defined by Fig. 5.4.2 and the Boolean equations:

$$F_{0S} = P_2 \overline{E} P_3 \qquad \text{(set } F_0\text{)}$$
$$F_{0R} = P_2 \overline{P}_3 + E \qquad \text{(reset } F_0\text{)}$$
$$P_{3S} = P_2 \overline{E} \, \overline{F}_0 \overline{P}_3 \qquad \text{(set } P_3\text{)}$$
$$P_{3R} = P_2 \overline{F}_0 P_3 + E \qquad \text{(reset } P_3\text{)}$$
$$P_{4S} = P_2 \overline{E} F_0 \overline{P}_4 \qquad \text{(set } P_4\text{)}$$
$$P_{4R} = P_2 F_0 P_4 + E \qquad \text{(reset } P_4\text{)}$$
$$P_{5S} = P_2 \overline{E} F_0 P_4 \overline{P}_5 \qquad \text{(set } P_5\text{)}$$
$$P_{5R} = P_2 F_0 P_4 P_5 + E \qquad \text{(reset } P_5\text{)}$$

The outputs of the timing unit are F_0, F_1 and F_2. The output F_0 is defined above. The signals which set and reset F_1 and F_2 are defined by Fig. 5.4.2 and the Boolean equations:

$$F_{1S} = \overline{E}F_0 \qquad \text{(set } F_1)$$
$$F_{2S} = \overline{E}F_0\overline{P}_4P_5 \qquad \text{(set } F_2)$$

Fig. 5.4.2 and the above Boolean equations define the design of the timing unit. Verification by the reader is advised.

5.5 QUESTIONS

5.5.1 Clock skew

The circuits of Fig. 5.5.1(a) and (b) represent alternative implementations for a part of a large sequential circuit. The function of this part is to count the number of ONEs produced

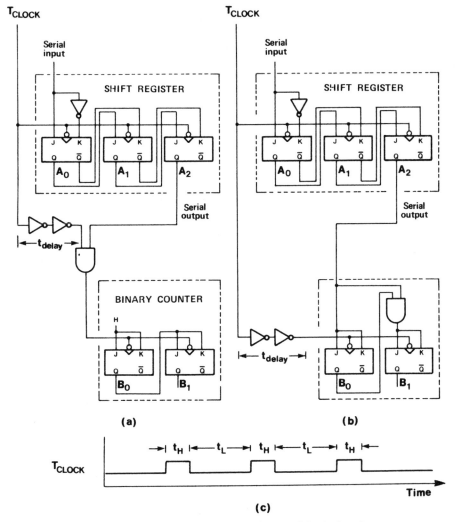

Fig. 5.5.1 Circuits and clock timing for question on 'clock skew'

by the serial output of a 3-bit shift-register. The waveform of the clock T_{CLOCK} is shown in Fig. 5.5.1(c). Each flip-flop of the circuits is a master-slave J–K flip-flop which transfers input data into the master flip-flop on the rising edge of the clock, and transfers the setting of the master into the slave flip-flop on the falling edge of the clock. The two inverters in series define a time delay (t_{delay}) between clocks used in various parts of the circuits. It is assumed for each implementation that the shift register may be loaded initially with a 3-bit number and that the counter may be initially cleared.

For the two alternative implementations, describe the limitations which must be placed on the value of the time delay t_{delay} for each circuit to function correctly. Briefly discuss the timing arrangements used in the circuits.

5.5.2   Timing signals for sector number

It is required to generate timing signals B_3, B_2, B_1 and B_0 from a 'sector clock' T. These timing signals are defined by the number sequence shown in Table 5.5.1, in which successive numbers in the sequence are represented by successive rows of the table. An examination of the sequence in decimal shows that each number is obtained from the preceding number by a subtraction of 3 (modulo-16). Four master-slave J–K flip-flops B_3, B_2, B_1 and B_0 are to be used in a clocked sequential circuit to generate the timing signals repetitively. The initial state of the circuit is given by $B_3 = 0$, $B_2 = 0$, $B_1 = 0$ and $B_0 = 0$. Show how such a circuit may be designed. (Hint: an examination of the two sequences for B_3, B_2, and B_1, B_0 will suggest an efficient design).

Table 5.5.1 Sector number sequence

NUMBER SEQUENCE				
DECIMAL	BINARY			
	B_3	B_2	B_1	B_0
0	0	0	0	0
13	1	1	0	1
10	1	0	1	0
7	0	1	1	1
4	0	1	0	0
1	0	0	0	1
14	1	1	1	0
11	1	0	1	1
8	1	0	0	0
5	0	1	0	1
2	0	0	1	0
15	1	1	1	1
12	1	1	0	0
9	1	0	0	1
6	0	1	1	0
3	0	0	1	1
0	0	0	0	0

5.5.3   Machine cycle with segment and digit periods

A timing unit receives a clock input T and a control input G. It generates output signals D_0, D_1, D_2, D_3, S_0, S_1, S_2, S_3 defined by Fig. 5.5.2.

It is to be noted that each 'machine cycle' consists of four 'segments' S_0, S_1, S_2, S_3 with each segment containing two, three or four 'digit periods'. The first digit period within a

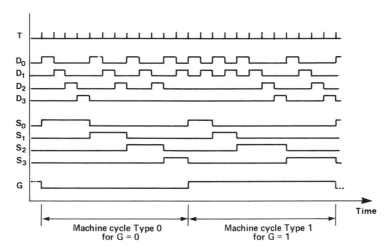

Fig. 5.5.2 Timing waveforms for question on machine cycle with segment and digit periods

segment is defined by the signal D_0, the second by D_1 and so on. The input control signal G is synchronised with the rising edge of the S_0 waveform. When G = 0 (which defines a type 0 machine cycle), the number of digit periods in S_0, S_1, S_2, S_3 are four, three, three, two respectively; and when G = 1 (which defines a type 1 machine cycle), the number of digit periods in S_0, S_1, S_2, S_3 are two, two, four, four respectively.

Sketch the circuit of the timing unit.

5.5.4 Phase logic

The instruction cycle of a computer consists of a sequence of phases from the six phases P_{FI}, P_{PO}, P_{ID}, P_{EO}, P_{E1} and P_{E2}. Control signals G_0, G_1 and G_2 are established by the computer before the rising edge of each pulse of a phase clock T. The phase logic is specified as follows.

    (a) From P_{FI}, the computer progresses to P_{EO} if $G_0 = 0$ and $G_1 = 0$; it progresses from P_{FI} to P_{PO} if $G_0 = 1$ and it progresses from P_{FI} to P_{ID} if $G_0 = 0$ and $G_1 = 1$.
    (b) From P_{PO}, it progresses to P_{EO} if $G_1 = 0$; and it progresses from P_{PO} to P_{ID} if $G_1 = 1$.
    (c) P_{EO} always follows P_{ID}.
    (d) From P_{EO}, it returns to P_{FI} if $G_2 = 0$; and it progresses from P_{EO} to P_{E1} if $G_2 = 1$.
    (e) P_{E2} always follows P_{E1}.
    (f) P_{FI} always follows P_{E2}.

Design the phase logic as specified using master-slave J–K flip-flops and NAND-gates. Draw a logic diagram of this phase logic.

5.5.5 Timing unit containing monostable multivibrators

Design a timing unit which has input signals X and T_{START}, and output signals T_{READ}, $T_{EXECUTE}$, T_{WRITE}, T_{END1}, $T_{START/STROBE}$, T_{STROBE}, $T_{OPERATE}$, T_{END2} and T_{END3}, as shown in Fig. 5.5.3. The timing unit is to have potentiometers which control the pulse widths T_R, T_X, T_W, T, T_{SS} and T_P. The output signals are described by Fig. 5.5.3 and the following description:

    T_{READ}:   A pulse of width T_R whose rising edge corresponds with the rising edge of T_{START}.

    $T_{EXECUTE}$:   A pulse of width T_X whose rising edge corresponds with the falling edge of T_{READ} when X = 1, or a signal which is ZERO when X = 0.

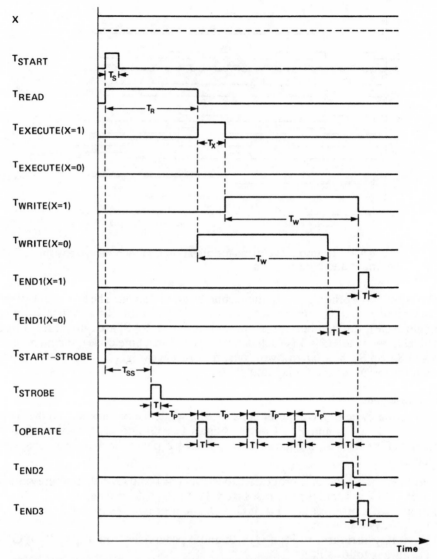

Fig. 5.5.3 Waveforms of timing unit containing monostable multivibrators

T_{WRITE}:	A pulse of width T_W whose rising edge corresponds with the falling edge of $T_{EXECUTE}$ when $X = 1$, or with the falling edge of T_{READ} when $X = 0$.
T_{END1}:	A pulse of width T whose rising edge corresponds with the falling edge of T_{WRITE}.
$T_{START/STROBE}$:	A pulse of width T_{SS} whose rising edge corresponds with the rising edge of T_{START}.
T_{STROBE}:	A pulse of width T whose rising edge corresponds with the falling edge of T_{SS}.
$T_{OPERATE}$:	A train of four pulses with width T, pulse spacing T_P and with the spacing between the rising edge of T_{STROBE} and the rising edge of the first pulse equal to T_P.

T_{END2}:   A pulse of width T corresponding to the fourth pulse of $T_{OPERATE}$.

T_{END3}:   A pulse of width T whose rising edge corresponds with the rising edge of either T_{END1} or T_{END2} depending on which rising edge occurs later in time.

5.5.6 Pushbutton and switch controlled timing unit

A timing unit under the control of a pushbutton and a switch X is to be designed. Whenever the pushbutton is depressed signals F_0 and F_1 are to be produced. These signals which are dependent on the setting of the switch X, are defined by Fig. 5.5.4 in which F_{00} and F_{10} are the required signals when X = 0; and F_{01} and F_{11} are the signals when X = 1. The edges of the signals F_0 and F_1 are defined by the rising edge of a given clock signal T_C. The signal T_I is a given 'power-on initialisation' signal. Design the timing unit using the approach described in Section 5.4.

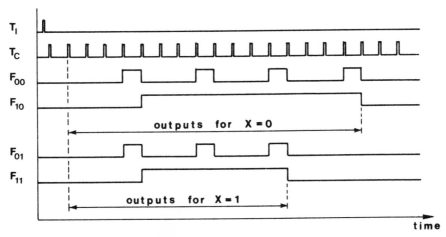

Fig. 5.5.4   Waveforms for question on pushbutton and switch controlled timing unit

6 PROGRAMMABLE-LOGIC-ARRAYS

Implementation of control signals for an arithmetic processor using field-programmable-logic-arrays

6.1 INTRODUCTION

A programmable-logic-array (PLA) is a two-level AND-OR circuit element with programmable interconnections which define the PLA's outputs in terms of Boolean functions of its inputs. The Boolean functions are in sum-of-products form and hence the programmable interconnections link:

(i) the inputs or their inverses to the AND-gates, and

(ii) AND-gate outputs to the OR-gates.

Programmable-logic-arrays are often used as component modules of very-large-scale-integrated circuits (VLSI) including microprocessors. For this purpose, very extensive computer-based aids are available for their design, testing and manufacture as part of a VLSI chip.

Programmable-logic-arrays are also available as circuit elements for use at the printed circuit board level. In these devices, known as 'field-programmable-logic-arrays' (FPLAs) every programmable interconnection is implemented as a fusible link, and 'programming' involves the (electronic) fusing of all links which are not required. This process is irreversible and hence a comprehensive verification of a circuit's design (perhaps by simulation) usually precedes the programming of FPLAs.

Compatibility with TTL circuits is a characteristic of some field-programmable-logic-arrays. Such devices can be used as substitutes for a large percentage of available small-scale and medium-scale TTL integrated circuits. In addition, however, they allow a very significant extension to the functional capability of these circuits, and hence implementations with good utilisation of FPLAs require a much smaller number of chips than those based on SSI and MSI components. This reduction can be by a factor of two or three.

Field-programmable-logic-arrays are available from different manufacturers in various configurations. These involve the following characteristics:

(i) number of inputs,

(ii) number of outputs,

(iii) number of AND-gates (i.e. product terms),

(iv) number of OR-gates,

(v) provision of a 'complement array' (i.e. EOR-gates) which allows a programmable AND-OR or AND-NOR configuration,

(vi) fixed or programmable interconnections from the outputs of the AND-gates to the inputs of the OR-gates,

(vii) provision of flip-flops defining circuit states and circuit outputs,

(viii) type and number of flip-flops,

(ix) interconnection between flip-flop outputs and AND-gate inputs,

(x) provision of an interconnection between an OR-gate output and AND-gate inputs.

Characteristic (vi) above was introduced so that devices such as the 'programmable-array-logic' devices (PALs) from Monolithic Memories Inc. can be included under the generic term 'field-programmable-logic-array'. Each PAL has a fixed interconnection between AND- and OR-gates. However, various configurations are possible from the family of PAL devices.

Some devices such as the 'field-programmable-gate-arrays' (FPGAs) from Signetics consist of an array of programmable AND-gates with no OR-gates at all.

Finally, the inclusion of flip-flops on chip provides an efficient implementation of complex sequential circuits or 'state machines'. The term 'field-programmable-logic-sequencer' (FPLS) has been used by Signetics to describe an LSI device which contains flip-flops in addition to a programmable AND-OR array. It is the term field-programmable-logic-sequencer (FPLS) which will be used in this book to describe the circuit extension of the field-programmable-logic-array (FPLA) by the addition of flip-flops with feedback interconnections.

The 'programmable read-only memory' (PROM) has an organisation similar to that of the FPLA, and may be used as well for function generation. The major difference between the two is that the PROM has a fixed AND array which performs the complete decoding of the input (address) lines. There are 2^n words (corresponding to 2^n AND-gates) in a PROM with n input (address) lines. When n is moderately large (say, 16) the PROM is much less efficient than the FPLA for the purpose of function generation.

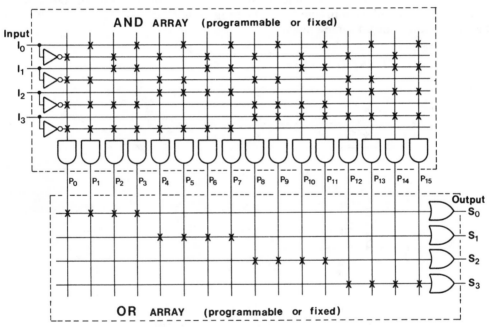

Fig. 6.1.1 Circuit of AND-OR arrays used to illustrate the difference between a PROM, PAL and FPLA

A circuit of an AND-OR array is shown in Fig. 6.1.1. The figure indicates that both the AND array and the OR array may be either programmable or fixed. These features may be used to illustrate the main differences between a PROM, PAL and FPLA. These differences are summarised by Table 6.1.1.

The organisations of a typical FPLA and a FPLS are described in Section 6.2. The design approach required for the implementation of control signals of an arithmetic processor using FPLAs is described in Section 6.3. Questions in Section 6.4 terminate the chapter.

6.2 ORGANISATION OF PROGRAMMABLE-LOGIC-ARRAYS

The organisation of a typical field-programmable-logic-array (FPLA) is shown in Fig. 6.2.1. This FPLA has sixteen inputs and eight outputs defined by 48 product terms. The

Table 6.1.1 Table illustrating differences between
a PROM, PAL and FPLA

	AND array	OR array
PROM	Fixed	Programmable
PAL	Programmable	Fixed
FPLA	Programmable	Programmable

FPLA consists of an AND array, an OR array, an EOR array and gates which control the
outputs via an 'enable' input. The AND array consists of 48 diode resistor AND-gates each
connected to sixteen 'true inputs' and sixteen 'complement inputs' via 32 fusible nichrome
links. The OR array consists of eight emitter follower OR-gates each connected to the 48
outputs of the AND array via 48 fusible links. The EOR array consists of eight EOR-gates.
One input of each EOR-gate is connected to the output of an OR-gate. The other input is
connected to ground via a fusible link. The programming of the FPLA is performed by
fusing (opening) the unwanted links.

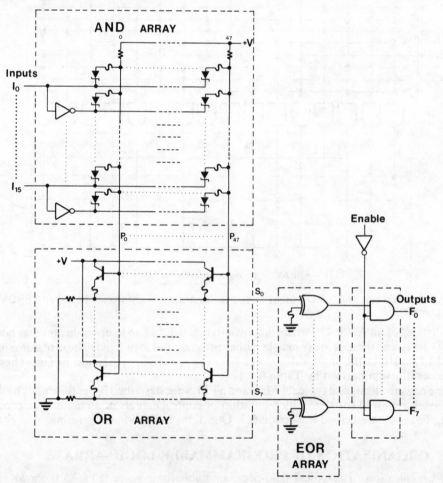

Fig. 6.2.1 Typical organisation of FPLA

The organisation of a typical field-programmable-logic-sequencer (FPLS) is shown in Fig. 6.2.2. This FPLS has sixteen inputs and eight outputs defined by the state of an eight-stage 'output register'. The FPLS consists of an AND array, an OR array, a complement array, an output register and a state register. The AND array contains 48 gates each with fusible link input connections to (i) the sixteen true inputs, (ii) sixteen complement inputs, (iii) true outputs of the state register, (iv) complement outputs of the state register and (v) the output of the complement array. The OR array contains 28 OR-gates each with fusible link connections to the outputs of the 48 AND-gates. The complement array contains a single NOR-gate with fusible link connections to the outputs of the 48 AND-gates. The

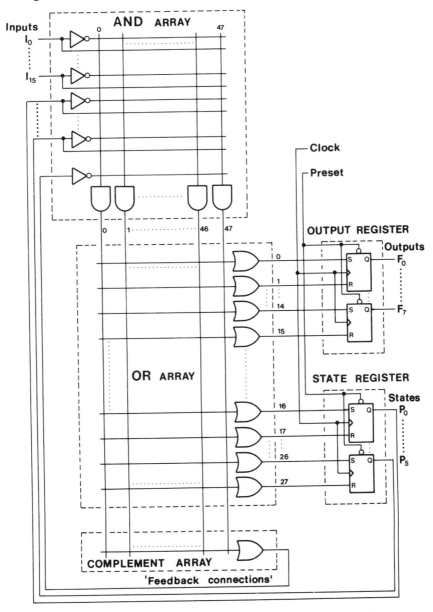

Fig. 6.2.2 Organisation of 'field-programmable-logic-sequencer'

output of this array provides a 'feedback' connection to the input of the AND array. The 28 outputs of the OR array provide the 'set' and 'reset' inputs of the fourteen clocked R–S flip-flops which comprise the eight-stage output register and the six-stage state register. The flip-flops have common 'preset' and 'clock' inputs.

The organisation of the FPLS of Fig. 6.2.2 is seen to be that of a synchronous sequential circuit. The six-stage state register provides the circuit with 2^6 internal states, while the eight-stage output register provides eight synchronous outputs. If additional internal states are required any of the flip-flops of the output register may be used as a state flip-flop by providing an external interconnection between the flip-flop output and an input of the FPLS.

6.3 IMPLEMENTATION OF CONTROL SIGNALS OF AN ARITHMETIC PROCESSOR USING PROGRAMMABLE-LOGIC-ARRAYS

Sections 6.3.1 to 6.3.6 (inclusive) describe the design of an arithmetic processor capable of the operations 'load', 'add', 'subtract', 'multiply' and 'divide'. Section 6.3.7 describes the implementation of the control signals for this arithmetic processor using programmable-logic-arrays.

6.3.1 Specification of arithmetic processor

The arithmetic processor to be designed is to operate on 4-bit, two's complement numbers. These numbers may be considered as either 'integers' or 'fractions' for the operations 'load', 'add' and 'subtract'. The 'divide' operation will utilise a non-restoring, binary division algorithm applicable to two's complement fractions, and hence both operands and the resultant quotient must be considered as two's complement fractions for this operation. For the 'multiply' operation, an 'add-shift' procedure is to be used, and the double-length product is to be formatted as a double-length fraction with the 'waste' bit set into the most-significant bit position of 'word 2' (i.e. with the format of the 4-bit equivalent of Fig. 4.2.3(a)).

The arithmetic processor is to contain a switch register M with outputs M_3, M_2, M_1, M_0, and two registers A and Q with outputs A_3, A_2, A_1, A_0 and Q_3, Q_2, Q_1, Q_0 respectively. When these registers contain single-length numbers, the subscript 3 refers to the sign bit and the subscript 0 refers to the least-significant magnitude bit.

For the multiply operation, the multiplicand is set into the M register and the multiplier is initially held in the Q register. The A register may be cleared initially or may be used to hold a number which is added to the double-length product. The final result is held in $A_3, A_2, A_1, A_0, Q_2, Q_1, Q_0$ with Q_3 set to 0. This result is equal to $M \times Q + 2^{-3}A$ where M, Q and A are the fractions held in registers M, Q and A respectively.

Table 6.3.1 Specification of arithmetic processor

R_2	R_1	R_0	OPERATION	DESCRIPTION
0	0	0	Load A	$M \rightarrow A$
0	0	1	Load Q	$M \rightarrow Q$
0	1	0	Add	$A + M \rightarrow A$
0	1	1	Subtract	$A - M \rightarrow A$
1	0	0	Multiply	$M \times Q + 2^{-3}A \rightarrow AQ$
1	0	1	Divide	$AQ \div M \rightarrow Q$

For the divide operation, the divisor is initially set into the M register and the double-length dividend into the A and Q registers, which may be considered to form a double-length register which we shall designate AQ. The quotient is produced in the Q register.

The arithmetic processor must be capable of six operations. The operation to be performed is specified by the setting of three toggle switches R_2, R_1, R_0 according to Table 6.3.1.

The operation specified by the toggle switches R_2, R_1, R_0 is to be initiated by pressing a pushbutton. Monitor lights connected to the flip-flops of the A and Q registers are to be used to verify results.

6.3.2 Structure of arithmetic processor required by the multiply and divide operations

The circuit of an 'add-shift multiplication' unit for two's complement fractions was given in Fig. 4.5.7, and the required timing waveforms were shown in Fig. 4.5.6. The essential features of this unit may be summarised as follows:

- (i) there is a 4-bit arithmetic unit which can produce at its outputs either (a) A, (b) A plus M, or (c) A minus M where A and M are the numbers held in the A and M registers respectively,
- (ii) there is an additional (sign extension) adder stage to eliminate arithmetic overflow,
- (iii) there is a data path from the A and M registers through the adder and back to the A register such that any one of the operations (a) 'pass-shift', (b) 'add-shift' or (c) 'subtract-shift' (where the direction of each shift operation is to the right) may be carried out using a single clock pulse,
- (iv) there is a data-selector which inhibits the shifting of the more significant half of the result for the last clock pulse so that the more significant half of the product is positioned correctly in the A register,
- (v) the Q register operates as as right shift-register,
- (vi) the multiplier bit presented at the Q_0 output and the timing waveform T_S (of Fig. 4.5.6) determine (a) which of the operations, A, A plus M or A minus M is to be performed, and (b) whether a shifting of the result is to take place as shown in Table 6.3.2.

Table 6.3.2 Control conditions and operations in an add-shift multiplication unit for two's-complement fractions

Q_0	T_S	OPERATION	SHIFT
0	0	A	YES
1	0	A+M	YES
0	1	A	NO
1	1	A−M	NO

The circuit of a 'non-restoring division' unit for two's complement fractions was given in Fig. 4.6.6, and the required timing waveforms shown in Fig. 4.6.7. The essential features of this unit may be summarised as follows:

- (i) there is a 4-bit arithmetic unit which can produce at its outputs either (a) A plus M, or (b) A minus M,
- (ii) there is a data path from the A and M registers through the adder and back to the A register such that either of the two operations (a) 'add-shift' or (b) 'subtract-shift' (where the direction of each shift operation is to the left) may be carried out using a single clock pulse,

(iii) the Q register operates as a left shift-register,
(iv) the add/subtract control signal X (X = 0 for add) is determined initially by the signs of the divisor (M_3) and dividend (A_3), and following each clock pulse by the previously determined quotient digit appearing in the Q_0 flip-flop, with X being specified by the Boolean equation:

$$X = (\overline{M}_3\overline{A}_3 + M_3A_3)T_1 + Q_0\overline{T}_1$$

(v) the quotient digit is determined by the signs of the divisor (M_3) and the remainder (S_3) according to the Boolean equation:

$$Q = \overline{M}_3\overline{S}_3 + M_3S_3$$

A circuit which satisfies the requirements of the 'add-shift multiplication' unit and the 'non-restoring division' unit as well as the other required operations of Table 6.3.1 may be structured as shown in Fig. 6.3.1. The essential features of this structure are:

(i) there is an arithmetic unit with inputs A_3, A_2, A_1, A_0 and B_3, B_2, B_1, B_0 representing two 4-bit numbers A and B respectively, and with outputs C_{n+4}, F_3, F_2, F_1, F_0 which can be used to represent either (a) A, (b) B, (c) A plus B, or (d) A minus B,

(ii) there are two 4-bit, 3-line-to-1-line data-selectors which determine the inputs to the A and Q registers,

(iii) there are data paths associated with the A register which allow the outputs of the arithmetic unit to be either (a) directly loaded into the A register, or (b) shifted one bit position to the right before being loaded into the A register, or (c) shifted one bit position to the left before being loaded into the A register,

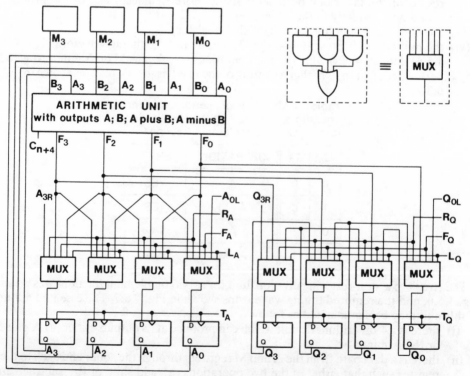

Fig. 6.3.1 Arithmetic processor for the operations ADD, SUBTRACT, MULTIPLY, DIVIDE, LOAD-A and LOAD-Q

(iv) there are data paths associated with the Q register which allow either (a) the outputs of the arithmetic unit to be directly loaded into the Q register, or (b) the contents of the Q register to be shifted to the right by one bit position, or (c) the contents of the Q register to be shifted to the left by one bit position.

The significance of the symbols introduced in Fig. 6.3.1 is as follows:

R_A : control signal for right shift of data into A
F_A : control signal for directly loading F (arithmetic unit outputs) into A
L_A : control signal for left shift of data into A
A_{3R} : data signal input to A_3 on right shift
A_{0L} : data signal input to A_0 on left shift
R_Q : control signal for right shift of Q
F_Q : control signal for directly loading F (arithmetic unit outputs) into Q
L_Q : control signal for left shift of Q
Q_{3R} : data signal input to Q_3 on right shift
Q_{0L} : data signal input to Q_0 on left shift
T_A : clock signal for A register
T_Q : clock signal for Q register

6.3.3 Structure of arithmetic processor using integrated circuits

The circuit represented by Fig. 6.3.1 may be implemented using six TTL MSI/LSI integrated circuits as shown in Fig. 6.3.2. The four types of integrated circuits used are:
(a) SN74181 Arithmetic logic unit/function generator
(b) SN7495A Four-bit parallel-access shift-register

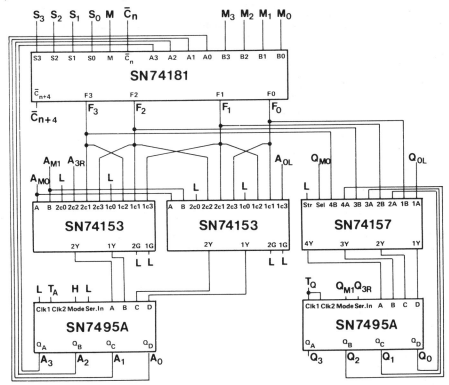

Fig. 6.3.2 Arithmetic processor for the operations ADD, SUBTRACT, MULTIPLY, DIVIDE, LOAD-A and LOAD-Q using six integrated circuits

(c) SN74153 Dual 4-line-to-1-line data-selector/multiplexer
(d) SN74157 Quadruple 2-line-to-1-line data-selector/multiplexer

The following points should be noted on inspection of Fig. 6.3.1 and Fig. 6.3.2.

   (i) the SN74181 is a 4-bit arithmetic logic unit capable of producing the required outputs A, B, A plus B and A minus B by appropriately defining the input control signals M, $\overline{C}_n$, S_3, S_2, S_1 and S_0,

  (ii) two SN7495A integrated circuits are used for the A and Q registers,

 (iii) two SN74153 integrated circuits are used to produce the input signals to the A register,

 (iv) the SN74157 and one SN7495A are used to produce a 4-bit bi-directional shift-register with parallel load inputs (and may be replaced by one integrated circuit in an alternate design).

The SN74153 data-selector uses two 'select' control signals to determine which one of four input signals is to be directed to the output. These signals are designated A_{M0} and A_{M1} in Fig. 6.3.2, and replace the three select control signals R_A, F_A and L_A in the preliminary design represented by Fig. 6.3.1.

Again the SN74157 data-selector uses one 'select' control signal, and the SN7495A uses one 'mode' control signal (defining parallel load or right shift). These signals are designated Q_{M0} and Q_{M1} in Fig. 6.3.2, and replace the three select control signals R_Q, F_Q and L_Q of Fig. 6.3.1. The remaining signals A_{3R}, A_{0L}, Q_{3R}, Q_{0L}, T_A and T_Q have the same significance in Fig. 6.3.2 as that of signals with the same designation in Fig. 6.3.1.

6.3.4 Detailed logical design of arithmetic processor

6.3.4.1 *Decoding of switches R_2, R_1 and R_0*

The three toggle switches R_2, R_1 and R_0 determine which of the six operations is to be performed according to Table 6.3.1. The switch outputs may therefore be *decoded* by defining the following control signals:

   (i) Load-A: $X_{LA} = \overline{R}_2\overline{R}_1\overline{R}_0$
  (ii) Load-Q: $X_{LQ} = \overline{R}_2\overline{R}_1R_0$
 (iii) Add: $X_A = \overline{R}_2R_1\overline{R}_0$
 (iv) Subtract: $X_S = \overline{R}_2R_1R_0$
  (v) Multiply: $X_M = R_2\overline{R}_1\overline{R}_0$
 (vi) Divide: $X_D = R_2\overline{R}_1R_0$

6.3.4.2 *SN74181 arithmetic logic unit control signals*

The SN74181 arithmetic logic unit is required to produce at its outputs one of the

Table 6.3.3 Required SN74181 inputs specified by the signals F_A, F_b, F_{A+B} and F_{A-B}

CONDITION	REQUIRED SN74181 OUTPUT	REQUIRED SN74181 INPUTS					
		S_3	S_2	S_1	S_0	M	$\overline{C}_n$
$F_A = 1$	F = A	L	L	L	L	L	H
$F_B = 1$	F = B	H	L	H	L	H	X
$F_{A+B} = 1$	F = A PLUS B	H	L	L	H	L	H
$F_{A-B} = 1$	F = A MINUS B	L	H	H	L	L	L

quantities A, B, A plus B and A minus B where A and B represent the two 4-bit input numbers. Four mutually exclusive signals F_A, F_B, F_{A+B} and F_{A-B} may be defined to represent the four conditions which require the SN74181 to produce A, B, A plus B and A minus B respectively. The control signals of the SN74181 which give these functions are shown in Table 6.3.3.

Hence, the SN74181 inputs may be defined in terms of F_A, F_B, F_{A+B} and F_{A-B} as follows:

   (i) $S_3 = F_B + F_{A+B}$
   (ii) $S_2 = F_{A-B}$
   (iii) $S_1 = F_B + F_{A-B}$
   (iv) $S_0 = F_{A+B}$
   (v) $M = F_B$
   (vi) $\overline{C}_n = F_A + F_{A+B}$

6.3.4.3   *The signals F_A, F_B, F_{A+B} and F_{A-B}*

The only condition which requires the arithmetic logic unit to produce A at its output (i.e. the condition $F_A = 1$) is the condition $Q_0 = 0$ in a multiply operation, hence:

$$F_A = X_M \overline{Q}_0$$

The two conditions which require the arithmetic logic unit to produce B at its output (i.e. the condition $F_B = 1$) are the conditions $X_{LA} = 1$ and $X_{LQ} = 1$ (i.e. load-A and load-Q operations). Hence:

$$F_B = X_{LA} + X_{LQ}$$

The three conditions which require the arithmetic logic unit to produce A+B at its output (i.e. the condition $F_{A+B} = 1$) are:
   (i)   an add operation,
   (ii)   a multiply operation when $Q_0 = 1$ and $T_S = 0$, and
   (iii)   a divide operation when $F_{SD} = 0$ (where F_{SD} is the condition for subtraction in a division operation). Hence:

$$F_{A+B} = X_A + X_M Q_0 \overline{T}_S + X_D \overline{F}_{SD}$$
$$F_{SD} = (\overline{M}_3 \overline{A}_3 + M_3 A_3) T_I + Q_0 \overline{T}_I$$

The three conditions which require the arithmetic logic unit to produce A−B at its output (i.e. the condition $F_{A-B} = 1$) are:
   (i)   a subtract operation,
   (ii)   a multiply operation when $Q_0 = 1$ and $T_S = 1$, and
   (iii)   a divide operation when $F_{SD} = 1$. Hence:

$$F_{A-B} = X_S + X_M Q_0 T_S + X_D F_{SD}$$

6.3.4.4   *Serial inputs to shift-registers*

The signal A_{3R} which is the input signal to the A_3 flip-flop of the A register during right shifts is required only for a multiply operation. This signal is the '*sum-difference output*' of a '*sign-extension*' *full adder-subtracter* as described in Section 4.5.3. The sign bit inputs of this full adder-subtracter are A_3 and $Q_0 M_3$. The carry-borrow input is defined by the timing signal T_S and the carry-borrow output $\overline{C}_{n+4}$ of the SN74181 integrated circuit. Addition is performed when $T_S = 0$, and subtraction when $T_S = 1$. The signal $\overline{C}_{n+4}$ is an active-LOW carry signal or an active-HIGH borrow signal as described in Section 4.4.4 and Section 4.4.5. Hence an active-HIGH carry-borrow signal is $\overline{T}_S \oplus \overline{C}_{n+4}$. When $Q_0 = 0$ it is necessary to make the carry-borrow input to the sign-extension adder-subtracter equal to zero so that $A_{3R} = A_3$. Hence this carry-borrow input is given by $Q_0(\overline{T}_S \oplus \overline{C}_{n+4})$, and the sum-difference output of the sign-extension adder-subtracter is defined as:

$$A_{3R} = (A_3 \oplus Q_0 M_3) \oplus Q_0(\overline{T}_S \oplus \overline{C}_{n+4})$$

The signal Q_{3R}, which is the input signal to the Q_3 flip-flop of the Q register during right shifts, is only required in the multiply operation. Fig. 4.5.7 shows that this signal is equal to the least-significant bit of the output of the parallel adder when $T_S = 0$, and is equal to zero when $T_S = 1$. In Fig. 6.3.2, the least significant bit of the output of the SN74181 arithmetic logic unit is designated F_0. Hence, Q_{3R} is defined by:

$$Q_{3R} = F_0 \overline{T}_S$$

It is to be noted that the effect of the $\overline{T}_S$ signal is to make the 'waste bit' of the double length product equal to zero.

The signal A_{0L}, which is the input signal to the A_0 flip-flop of the A register during left shifts, is only required for a divide operation. Fig. 4.6.6 shows that this signal is equal to Q_3. Hence:

$$A_{0L} = Q_3$$

It is to be noted that it is this signal which causes the division process to operate on a double-length dividend initially set into the AQ register. If the division process is to operate on a single-length dividend initially set into the A register, then we must set $A_{0L} = 0$.

The signal Q_{0L}, which is the input signal to the Q_0 flip-flop of the Q register during left shifts, is only required for a divide operation. Fig. 4.6.6 shows that the quotient digit Q is shifted into Q_0. Hence:

$$Q_{0L} = Q = \overline{M}_3 \overline{F}_3 + M_3 F_3$$

6.3.4.5 *Select signals of data-selectors*

An examination of the functional circuit diagram of the SN74153 data-selectors and of their wiring in Fig. 6.3.2 will confirm the entries of the first three columns of Table 6.3.4.

Table 6.3.4   Select signals of data-selectors

A_{M1}	A_{M0}	OPERATION	CONDITIONS
B of SN74153	A of SN74153		
0	0	—	
0	1	$F \rightarrow A$	$X_{LA}, X_A, X_S, (X_{LQ}), X_M T_S$
1	0	Right shift	$X_M \overline{T}_S$
1	1	Left shift	X_D

The fourth column of Table 6.3.4 lists the conditions which determine the select signals of the SN74153 data-selectors used in Fig. 6.3.2. It is to be noted that X_{LQ} may be added to Table 6.3.4 as shown as this may be considered a 'don't care' condition. For a load-Q operation, the SN74153 data-selector may produce F at its outputs, but this will do no harm as it is not clocked into the A register. Table 6.3.4 now enables the following equations to be established:

$$A_{M0} = \overline{X}_M + T_S$$

$$A_{M1} = X_M \overline{T}_{S+} X_D$$

An examination of the functional circuit diagrams of the SN7495A and SN74157 integrated circuits, and of their wiring in Fig. 6.3.2 will verify the entries in the first three columns of Table 6.3.5.

Table 6.3.5 Mode control of SN7495A and select signal of SN74157

Q_{M1}	Q_{M0}	OPERATION	CONDITIONS
Mode control SN7495A	Select SN74157		
0	0	Right shift	X_M
0	1	Right shift	X_M
1	0	Left shift	X_D
1	1	$F \rightarrow Q$	X_{LQ}

The fourth column of Table 6.3.5 follows from earlier descriptions. It is to be noted that the Q register is right shifted only for the multiply operation, and at other times, it is loaded from the SN74157 output. Hence:

$$Q_{M1} = \overline{X}_M$$

Again, the Q register is left shifted only for a divide operation, and hence the following equation may be used:

$$Q_{M0} = \overline{X}_D$$

6.3.4.6 *Timing signals and clocks*
The timing waveforms required for the 'add-shift multiplication' unit of Fig. 4.5.7 are shown in Fig. 4.5.6 and the timing waveforms for the 'non-restoring division' unit of Fig. 4.6.6 are shown in Fig. 4.6.7. These waveforms must now be modified to suit the requirements of the circuit of Fig. 6.3.2. The following points should be noted:
  (i) the outputs of the master-slave flip-flops in the SN7495A shift-registers change state on the falling edge of the clock pulse, and hence the T_S and T_I waveforms must be modified so that they change state also on the falling edge of the clock pulse (T_0), and
  (ii) the four clock pulses (T_0) are required only for the multiply and divide operations, and a single clock pulse for the A and Q registers would be adequate for all other operations.

An examination of Table 6.3.1 will show that the R_2 signal may be used to specify whether the timing unit is to produce one or four clock pulses. Hence, the timing unit to be designed has as inputs (i) R_2, and (ii) the output of the START pushbutton. The output waveforms of the timing unit are shown in Fig. 6.3.3.

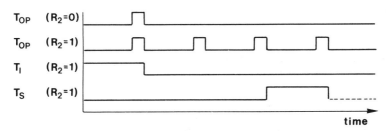

Fig. 6.3.3 Timing waveforms for the arithmetic processor

The A register is clocked by T_{OP} except for the 'load-Q' operation. Hence:

$$T_A = T_{OP}\overline{X}_{LQ}$$

The Q register is clocked by T_{OP} for the 'load-Q', 'multiply' and 'divide' operations, and hence:

$$T_Q = T_{OP}X_{LQ}+T_{OP}R_2$$

6.3.5 Summary of equations

The detailed logical design of the arithmetic processor described in the previous section may now be summarised by the following equations:

$$
\begin{align}
&\text{(i)} &X_{LA} &= \overline{R}_2\overline{R}_1\overline{R}_0 \\
&\text{(ii)} &X_{LQ} &= \overline{R}_2\overline{R}_1R_0 \\
&\text{(iii)} &X_A &= \overline{R}_2R_1\overline{R}_0 \\
&\text{(iv)} &X_S &= \overline{R}_2R_1R_0 \\
&\text{(v)} &X_M &= R_2\overline{R}_1\overline{R}_0 \\
&\text{(vi)} &X_D &= R_2\overline{R}_1R_0 \\
&\text{(vii)} &F_A &= X_M\overline{Q}_0 \\
&\text{(viii)} &F_B &= X_{LA}+X_{LQ} \\
&\text{(ix)} &F_{SD} &= (\overline{M}_3\overline{A}_3+M_3A_3)T_I+Q_0\overline{T}_I \\
&\text{(x)} &F_{A+B} &= X_A+X_MQ_0\overline{T}_S+X_D\overline{F}_{SD} \\
&\text{(xi)} &F_{A-B} &= X_S+X_MQ_0T_S+X_DF_{SD} \\
&\text{(xii)} &S_3 &= F_{A+B}+F_B \\
&\text{(xiii)} &S_2 &= F_{A-B} \\
&\text{(xiv)} &S_1 &= F_{A-B}+F_B \\
&\text{(xv)} &S_0 &= F_{A+B} \\
&\text{(xvi)} &M &= F_B \\
&\text{(xvii)} &\overline{C}_n &= F_A+F_{A+B} \\
&\text{(xviii)} &A_{3R} &= (A_3\oplus Q_0M_3)\oplus Q_0(\overline{T}_S\oplus\overline{C}_{n+4}) \\
&\text{(xix)} &Q_{3R} &= F_0\overline{T}_S \\
&\text{(xx)} &A_{0L} &= Q_3 \\
&\text{(xxi)} &Q_{0L} &= \overline{M_3\oplus F_3} \\
&\text{(xxii)} &A_{M0} &= \overline{X}_M+T_S \\
&\text{(xxiii)} &A_{M1} &= X_M\overline{T}_S+X_D \\
&\text{(xxiv)} &Q_{M0} &= \overline{X}_D \\
&\text{(xxv)} &Q_{M1} &= \overline{X}_M \\
&\text{(xxvi)} &T_A &= T_{OP}\overline{X}_{LQ} \\
&\text{(xxvii)} &T_Q &= T_{OP}X_{LQ}+T_{OP}R_2
\end{align}
$$

6.3.6 Summary of design

Up to this point, the design of the arithmetic processor whose specifications were given in Section 6.3.1 may be represented by:

(i) the circuit of Fig. 6.3.2,
(ii) the timing waveforms of Fig. 6.3.3, and
(iii) the Boolean equations of Section 6.3.5.

The implementation of the Boolean equations of Section 6.3.5 using MSI/LSI integrated circuits is an instructive exercise, and forms the basis of one of the questions in

Section 6.4. The implementation of these equations using field-programmable-logic-arrays will be described in Section 6.3.7.

6.3.7 Implementation of control logic using FPLAs

The Boolean equations of Section 6.3.5 define the following control signals, data signals and clocks:

$$S_3, S_2, S_1, S_0, M, \overline{C}_n : \text{control inputs of SN74181}$$

A_{M0}, A_{M1} : select inputs of SN74153

Q_{M0} : select input of SN74157

Q_{M1} : mode input of SN7495A of Q register

A_{3R} : serial input to A_3 for right shift

A_{0L} : serial input to A_0 for left shift

Q_{3R} : serial input to Q_3 for right shift

Q_{0L} : serial input to Q_0 for left shift

T_A, T_Q : clocks for A and Q registers

The equation $A_{0L} = Q_3$ represents a direct connection from the Q_3 output to the A_{0L} input. The remaining 15 signals and clocks are defined in terms of:

R_2, R_1, R_0, M_3 : switch inputs

$F_3, F_0, \overline{C}_{n+4}$: outputs of SN74181

A_3, Q_0 : outputs of A and Q registers

T_I, T_S, T_{OP} : timing waveforms

The fifteen signals and clocks may be generated using two FPLAs. The incorporation of these two elements (shown as PLA1 and PLA2) with other integrated circuits of the arithmetic processor is depicted in Fig. 6.3.4. The organisation of each FPLA is assumed to be that of Fig. 6.2.1.

The programming of the FPLAs requires that each output (or its complement) should be expressed as a sum-of-products expression in terms of its inputs. This requires considerable manipulation of the Boolean equations of Section 6.3.5. The resultant equations (which may be verified by the reader) are as follows:

$$S_3 = \overline{R}_2 R_1 \overline{R}_0 + R_2 \overline{R}_0 Q_0 \overline{T}_S + R_2 \overline{R}_0 \overline{Q}_0 \overline{T}_I + R_2 R_0 M_3 \overline{A}_3 T_I + R_2 R_0 \overline{M}_3 A_3 T_I + \overline{R}_2 R_1$$

$$S_2 = \overline{R}_2 R_1 R_0 + R_2 \overline{R}_0 Q_0 \overline{T}_S + R_2 R_0 \overline{M}_3 \overline{A}_3 T_I + R_2 R_0 M_3 A_3 T_I + R_2 R_0 Q_0 \overline{T}_I$$

$$S_1 = \overline{R}_2 R_1 R_0 + R_2 \overline{R}_0 Q_0 \overline{T}_S + R_2 R_0 \overline{M}_3 \overline{A}_3 T_I + R_2 R_0 M_3 A_3 T_I + R_2 R_0 Q_0 \overline{T}_I + \overline{R}_2 R_1$$

$$S_0 = \overline{R}_2 R_1 \overline{R}_0 + R_2 \overline{R}_0 Q_0 \overline{T}_S + R_2 R_0 \overline{Q}_0 \overline{T}_I + R_2 R_0 M_3 \overline{A}_3 T_I + R_2 R_0 \overline{M}_3 A_3 T_I$$

$$M = \overline{R}_2 R_1$$

$$\overline{C}_n = R_2 \overline{R}_1 \overline{R}_0 \overline{Q}_0 + \overline{R}_2 R_1 \overline{R}_0 + R_2 \overline{R}_0 Q_0 \overline{T}_S + R_2 R_0 \overline{Q}_0 \overline{T}_I + R_2 R_0 M_3 \overline{A}_3 T_I + R_2 R_0 \overline{M}_3 A_3 T_I$$

$$A_{3R} = A_3 \overline{Q}_0 + M_3 \overline{A}_3 Q_0 C_{n+4} T_S + M_3 \overline{A}_3 Q_0 \overline{C}_{n+4} \overline{T}_S + \overline{M}_3 \overline{A}_3 Q_0 \overline{C}_{n+4} T_S + \overline{M}_3 \overline{A}_3 Q_0 C_{n+4} \overline{T}_S$$
$$\qquad + \overline{M}_3 A_3 \overline{C}_{n+4} \overline{T}_S + \overline{M}_3 A_3 C_{n+4} T_S + M_3 A_3 \overline{C}_{n+4} T_S + M_3 A_3 C_{n+4} \overline{T}_S$$

$$Q_{3R} = F_0 \overline{T}_S$$

$$Q_{0L} = M_3 F_3 + \overline{M}_3 \overline{F}_3$$

$$A_{M0} = \overline{R}_2 + R_0 + T_S$$

$$A_{M1} = R_2 \overline{R}_0 \overline{T}_S + R_2 R_0$$

$$Q_{M0} = \overline{R}_2 + \overline{R}_0$$

$$Q_{M1} = \overline{R}_2 + R_0$$

$$T_A = R_2 T_{OP} + R_1 T_{OP} + \overline{R}_0 T_{OP}$$

$$T_Q = \overline{R}_2 \overline{R}_1 R_0 T_{OP} + R_2 T_{OP}$$

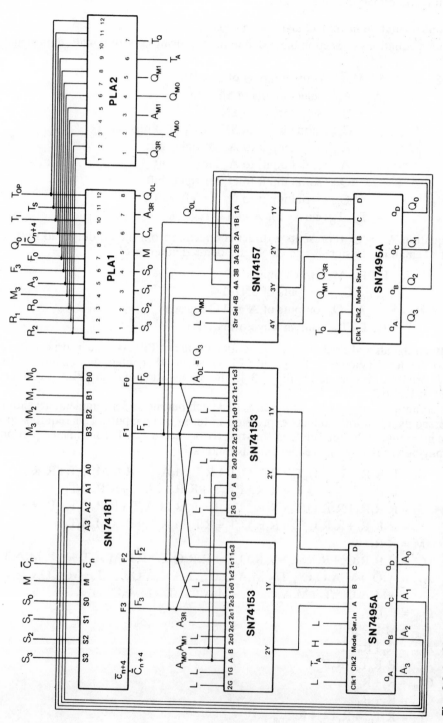

Fig. 6.3.4 Circuit of the arithmetic processor showing the input and output connections to the two programmable-logic-arrays

The above fifteen equations provide sufficient data for the programming of the FPLAs labelled PLA1 and PLA2 in Fig. 6.3.4.

6.4   QUESTIONS

6.4.1   Verification of FPLA design equations
Derive the set of equations in sum-of-products form given in Section 6.3.7 from the equations given in Section 6.3.5.

6.4.2   Implementation of design equations using SSI and MSI/LSI integrated circuits
Design equations defining control inputs, data inputs and clocks for an arithmetic processor were given in Section 6.3.5. The implementation of these equations using two FPLAs was described in Section 6.3.7. Obtain an implementation of the same equations using commercially available SSI and MSI/LSI integrated circuits. A comparison of the required number of chips is of interest.

6.4.3   Consideration of possible PLA substitution for MSI/LSI integrated circuits
Consider whether it would be possible to program a FPLA with the organisation of Fig. 6.2.1 so that it has the same logical function of each of the following MSI/LSI integrated circuits:

TYPE NUMBER	DESCRIPTION
SN74153	Dual 4-line-to-1-line data-selector
SN74148	Cascadable octal priority encoder
SN7485	4-bit magnitude comparator
SN74180	8-bit odd/even parity generator/checker
SN74S275	7-bit slice Wallace tree
SN74H87	4-bit true/complement/zero/one element

6.4.4   7-bit parallel incrementer
Consider the design of a 7-bit 'parallel incrementer' with the following specifications:

$$A_6 \text{---} A_0 : \text{7-bit data input}$$
$$C_0 : \text{increment input}$$
$$S_6 \text{---} S_0 : \text{7-bit data output}$$
$$C_{n+7} : \text{carry output}$$

The 8-bit binary number $C_{n+7}, S_6 \text{---} S_0$ is required to be equal to the 7-bit binary number $A_6 \text{---} A_0$ plus C_0. Specify the programming of a FPLA which will provide the above input-output relationship. (Hint: one approach which will readily lead to equations for the outputs is to consider the equations for a zero-level carry-lookahead adder with one input number equal to zero.)

6.4.5   PLA implementation of control signals for an arithmetic processor capable of eight operations
Consider an arithmetic processor with a basic structure defined by Fig. 6.3.2. The arithmetic processor is controlled by three switches R_2, R_1, R_0 and a pushbutton. When the pushbutton is depressed the operation corresponding to the switch settings, defined by Table 6.4.1, is to be performed.

Table 6.4.1   Specification of arithmetic processor

R_2	R_1	R_0	OPERATION	DESCRIPTION
0	0	0	Load A	$M \rightarrow A$
0	0	1	Load Q	$M \rightarrow Q$
0	1	0	Add	$A + M \rightarrow A$
0	1	1	Subtract	$A - M \rightarrow A$
1	0	0	Multiply	$M \times Q + 2^{-3}A \rightarrow AQ$
1	0	1	Divide	$AQ \div M \rightarrow Q$
1	1	0	Shift A left	$A_2A_1A_00 \rightarrow A$
1	1	1	Shift A right	$0A_3A_2A_1 \rightarrow A$

Following the approach described in Section 6.3 specify the interconnections and programming of PLAs for generation of the control signals, data signals and clocks required by the circuit of Fig. 6.3.2.

6.4.6   PLA implementation of control signals for an arithmetic processor capable of 16 operations

Again consider an arithmetic processor with the same basic structure defined by Fig. 6.3.2. This arithmetic processor is controlled by four switches R_3, R_2, R_1, R_0 and a pushbutton. When the pushbutton is depressed one of the operations defined by Table 6.4.2 is to be performed.

Table 6.4.2   Specification of arithmetic processor

R_3	R_2	R_1	R_0	OPERATION	DESCRIPTION
0	0	0	0	Load A	$M \rightarrow A$
0	0	0	1	Load Q	$M \rightarrow Q$
0	0	1	0	Add	$A + M \rightarrow A$
0	0	1	1	Subtract	$A - M \rightarrow A$
0	1	0	0	Multiply	$M \times Q + 2^{-3}A \rightarrow AQ$
0	1	0	1	Divide	$AQ \div M \rightarrow Q$
0	1	1	0	Shift A left	$A_2A_1A_00 \rightarrow A$
0	1	1	1	Shift A right	$0A_3A_2A_1 \rightarrow A$
1	0	0	0	Shift Q left	$Q_2Q_1Q_00 \rightarrow Q$
1	0	0	1	Shift Q right	$0Q_3Q_2Q_1 \rightarrow Q$
1	0	1	0	Shift AQ cyclic left	$A_2A_1A_0Q_3Q_2Q_1Q_0A_3 \rightarrow AQ$
1	0	1	1	Shift AQ cyclic right	$Q_0A_3A_2A_1A_0Q_3Q_2Q_1 \rightarrow AQ$
1	1	0	0	And	M_n AND $A_n \rightarrow A_n (n = 0, 1, 2, 3)$
1	1	0	1	Exclusive-OR	M_n EOR $A_n \rightarrow A_n$ $(n = 0, 1, 2, 3)$
1	1	1	0	Complement A	$\overline{A}_n \rightarrow A_n$ $(n = 0, 1, 2, 3)$
1	1	1	1	Clear A	$0 \rightarrow A$

Again follow the approach described in Section 6.3 and specify the PLAs required to generate the control signals, data signals and clocks for the circuit of Fig. 6.3.2.

BIBLIOGRAPHY

BOOKS

AGAJANIAN, A. H., *Computer Technology, Logic, Memory and Microprocessors, a Bibliography*, Plenum, 1978.

BARNA, A., *High Speed Pulse and Digital Techniques*, Wiley-Interscience, 1980.

BARTEE, T. C., *Digital Computer Fundamentals*, McGraw-Hill International Student Edition, 1960.

BARTEE, T. C., LEBOW, I. L. and REED, I. S., *Theory and Design of Digital Machines*, McGraw-Hill, 1962.

BELL, C. G. and NEWELL, A., *Computer Structures: Readings and Examples*, McGraw-Hill, 1971.

BELL, C. G., MUDGE, J. C. and McNAMARA, J. E., *Computer Engineering—a DEC View of Hardware Systems Design*, Digital Press, 1978.

BELOVE, C., *Digital and Analog Systems, Circuits and Devices: An Introduction*, McGraw-Hill, 1973.

BLAKESLEE, T. R., *Digital Design with Standard MSI and LSI*, 2nd Edition: Design Techniques for the Microcomputer Age, Wiley Interscience, 1979.

BOOTH, T. L., *Digital Networks and Computer Systems*, Wiley International, 1971.

BOWEN, B. A. and BUHR, R. J. A., *The Logical Design of Multiple-Microprocessor Systems*, Prentice-Hall, 1980.

BOYCE, J. C., *Digital Computer Fundamentals*, Prentice-Hall, 1977.

CHU, Y., *Digital Computer Design Fundamentals*, McGraw-Hill, 1962.

CLARE, C., *Designing Logic Systems Using State-Machines*, McGraw-Hill, 1973.

DAVIS, G. B., *Introduction to Computers*, (3rd Edition), McGraw-Hill, 1977.

DIGITAL EQUIPMENT CORPORATION, *Microcomputer Processor Handbook*, Digital Press, 1979.

DEMPSEY, J. A., *Basic Digital Electronics with MSI Applications*, Addison-Wesley, 1977.

DEMPSEY, J. A., *Experimentation with Digital Electronics*, Addison-Wesley, 1977.

EDWARDS, F. H., *The Principles of Switching Circuits*, M.I.T. Press, 1973.

FLETCHER, W. I., *An Engineering Approach to Digital Design*, Prentice-Hall, 1980.

FLORES, I., *The Logic of Computer Arithmetic*, Prentice-Hall, 1963.

FRIEDMAN, A. D., *Logical Design of Digital Systems*, Pitman, 1975.

GARLAND, H., *Introduction to Microprocessor System Design*, McGraw-Hill, 1979.

GEAR, C. W., *Computer Organisation and Programming*, McGraw-Hill, 1980.

GIVONE, D. D. and ROESSER, R. P., *Microprocessors/Microcomputers: An Introduction*, McGraw-Hill, 1980.

GOTHMAN, W. H., *Digital Electronics—an Introduction to Theory and Practice*, Prentice-Hall, 1977.

GRABBE, E. M., RAMO, S. and WOOLDRIDGE, D. E., *Handbook of Automation, Computation and Control*, Vol. 2, Computers and Data Processing, John Wiley, 1959.

GRAY, H. J., *High-Speed Digital Memories and Circuits*, Addison-Wesley Advances in Modern Engineering Series, 1976.

GRAY, J. P. (Ed.), *VLSI81 Very Large Scale Integration*, (Proceedings of the first International Conference on Very Large Scale Integration, Edinburgh, August 1981), Academic Press, 1981.

GREENFIELD, S. E., *The Architecture of Microcomputers*, Winthrop Computer Systems Series, 1980.

GROGONO, P., *Programming in PASCAL* (Revised Edition), Addison-Wesley, 1980.

HEATH, F. G., *Digital Computer Design*, Oliver and Boyd, 1969.

HELLERMAN, H. and CONROY, T. F., *Computer System Performance*, McGraw-Hill, 1975.

HILBURN, J. L. and JULICH, P. M., *Microcomputers/Microprocessors: Hardware, Software and Applications*, Prentice-Hall, 1976.

HILL, F. J. and PETERSON, G. R., *Introduction to Switching Theory and Logical Design* (2nd Edition), (Wiley International Edition), John Wiley, 1974.

HILL, F. J. and PETERSON, G. R., *Digital Systems Hardware Organisation and Design* (2nd Edition), John Wiley, 1978.

HOLT, C. A., *Electronic Circuits—Digital and Analog,* John Wiley, 1978.

HOPE, G. S., *Integrated Devices in Digital Circuit Design,* Wiley-Interscience, 1980.

HOPPER, A. and WHEELER, D., *Local Area Networks: The Cambridge Ring,* Addison-Wesley, 1983.

HOWES, M. J. and MORGAN, D. V. (Ed.), *Charge Coupled Devices and Systems,* Wiley-Interscience, 1979.

HURST, S. L., *The Logical Processing of Digital Signals,* Edward Arnold, 1978.

HUSKEY, H. D. and KORN, G. A. (Ed.), *Computer Handbook,* McGraw-Hill, 1962.

HWANG, K., *Computer Arithmetic, Principles, Architecture and Design,* John Wiley, 1978.

INTEL MARKETING COMMUNICATIONS, *The Semiconductor Memory Book,* Wiley-Interscience, 1978.

JENSEN, R. W. and TONIES, C. C., *Software Engineering,* Prentice-Hall, 1979.

KARBOWIAK, A. E. and HUEY, R. M. (Ed.), *Information, Computers, Machines and Man,* John Wiley, 1971.

KATZAN, H. Jr., *Microprogramming Primer,* McGraw-Hill, 1977.

KLINGMAN, E. E., *Microprocessor Systems Design,* Prentice-Hall, 1977.

KORN, G. A., *Minicomputers for Engineers and Scientists,* McGraw-Hill, 1973.

KOSTOPOULOS, G. K., *Digital Engineering,* Wiley-Interscience, 1974.

KRUTZ, R. L., *Microprocessors and Logic Design,* John Wiley, 1980.

KUCK, D. L., *The Structure of Computers and Computations,* Vol. 1, John Wiley, 1978.

KUO, B. C., *Analysis and Synthesis of Sampled-Data Control Systems,* Prentice-Hall, 1963.

KUO, B. C., *Digital Control Systems,* Holt, Rinehart and Winston, 1980.

LEDLEY, R. S., *Digital Computer and Control Engineering,* McGraw-Hill, 1962.

LEE, S. C., *Digital Circuits and Logic Design,* Prentice-Hall, 1976.

LEE, S. C., *Modern Switching Theory and Digital Design,* Prentice-Hall, 1978.

LEVENTHAL, L. A., *Introduction to Microprocessors: Software, Hardware, Programming,* Prentice-Hall, 1978.

LEVY, H. M. and ECKHOUSE, R. H. Jr., *Computer Programming and Architecture—The VAX-11,* Digital Press, 1980.

LEWIN, D., *Theory and Design of Digital Computers,* Nelson, 1972.

LEWIN, D., *Logical Design of Switching Circuits* (2nd Edition), Nelson, 1974.

LEWIS, R. and TAGG, E. D. (Ed.), *Computers in Education,* (Proceedings of the IFIP TC-3 3rd World Conference on Computers in Education—WCCE81, Lausanne, Switzerland, July 1981), North Holland, 1981.

LIN, W. C. (Ed.), *Microprocessors: Fundamentals and Applications,* IEEE Press, 1977.

LIND, L. F. and NELSON, J. C. C., *Analysis and Design of Sequential Digital Systems,* Macmillan, 1977.

MacEWEN, G. H., *Introduction to Computer Systems: Using the PDP-11 and Pascal,* McGraw-Hill, 1980.

MALEY, G. A. and EARLE, J., *The Logic Design of Transistor Digital Computers,* Prentice-Hall, 1963.

MALY, K. and HANSON, A. R., *Fundamentals of the Computer Sciences,* Prentice-Hall, 1978.

MARTIN, J., *Programming Real-Time Computer Systems,* Prentice-Hall, 1965.

MARTIN, J., *Design of Real-Time Computer Systems,* Prentice-Hall, 1967.

McCLUSKEY, E. J., *Introduction to the Theory of Switching Circuits,* McGraw-Hill, 1965.

McNAMARA, J. E., *Technical Aspects of Data Communication,* Digital Press, 1977.

MEAD, C. and CONWAY, L., *Introduction to VLSI Systems,* Addison-Wesley, 1980.

MITRA, S.K., *An Introduction to Digital and Analog Integrated Circuits and Applications,* Harper and Row, 1980.

MORRIS, N. M., *Semiconductor Devices,* Macmillan Basis Books in Electronics, 1976.

MOWLE, F. J., *A Systematic Approach to Digital Logic Design,* Addison-Wesley, 1976.

MUROGA, S., *Logical Design and Switching Theory,* Wiley-Interscience, 1979.

MYERS, G. J., *Digital System Design and LSI Bit-Slice Logic,* Wiley-Interscience, 1980.

PEATMAN, J. B., *The Design of Digital Systems,* McGraw-Hill, 1972.

PEATMAN, J. B., *Microcomputer-Based Design,* McGraw-Hill, 1977.

PEATMAN, J. B., *Digital Hardware Design,* McGraw-Hill, 1980.

PHISTER, M. Jr., *Logical Design of Digital Computers,* John Wiley, 1958.

PHISTER, M. Jr., *Data Processing Technology and Economics* (2nd Edition), Digital Press, 1979.

PRATHER, R. E., *Introduction to Switching Theory: A Mathematical Approach,* Allyn and Bacon, 1967.

RICHARDS, R. K., *Arithmetic Operations in Digital Computers,* Van Nostrand, 1955.

RICHARDS, R. K., *Electronic Digital Systems,* John Wiley, 1966.

RICHARDS, R. K., *Digital Design*, Wiley-Interscience, 1971.

ROSE, A., *Computer Logic*, Wiley-Interscience, 1971.

SANDIGE, R. S., *Digital Concepts Using Standard Integrated Circuits*, McGraw-Hill, 1978.

SWARTZLANDER, E. E. Jr., (Ed.), *Computer Arithmetic*, (Benchmark Papers in Electrical Engineering and Computer Science/21), Dowden, Hutchinson and Ross, 1980.

SZE, S. M., *Physics of Semiconductor Devices* (2nd Edition), Wiley, 1981.

TAUB, H. and SCHILLING, D., *Digital Integrated Electronics*, McGraw-Hill Electrical and Electronic Engineering Series, 1977.

TEXAS INSTRUMENTS INC., *Supplement to the TTL Data Book for Design Engineers*, Texas Instruments Inc., 1974.

TEXAS INSTRUMENTS INC., *The TTL Data Book for Design Engineers* (2nd Edition), Texas Instruments Inc., 1976.

TOCCI, R. J., *Digital Systems—Principles and Applications*, Prentice-Hall, 1977.

WEBER, S. (Ed.), *Large and Medium Scale Integration—Devices and Applications*, McGraw-Hill, 1974.

WEITZMAN, C., *Distributed Micro/Minicomputer Systems—Structure, Implementation and Application*, Prentice-Hall, 1980.

WIATROWSKI, C. A. and HOUSE, C. H., *Logic Circuits and Microcomputer Systems*, McGraw-Hill, 1980.

WOOLLONS, D. J., *Introduction to Digital Computer Design*, McGraw-Hill, 1972.

ZACHAROV, B., *Digital Systems Logic and Circuits*, George Allen and Unwin, 1968.

ZISSOS, D., *System Design with Microprocessors*, Academic Press, 1978.

PUBLISHED PAPERS AND SPECIAL ISSUES OF JOURNALS

ABADIR, M. S. and REGHBATI, H. K., 'LSI Testing Techniques', *IEEE Micro*, Feb. 1983, pp. 34–51.

AGRAWAL, D. P., 'High-Speed Arithmetic Arrays', *IEEE Trans. on Computers*, C–28, 3, Mar. 1979, pp. 215–24.

ALLEN, M. W. et al., 'CIRRUS, An Economical Multiprogram Computer with Microprogram Control', *IEEE Trans.*, EC–12, 6, Dec. 1963, pp. 663–71.

ANDERSON, D. A., 'Operating Systems' (Tutorial Series 9), *Computer*, June 1981, pp. 69–82.

BARBACCI, M. R., 'Instruction Set Processor Specifications (ISPS): The Notation and Its Applications', *IEEE Trans. on Computers*, C–30, 1, Jan. 1981, pp. 24–40.

BARBE, D. F., 'VHSIC Systems and Technology', *Computer*, Feb. 1981, pp. 13–22.

BARTOLINI, R. A., 'Optical Recording: High-Density Information Storage and Retrieval', *Proc. IEEE*, 70, 6, June 1982, pp. 589–97.

BECKMAN, F. S., BROOKS, F. P. Jr. and LAWLESS, W. J., 'Developments in the Logical Organisation of Computer Arithmetic and Control Units', *Proc. IRE*, Jan. 1961, pp. 53–65.

BERESFORD, R., 'Advances in Customization Free VLSI System Designers', *Electronics*, Feb. 10, 1983, pp. 134–45.

BERLEKAMP, E. R., 'The Technology of Error-Correcting Codes', *Proc. IEEE*, 68, 5, May 1980, pp. 564–93.

BERNHARD, R., 'Computing at the Speed Limit', *IEEE Spectrum*, July 1982, pp. 26–31.

BHANDARKAR, D. P., 'The Impact of Semiconductor Technology on Computer Systems', *Computer*, Sep. 1979, pp. 92–8.

BORGERS, E. M., 'Characteristics of Priority Interrupts', *Datamation*, June 1965, pp. 31–4.

BORRILL, P. L., 'Microprocessor Bus Structures and Standards', *IEEE Micro*, Feb. 1981, pp. 84–95.

BOTEZ, D. and HERSKOWITZ, G. J., 'Components for Optical Communications Systems: A Review', *Proc. IEEE*, 68, 6, June 1980, pp. 689–731.

BREUER, M. A., FRIEDMAN, A. D. and IOSUPOVICZ, A., 'A Survey of the State of the Art of Design Automation', *Computer*, Oct. 1981, pp. 58–75.

BUDZINSKI, R., LINN, J. and THATTE, S., 'A Restructurable Integrated Circuit for Implementing Programmable Digital Systems', *Computer*, Mar. 1982, pp. 43–54.

BUEHLER, M. G. and SIEVERS, M. W., 'Off-Line, Built-In Test Techniques for VLSI Circuits', *Computer*, June 1982, pp. 69–82.

BULTHUIS, K. et al., 'Ten Billion Bits on a Disk', *IEEE Spectrum*, Aug. 1979, pp. 26–33.

CARNEY, P. C., 'Selecting On-Board Satellite Computer Systems', *Computer*, Apr. 1983, pp. 35–41.

CASSOLA, R. L., 'A Floating Point Module for Military Computers', *Computer Design,* Feb. 1982, pp. 67–76.

CAVLAN, N. and DURHAM, S. J., 'Field-Programmable Arrays: Powerful Alternatives to Random Logic', *Electronics,* July 5, 1979, pp. 109–14.

CAVLAN, N. and DURHAM, S. J., 'Sequences and Arrays Transform Truth Tables into Working Systems', *Electronics,* July 19, 1979, pp. 132–9.

CHAMPINE, G. A., 'Back-End Technology Trends', *Computer,* Feb. 1980, pp. 50–58.

CHARLESWORTH, A. E., 'An Approach to Scientific Array Processing: The Architectural Design of the AP-120B/FPS-164 Family', *Computer,* Sep. 1981, pp. 18–27.

CHEN, I. and WILLONER, R., 'An O(n) Parallel Multiplier with Bit-Sequential Input and Output', *IEEE Trans. on Computers,* **C–28,** 10, Oct. 1979, pp. 721–7.

CHEN, X. and HURST, S. L., 'A Comparison of Universal-Logic-Module Realizations and their Application in the Synthesis of Combinatorial and Sequential Logic Networks', *IEEE Trans. on Computers,* **C–31,** 2, Feb. 1982, pp. 140–47.

CHEN, X. and WU, X., 'Derivation of Universal Logic Modules for $n \geqslant 3$, by Algebraic Means', *IEE Proc.,* **128,** Pt. E, 5, Sep. 1981, pp. 205–11.

CHI, C. S., 'Higher Densities for Disk Memories', *IEEE Spectrum,* Mar. 1981, pp. 39–43.

CHI, C. S., 'Advances in Computer Mass Storage Technology', *Computer,* May 1982, pp. 60–74.

CHRISTIANSEN, D. (Ed.) et al., 'Reliability', *IEEE Spectrum,* Oct. 1981, pp. 34–104.

CODY, W. J., 'Analysis of Proposals for the Floating-Point Standard', *Computer,* Mar. 1981, pp. 63–8.

COHLER, E. V. and STORER, J. E., 'Functionally Parallel Architecture for Array Processors', *Computer,* Sep. 1981, pp. 28–36.

CONKLIN, P. F. and RODGERS, D. P., 'Advanced Minicomputer Designed by Team Evaluation of Hardware/Software Tradeoffs', *Computer Design,* Apr. 1978, pp. 129–37.

COONEN, J. T., 'An Implementation Guide to a Proposed Standard for Floating-Point Arithmetic', *Computer,* Jan. 1980, pp. 68–79.

COONEN, J. T., 'Underflow and the Denormalized Numbers', *Computer,* Mar. 1981, pp. 75–87.

COOPER, J. A., 'Limitations on the Performance of Field-Effect Devices for Logic Applications', *Proc. IEEE,* **69,** 2, Feb. 1981, pp. 226–31. (Special issue on Fundamental Limits in Electrical Engineering)

CRAGON, H. G., 'The Elements of Single-Chip Microcomputer Architecture', *Computer,* Oct. 1980, pp. 27–40.

CRESPI-REGHIZZI, S., CORTI, P. and DAPRA', A., 'A Survey of Microprocessor Languages', *Computer,* Jan. 1980, pp. 48–66.

CURNOW, H. and WICKMAN, B., 'A Synthetic Benchmark', *The Computer J.,* **19,** 1, Feb. 1976, pp. 43–9.

DADDA, L., 'Some Schemes for Parallel Multipliers', *Alta Frequenza,* **34,** Mar. 1965, pp. 349–56.

DA SILVA, J. G. D. and WOODS, J. V., 'Design of a Processing Subsystem for the Manchester Data-Flow Computer', *IEE Proc.,* **128,** Pt. E, 5, Sep. 1981, pp. 219–24.

DA SILVA, J. G. D. and WATSON, J., 'Pseudo-Associative Store with Hardware Hashing', *IEE Proc.,* **130,** Pt. E, 1, Jan. 1983, pp. 19–24.

DENNIS, J. B., 'Data Flow Supercomputers', *Computer,* Nov. 1980, pp. 48–56.

DICKIE, A. A., 'Computer-Assisted Design of PROM-Controlled State-Machine Circuits for Logical Applications', *IEE Proc.,* **128,** Pt. E, 3, May 1981, pp. 123–8.

DIFFIE, W. and HELLMAN, M. E., 'Privacy and Authentication: An Introduction to Cryptography', *Proc. IEEE,* **67,** 3, Mar. 1979, pp. 397–427.

DORROS, I., 'Telephone Nets Go Digital', *IEEE Spectrum,* Apr. 1983, pp. 48–53.

EDEN, R. C., 'Comparison of GaAs Device Approaches for Ultrahigh-Speed VLSI', *Proc. IEEE,* **70,** 1, Jan. 1982, pp. 5–12.

ELEKTOR, '16-Bit Microprocessors', *Elektor,* Apr. 1981, Special Supplement, pp. 1–24.

FAIRBAIRN, D. G., 'VLSI: A New Frontier for Systems Designers', *Computer,* Jan. 1982, pp. 87–96.

FATHI, E. T. and KRIEGER, M., 'Multiple Microprocessor Systems: What, Why, and When', *Computer,* Mar. 1983, pp. 23–32.

FENG, T. Y., 'A Survey of Interconnection Networks', *Computer,* Dec. 1981, pp. 12–27.

FISCHER, W. P., 'Microprocessor Assembly Language Draft Standard', (IEEE Task P694/D11), *Computer,* Dec. 1979, pp. 96–109.

FLEISHER, H. and MAISSEL, L. I., 'An Introduction to Array Logic', *IBM J. Res. Develop.*, **19**, Mar. 1975, pp. 98–109.

FLYNN, M. J., 'Directions and Issues in Architecture and Language', *Computer*, Oct. 1980, pp. 5–22.

FOSTER, M. J. and KUNG, H. T., 'The Design of Special-Purpose VLSI Chips', *Computer*, Jan. 1980, pp. 26–40.

FOWLER, M., 'Personal-Computer Networks', *Electronics and Power*, Nov./Dec. 1981, pp. 805–9.

FRANKEL, S. P., 'The Logical Design of a Simple General Purpose Computer', *Trans. IRE*, PGEC, **EC–6**, 1, Mar. 1957., pp. 5–14.

GHEEWALA, T., 'The Josephson Technology', *Proc. IEEE*, **70**, 1, Jan. 1982, pp. 26–34.

GILBERT, R., 'The General-Purpose Interface Bus', *IEEE Micro*, Feb. 1982, pp. 41–51.

GOTTLIEB, A. and SCHWARTZ, J. T., 'Networks and Algorithms for Very-Large-Scale Parallel Computation', *Computer*, Jan. 1982, pp. 27–36.

GOTTLIEB, A. et al., 'The N.Y.U. Ultracomputer—Designing an MIMD Shared Memory Parallel Computer', *IEEE Trans. on Computers*, **C–32**, 2, Feb. 1983, pp. 175–89.

GRIERSON, J. R., 'Modern Developments in Gate Arrays', *Electronics and Power*, Mar. 1982, pp. 244–8.

GUPTA, A. and TOONG, H. D., 'An Architectural Comparison of 32–Bit Microprocessors', *IEEE Micro*, Feb. 1983, pp. 9–22.

HACHTEL, G. D. and SANGIOVANNI-VINCENTELLI, A. S., 'A Survey of Third-Generation Simulation Techniques', *Proc. IEEE*, **69**, 10, Oct. 1981, pp. 1264–80.

HAFER, L. J. and PARKER, A. C., 'Automated Synthesis of Digital Hardware', *IEEE Trans. on Computers*, **C–31**, 2, Feb. 1982, pp. 93–109.

HAYES, J., 'MOS Scaling', *Computer*, Jan. 1980, pp. 8–13.

HAYES, J. P., 'A Unified Switching Theory with Applications to VLSI Design', *Proc. IEEE*, **70**, 10, Oct. 1982, pp. 1140–51.

HAYNES, L. S., LAU, R. L., SIEWIOREK, D. P. and MIZELL, D. W., 'A Survey of Highly Parallel Computing', *Computer*, Jan. 1982, pp. 9–24.

HNATEK, E. R., 'Semiconductor Memory Update—Part 1: ROMs', *Computer Design*, Dec. 1979, pp. 67–77.

HOAGLAND, A. S., 'Storage Technology: Capabilities and Limitations', *Computer*, May 1979, pp. 12–18.

HOOPER, D. E. and ROBERTS, D. H., 'Silicon Systems', *GEC Journal of Science and Technology*, **48**, 2, 1982 (Special Issue—Microelectronics in GEC), pp. 52–5.

HÖRBST, E., 'Case Studies on the Interaction between Process Technology, Architecture and Design Methodology', Preprints of papers, Microelectronics '82, Conference, Adelaide, May 1982.

HOUSE, C. H., 'Perspectives on Dedicated and Control Processing', *Computer*, Dec. 1980, pp. 35–49.

HUNT, J. W., 'Programming Languages' (Tutorial Series 15), *Computer*, Apr. 1982, pp. 70–88.

HWANG, K., 'Global and Modular Two's Complement Cellular Array Multipliers', *IEEE Trans. on Computers*, **C–28**, 4, Apr. 1979, pp. 300–306.

IEEE COMPUTER, 'Fault-Tolerant Computing' (Theme features), *Computer*, Mar. 1980.

IEEE COMPUTER, 'Advances in Hardware: Chips to Systems' (Theme features), *Computer*, Feb. 1981.

IEEE COMPUTER, 'Array Processor Architecture' (Theme), *Computer*, Sep. 1981.

IEEE COMPUTER, 'Highly Parallel Computing', *Computer*, Jan. 1982.

IEEE COMPUTER, 'Data Flow Systems' (Theme), *Computer*, Feb. 1982.

IEEE COMPUTER, 'Mass Storage Systems and Data Center Architectures' (Theme features), *Computer*, July 1982.

IEEE PROCEEDINGS, 'Special Issue on Computers', *IEEE Proc.*, Dec. 1966.

IEEE PROCEEDINGS, 'Special Issue on Software Engineering', *IEEE Proc.*, Sep. 1980.

IEEE PROCEEDINGS, 'Fundamental Limits in Electrical Engineering', *IEEE Proc.*, Feb. 1981.

IEEE PROCEEDINGS, 'Special Issue on Computer-Aided Design', *IEEE Proc.*, Oct. 1981.

IEEE PROCEEDINGS, 'Special Issue on Very Fast Solid-State Technology', *IEEE Proc.*, Jan. 1982.

IEEE SPECTRUM, 'Special Issue on Productivity', *Spectrum*, Oct. 1978.

IEEE SPECTRUM, 'Special Issue on Reliability', *Spectrum*, Oct. 1981.

IEEE SPECTRUM, 'Technology '83', *Spectrum*, Jan. 1983.

IEEE TASK P754, 'A Proposed Standard for Binary Floating-Point Arithmetic', *Computer*, Mar. 1981, pp. 51–62.

IEEE TASK P755, 'A Proposed Standard for Extending High-Level Languages for Microprocessors', *IEEE Micro,* May 1981, pp. 70–75.

IEEE TRANSACTIONS, 'Joint Special Issue on Microprocessors and Microcomputers', (Also published in *IEEE Journal of Solid-State Circuits,* **SC–15**, 1), *IEEE Trans. on Computers,* **C–29**, 2, Feb. 1980.

IEEE TRANSACTIONS, 'Special Issue on Fault-Tolerant Computing', *IEEE Trans. on Computers,* **C–29**, 6, June 1980.

IEEE TRANSACTIONS, 'Special Issue on Parallel Processing', *IEEE Trans. on Computers,* **C–29**, 9, Sep. 1980.

IEEE TRANSACTIONS, 'Special Issue on Distributed Processing Systems', *IEEE Trans. on Computers,* **C–29**, 12, Dec. 1980.

IEEE TRANSACTIONS, 'Special Issue on Interconnection Networks for Parallel and Distributed Processing', *IEEE Trans. on Computers,* **C–30**, 4, Apr. 1981.

IEEE TRANSACTIONS, 'Special Issue on Microprogramming Tools and Techniques', *IEEE Trans. on Computers,* **C–30**, 7, July 1981.

IEEE TRANSACTIONS, 'Joint Special Issue on Design for Testability', (also published in *IEEE Trans. on Circuits and Systems,* **CAS–28**, 11, Nov. 1981), *IEEE Trans. on Computers,* **C–30,** 11, Nov. 1981.

JENSEN, R. W., 'Structural Programming' (Tutorial Series 16), *Computer,* Mar. 1981, pp. 31–48.

KARPLUS, W. J. and COHEN, D., 'Architectural and Software Issues in the Design and Application of Peripheral Array Processors', *Computer,* Sep. 1981, pp. 11–17.

KARTASHEV, S. I. and KARTASHEV, S. P., 'Problems of Designing Supersystems with Dynamic Architectures', *IEEE Trans. on Computers,* **C–29**, 12, Dec. 1980, pp. 1114–32.

KEYES, R. W., 'Fundamental Limits in Digital Information Processing', *Proc. IEEE,* **69**, 2, Feb. 1981, pp. 267–78.

KORN, G. A., 'Multiprocessor Designs Surpass Supermini Alternatives for Continuous System Simulation', *Computer Design,* May 1981, pp. 95–101.

KOZDROWICKI, E. W. and THEIS, D. J., 'Second Generation of Vector Supercomputers', *Computer,* Nov. 1980, pp. 71–83.

KUNG, H. T., 'Why Systolic Architectures?', *Computer,* Jan. 1982, pp. 37–46.

LERNER, E. J., 'Reliable Systems: Design and Tests', *IEEE Spectrum,* Oct. 1981, (Special Issue on Reliability), pp. 50–55.

LESLIE, I. M., 'Master Clock Repeater for the Cambridge Digital Communication Ring', IEE Proc., **128**, Pt. E, 2, Mar. 1981, pp. 64–6.

LEVY, H. M. and LIPMAN, P. H., 'Virtual Memory Management in the VAX/VMS Operating System', *Computer,* Mar. 1982, pp. 35–41.

LINCOLN, N. R., 'Technology and Design Tradeoffs in the Creation of a Modern Supercomputer', *IEEE Trans. on Computers,* **C–31**, 5, May 1982, pp. 349–62.

LOHSTROH, J., 'Devices and Circuits for Bipolar (V)LSI', *Proc. IEEE,* **69**, 7, July 1981, pp. 812–26.

LONG, S. I. et al., 'High Speed GaAs Integrated Circuits', *Proc. IEEE,* **70**, 1, Jan. 1982, pp. 35–45.

LOUIE, T., 'Array Processors: A Selected Bibliography', *Computer,* Sep. 1981, pp. 53–7.

MacSORLEY, O. L., 'High-Speed Arithmetic in Binary Computers', *IRE Proc.,* **49**, 1961, pp. 67–91.

MANUEL, T. et al., 'Computers People Can Count On', *Electronics,* Jan. 27, 1983, pp. 93–105.

MARCUS, M. J., 'Some System Implications of a Josephson Computer Technology', *Proc. IEEE,* **69**, 4, Apr. 1981, pp. 404–9.

MARSHALL, M. and WALLER, L., 'VLSI Pushes Super-CAD Techniques', *Electronics,* July 31, 1980, pp. 73–80.

MAUNDER, A. W., 'Concepts Involved in Algorithms Used in the Digital Logic Simulation Program SIMODL', *Elec. Engg. Trans., I.E. Aust.,* **EE15**, 3, 1979, pp. 103–9.

MAUNDER, A. W. and WONG, D. G., 'The Application of the Digital Logic Simulation Program "SIMODL" to Teaching in the Field of Digital Systems Design', *Elec. Engg. Trans., I.E. Aust.,* **EE15**, 3, 1979, pp. 110–16.

McCREA, P. G. and MATHESON, W. S., 'Design of High-Speed Fully Serial Tree Multiplier', *IEE Proc.,* **128**, Pt. E, 1, Jan. 1981, pp. 13–20.

McDONOUGH, K., CAUDEL, E., MAGAR, S. and LEIGH, A., 'Microcomputer with 32-bit Arithmetic Does High-Precision Number Crunching', *Electronics,* Feb. 24, 1982, pp. 105–10.

MILLER, S. E., 'Overview of Telecommunications Via Optical Fibers', *Proc. IEEE,* **68**, 10, Oct. 1980 (Special Issue on Optical-Fiber Communications).

MOORE, G., 'VLSI: Some Fundamental Challenges', *IEEE Spectrum,* Apr. 1979, pp. 30–37.

MORALEE, D., 'ADA: Software Engineering Language of the Future', *Electronics and Power,* July/Aug. 1981, pp. 556–62.

MUDGE, J. C., 'Design Decisions Achieve Price/Performance Balance in Mid-Range Minicomputers', *Computer Design,* Aug. 1977, pp. 87–95.

MURPHY, B. T., THOMAS, L. C. and MACRAE, A. V., 'Twin Tubs, Domino Logic, CAD Speed Up 32–bit Processor', *Electronics,* Oct. 6, 1981, pp. 106–11.

MYERS, W., 'CAD/CAM: The Need for a Broader Focus', *Computer,* Jan. 1982, pp. 105–16.

NAU, D. S., 'Expert Computer Systems', *Computer,* Feb. 1983, pp. 63–85.

NEWTON, A. B., 'Computer-Aided Design of VLSI Circuits', *Proc. IEEE,* **69**, 10, Oct. 1981, pp. 1189–99.

NISENOFF, N., 'Hardware for Information Processing Systems: Today and in the Future', *Proc. IEEE,* **54**, 12, Dec. 1966, pp. 1820–35.

NOAKS, D. R. and BURTON, D. P., 'A High-Speed, Asynchronous, Digital Multiplier', *The Radio and Electronic Engineer,* Dec. 1968, pp. 357–65.

NOYCE, R. N. and HOFF, M. E., 'A History of Microprocessor Development at Intel', *IEEE Micro,* Feb. 1981, pp. 8–21.

PATTERSON, D. A. and SÉQUIN, C. H., 'Design Considerations for Single-Chip Computers of the Future', *IEEE Trans. on Computers,* **C–29**, 2, Feb. 1980, pp. 108–16.

PEARCEY, T., 'The Effect of Large Scale Integration and Batch Fabrication on the Architecture of Large Data Systems', *Aust. Computer Journal,* **6**, 2, July 1974, pp. 61–70.

PIVNICHNY, J. R., 'High Speed Decimal Multipliers', *IBM Technical Disclosure Bulletin,* **24**, 5, Oct. 1981, pp. 2612–17.

POHM, A. V. and SMAY, T. A., 'Computer Memory Systems' (Tutorial Series 13), *Computer,* Oct. 1981, pp. 93–110.

POSA, J. G., 'Peripheral Chips Shift Microprocessor Systems into High Gear', *Electronics,* Aug. 16, 1979, pp. 93–106.

POSA, J. G., 'Gate Arrays—A Special Report', *Electronics,* Sep. 25, 1980, pp. 145–58.

PRADHAN, D. K. and STIFFLER, J. J., 'Error-Correcting Codes and Self-Checking Circuits', *Computer,* Mar. 1980, pp. 27–37.

PRINCE, S. M. and SLOMAN, M. S., 'Communication Requirements of a Distributed Computer Control System', *IEE Proc.,* **128**, Pt. E, 1, Jan. 1981, pp. 21–34.

PROUDFOOT, J. T., 'Programmable Logic Arrays', *Electronics and Power,* Nov./Dec. 1980, pp. 883–7.

RAJCHMAN, J. A., 'Computer Memories: A Survey of the State-of-the-Art', *Proc. IRE,* Jan. 1961, pp. 104–27.

RALLAPALLI, K. and KROEGER, J., 'Chips Make Fast Math a Snap for Microprocessors', *Electronics,* Apr. 24, 1980, pp. 153–7.

RASMUSSEN, R. A., 'Automated Testing of LSI' (Tutorial Series 14), *Computer,* Mar. 1982, pp. 69–78.

RAUSCHER, T. G. and ADAMS, P. M., 'Microprogramming: A Tutorial and Survey of Recent Developments', *IEEE Trans. on Computers,* **C–29**, 1, Jan. 1980, pp. 2–20.

RAYMOND, T. C., 'LSI-VLSI Design Automation' (Tutorial Series 10), *Computer,* **14**, 7, July 1981, pp. 89–101.

REGHBATI, H. K., 'An Overview of Data Compression Techniques', *Computer,* Apr. 1981, pp. 71–4.

REISER, M., 'Performance Evaluation of Data Communication Systems', *Proc. IEEE,* **70**, 2, Feb. 1982, pp. 171–96.

RENNELS, D. A., 'Distributed Fault-Tolerant Computer Systems', *Computer,* Mar. 1980, pp. 55–65.

ROBERTS, L., 'The Evolution of Packet Switching', *Proc. IEEE,* **66**, 11, Nov. 1978, pp. 1307–13.

RODRIGUE, G., GIROUX, E. D. and PRATT, M., 'Perspectives on Large-Scale Scientific Computation' (Tutorial Series 1), *Computer,* Oct. 1980, pp. 65–80.

RODRIGUES, M. R. D., ZURAWSKI, J. H. P. and GOSLING, J. B., 'Hardware Evaluation of Mathematical Functions', *IEE Proc.,* **128**, Pt. E, 4, July 1981, pp. 155–64.

ROSENFELD, A., 'Parallel Image Processing Using Cellular Arrays', *Computer,* Jan. 1983, pp. 14–20.

RUBINSTEIN, E. (Ed.) et al., 'Technology in War and Peace', *IEEE Spectrum,* Oct. 1982, pp. 34–114.

SABO, D., 'New Technologies and Their Influence on Future System Design', 1st International Conference on Semi-Custom ICs, London, Nov. 1981.

SALLET, H. W., 'Magnetic Tape: A High Performer', *IEEE Spectrum,* July 1977, pp. 26–31.

SARIDIS, G. N., 'Toward the Realization of Intelligent Controls', *Proc. IEEE,* **67**, 8, Aug. 1979, pp. 1115–33.

SATYANARAYANAN, M., 'Multiprocessing: An Annotated Bibliography', *Computer,* May 1980, pp. 101–16.

SCHNEIDER, G. M., 'Computer Network Protocols: A Hierarchical Viewpoint', *Computer,* Sep. 1979, pp. 8–10.

SCHWEPPE, F. C., 'Power Systems '2000': Hierarchical Control Strategies', *IEEE Spectrum,* July 1978, pp. 42–7.

SCIENTIFIC AMERICAN, 'Microelectronics', *Scientific American,* Sep. 1977.

SERRELL, R. et al., 'The Evolution of Computing Machines and Systems', *Proc. IRE,* May 1962, pp. 1039–58.

SHIVA, S. G., 'Computer Hardware Description Languages—A Tutorial', *Proc. IEEE,* **67**, 12, Dec. 1979, pp. 1605–15.

SIEGEL, H. J. and McMILLEN, R. J., 'Using the Augmented Data Manipulator Network in PASM', *Computer,* Feb. 1981, pp. 25–33.

SIEWIOREK, D. P. and LAI, L. K. W., 'Testing of Digital Systems', *Proc. IEEE,* **69**, 10, Oct. 1981, pp. 1321–33.

SLANA, M. F. and LEHMAN, H. R., 'Data Communication Using the Telecommunication Network', *Computer,* May 1981, pp. 73–88.

SNYDER, L., 'Introduction to the Configurable Highly Parallel Computer', *Computer,* Jan. 1982, pp. 47–56.

SOLOMON, P. M., 'A Comparison of Semiconductor Devices for High-Speed Logic', *Proc. IEEE,* **70**, 5, May 1982, pp. 489–509.

SUMNEY, L. W., 'VHSIC: A Status Report', *IEEE Spectrum,* Dec. 1982, pp. 34–9.

SZE, S. M., 'Semiconductor Device Development in the 1970's and 1980's—A Perspective', *Proc. IEEE,* **69**, 9, Sep. 1981, pp. 1121–31.

TABACHNICK, R. L., ZSOMBOR-MURPHY, P. J., VROOMEN, L. J. and LE-NGOC, T., 'Sequence Controllers with Standard Hardware and Custom Firmware', *IEEE Micro,* May 1981, pp. 9–25.

THEIS, D. J., 'Spacecraft Computers: State-of-the-Art Survey', *Computer,* Apr. 1983, pp. 85–97.

THOMAS, D. E., 'The Automatic Synthesis of Digital Systems', *Proc. IEEE,* **69**, 10, Oct. 1981, pp. 1200–1211.

THORNTON, J. E., 'Back-End Network Approaches', *Computer,* Feb. 1980, pp. 10–17.

TOBIAS, J. R., 'LSI/VLSI Building Blocks' (Tutorial Series 11), *Computer,* Aug. 1981, pp. 83–101.

TODD, C. D., 'An Annotated Bibliography on NOR and NAND Logic', *IEEE Trans.,* **EC–12**, 5, Oct. 1963, pp. 462–4.

TOONG, H. D. and GUPTA, A., 'An Architectural Comparison of Contemporary 16–Bit Microprocessors', *IEEE Micro,* May 1981, pp. 26–37.

WALLACE, C. S., 'A Suggestion for a Fast Multiplier', *IEEE Trans. Electronic Computers,* **EC–13**, Feb. 1964, pp. 14–17.

WARD, W. P., 'Minicomputer Blasts Through 4 Million Instructions a Second', *Electronics,* Jan. 13, 1982, pp. 155–9.

WARE, F. and McALLISTER, W., 'C-MOS Chip Set Streamlines Floating-Point Processing', *Electronics,* Feb. 10, 1982, pp. 149–52.

WASER, S., 'High-Speed Monolithic Multipliers for Real-Time Digital Signal Processing', *Computer,* Oct. 1978, pp. 19–29.

WATSON, I. and GURD, J., 'A Practical Data Flow Computer', *Computer,* Feb. 1982, pp. 51–7.

WATSON, R. W., 'Network Architecture Design for Back-End Storage Networks', *IEEE Computer,* Feb. 1980, pp. 32–48.

WILHELM, W., 'Gate Arrays: State of the Art, Problems and Solutions', Proceedings 1981 European Solid State Circuits Conference (ESSCIRC 81), Freiburg, W. Germany, Sep. 1981, pp. 137–46.

WILKES, M. V., 'The Impact of Wide-Band Local Area Communication Systems on Distributed Computing', *Computer,* Sep. 1980, pp. 22–5.

WILKES, M. V. and STRINGER, J. B., 'Microprogramming and the Design of the Control Circuits in an Electronic Digital Computer', *Proc. Cambridge Phil. Soc.,* Pt. 2, **49**, Apr. 1953, pp. 30–38.

WILLIAMS, T. W. and PARKER, K. P., 'Design for Testability—A Survey', *IEEE Trans. on Computers,* **C–31**, 1, Jan. 1982, pp. 2–15.

WONG, D. G., 'The Logical Design of the General Purpose Digital Computer SNOCOM', *Journal I.E. Aust.,* June 1962, pp. 125–36.

WONG. D. G., 'Laboratory Equipment for Teaching Digital Computer Fundamentals', *Proc. IREE Aust.,* Feb. 1965, pp. 77–83.

WONG, D. G., 'The Design and Construction of the Digital Computer ARCTURUS', Proc. Third Australian Computer Conference, Canberra, May 1966.

WULF, W. A., 'Trends in the Design and Implementation of Programming Languages', *Computer,* Jan. 1980, pp. 14–25.

ZURAWSKI, J. H. P. and GOSLING, J. B., 'Design of High-Speed Digital Divider Units', *IEEE Trans. on Computers,* **C–30**, 9, Sep. 1981, pp. 691–9.

INDEX